BIRDS OF THE US-MEXICO BORDERLANDS: DISTRIBUTION, ECOLOGY, AND CONSERVATION

Janet M. Ruth, Timothy Brush, and David J. Krueper
Associate Editors

Studies in Avian Biology No. 37

A PUBLICATION OF THE COOPER ORNITHOLOGICAL SOCIETY

Front cover photographs, clockwise from upper left: San Pedro River, Arizona by David J. Krueper, Yellow-breasted Chat (*Icteria virens*) by David J. Krueper, San Rafael Valley grasslands, Arizona by Janet Ruth, Arizona Grasshopper Sparrow (*Ammodramus savannarum ammolegus*) by Rick Bowers, Chisos Mountains from the Rio Grande Valley, Texas by Roland Wauer, Mangrove Yellow Warbler (probably *Dendroica petechia oraria*) by Scarlet Colley, Cabeza Prieta National Wildlife Refuge, Arizona by John and Karen Hollingsworth, Broad-billed Hummingbird (*Cynanthus latirostris*) by David J. Krueper, Cave Creek Canyon and Chiricahua Mountains, Arizona by Helen Snyder, Tufted Flycatcher (*Mitrephanes phaeocercus*) byTony Godfrey, Cienega de Santa Clara, Colorado River delta, Sonora, Mexico by Carlos Valdes, Golden-fronted Woodpecker (*Melanerpes aurifrons*) by Lee Baines, Chihuahuan Desert, Arizona by Janet M. Ruth, Royal Tern (*Thalasseus maximus*) by George Jameson. Center: relief map of the US–Mexico borderlands. Source: The National Map, USGS, http://www.nationalmap.gov.

STUDIES IN AVIAN BIOLOGY

Edited by

Carl D. Marti
1310 East Jefferson Street
Boise, ID 83712

Studies in Avian Biology is a series of works too long for *The Condor*, published at irregular intervals by the Cooper Ornithological Society. Manuscripts for consideration should be submitted to the editor. Style and format should follow those of previous issues.

Price $20.00. To order this and other SAB volumes, please go to the Cooper Ornithological Society website: http://cooper.org.

ISBN: 978-0-943610-84-9

Library of Congress Control Number: 2008935582

Printed at Cadmus Professional Communications, Ephrata, Pennsylvania 17522

Issued: September 2008

CONTENTS

iv

LIST OF AUTHORS

LAURIE B. ABBOTT
Department of Animal and Range Sciences
P.O. Box 30003, MSC 3-I
New Mexico State University
Las Cruces, NM 88003

M. SOFIA AGUDELO
Department of Fish, Wildlife and Conservation
    Ecology
P.O. Box 30003, MSC 4901
New Mexico State University
Las Cruces, NM 88003

TIMOTHY BRUSH
Department of Biology
University of Texas-Pan American
1201 West University Drive
Edinburg, TX 78539

ALEJANDRA CALVO-FONSECA
Pronatura Noroeste
Avenida Jalisco 903
San Luis Río Colorado
Sonora, México 83440

CHARLES T. COLLINS
Department of Biological Sciences
California State University
Long Beach, CA 90840

MARTHA J. DESMOND
Department of Fish, Wildlife and Conservation
    Ecology
P.O. Box 30003, MSC 4901
New Mexico State University
Las Cruces, NM 88003

ROBERT H. DIEHL
Department of Biological Sciences
Box 5018
University of Southern Mississippi
Hattiesburg, MS 39406

RODNEY FELIX, JR.
Department of Biological Sciences
Box 5018
University of Southern Mississippi
Hattiesburg, MS 39406

AARON D. FLESCH
School of Natural Resources
University of Arizona
325 Biological Sciences East
Tucson Arizona 85721

MARK FLIPPO
Big Bend National Park Service
P.O. Box 129
Big Bend National Park, TX 79834

OSVEL HINOJOSA-HUERTA
Pronatura Noroeste
Avenida Jalisco 903
San Luis Río Colorado
Sonora, México 83440

HELENA ITURRIBARRÍA-ROJAS
Pronatura Noroeste
Avenida Jalisco 903
San Luis Río Colorado
Sonora, México 83440

DAVID J. KRUEPER
U.S. Fish and Wildlife Service (MBO)
P.O. Box 1306
Albuquerque, NM 87103

DAVID MEHLMAN
The Nature Conservancy
1303 Rio Grande Boulevard NW, Suite 5
Albuquerque, NM 87107

CESAR MENDEZ-GONZALEZ
Department of Animal and Range Sciences
P.O. Box 30003, MSC 3-I and
Department of Fish, Wildlife and
    Conservation Ecology
P.O. Box 30003, MSC 4901
New Mexico State University
Las Cruces, NM 88003

LEIGH MURRAY
University Statistics Center
P.O. Box 30001, MSC 3CQ
New Mexico State University
Las Cruces, NM 88003

EDUARDO PALACIOS
Departmento de Biologia Conservacion
Centro de Investigación Científica y de Educación
    Superior de Ensenada (CICESE)
Unidad La Paz. Miraflores 334 Fracc. Bellavista
La Paz, BCS, México 23050

JUAN JOSÉ RIVERA-DÍAZ
Pronatura Noroeste
Avenida Jalisco 903
San Luis Río Colorado
Sonora, México 83440

JANET M. RUTH
U.S. Geological Survey
Fort Collins Science Center
Arid Lands Field Station
Biology Department
University of New Mexico
Albuquerque, NM 87131

José Fernando Villaseñor-Gómez
Luís de Velasco # 155
Morelia, Michoacán
México 58000

Roland H. Wauer
315 Padre Lane
Victoria, TX 77905

Enrique Zamora-Hernández
Pronatura Noroeste
Avenida Jalisco 903
San Luis Río Colorado
Sonora, México 83440

Studies in Avian Biology No. 37:1–9

PREFACE

Janet M. Ruth, Timothy Brush, and David J. Krueper

The concept for this volume began as a scientific symposium at the North American Ornithological Conference (NAOC) in Veracruz, Mexico in October 2006. The symposium was entitled "Avian Distributional Change, Anthropogenic Challenges, and Recent Avian Research and Technological Advances within the US–Mexico Border Region," and was co-chaired by two of us (DJK and TB) along with Carol Beardmore (Sonoran Joint Venture) and Bill Howe (USDI Fish and Wildlife Service). In light of the importance of the borderland region for birds and bird conservation, and because of the great need for additional information about this poorly studied region, we have compiled this volume to present new information about bird distribution, ecology, and conservation.

GEOGRAPHY AND HUMAN POPULATION

The US–Mexico borderlands region, stretching from the Gulf of Mexico to the Pacific Ocean, includes southern portions of Texas, New Mexico, Arizona, and California in the US and northern portions of Tamaulipas, Coahuila, Nuevo León, Chihuahua, Sonora, and Baja California in Mexico (Fig. 1). For purposes of this introduction we are defining the borderlands region as roughly 325 km (202 miles) on either side of the border. However, this is a somewhat arbitrary assignment; although most of the information presented in this volume falls within these boundaries, the reader will note that some chapters include study sites outside this area.

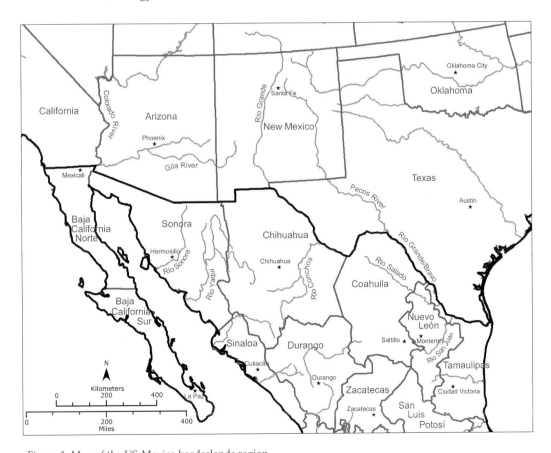

Figure 1. Map of the US-Mexico borderlands region.

At its core, the borderlands comprises portions of the following cross-border Bird Conservation Regions (BCRs) as defined by the North American Bird Conservation Initiative (NABCI), from east to west: Gulf Coastal Prairie (BCR 37), Tamaulipan Brushlands (BCR 36); Edwards Plateau (BCR 20), Chihuahuan Desert (BCR 35); Sierra Madre Occidental (BCR 34); Sonoran and Mohave Deserts (BCR 33); and Coastal California (BCR 32) (http://www.nabci-us.org/map.html). At its northern periphery, the borderlands includes the southern portions of several US BCRs: Oaks and Prairies (BCR 21); Central Mixed-grass Prairie (BCR 19); Shortgrass Prairie (BCR 18); and Southern Rockies–Colorado Plateau (BCR 16). At its southern periphery, it includes the northern portions of several Mexican BCRs: Sierra Madre Oriental (BCR 48), Planicie Costera, Lomeríos y Cañones de Occidente (BCR 43), Sierras de Baja California (BCR 39), and Desierto de Baja California (BCR 40) (http://www.nabci-us.org/mxbcrmap.html).

Important watersheds draining the borderlands region include the following rivers (ríos): Grande (known as Bravo in Mexico), San Juan, Salado, Nueces, Pecos, Conchos, Yaqui, Sonora, Gila, San Pedro, Santa Cruz, and Colorado (Fig. 1).

In 1854 <80,000 people were living in the borderlands region and it remained largely uninhabited or sparsely settled until after World War II (Webster and Bahre 2001). Although the borderlands remain relatively unpopulated, today a number of major population centers have developed in the region. In addition to cities near the border in the US (San Antonio, Tucson, Phoenix, and Los Angeles) and Mexico (Monterrey, Saltillo, Chihuahua, Hermosillo, and Mexicali), major bi-national metropolitan areas have developed around Brownsville-Matamoros, McAllen-Reynosa, Laredo-Nuevo Laredo, El Paso-Ciudad Juarez, Yuma-San Luis, and San Diego-Tijuana. In fact, with the exception of Mexico City, La Frontera is Mexico's fastest growing region (Webster and Bahre 2001). The populations in these areas are expanding and impacting the surrounding, less-developed regions along the border via increased water demands, exurbanization, and increased transportation needs. An assessment of diversity in the Sonoran Desert region of the borderlands identified the four most significant threats to this region as: (1) urbanization and resulting habitat conversion and fragmentation, (2) population increases and resulting increases in resource consumption, (3) surface water impoundment and diversion away from natural ecosystems, and (4) inappropriate livestock grazing (Nabhan and Holdsworth 1999).

BIOTIC COMMUNITY CHARACTERISTICS

The southwestern US and northern Mexico support a broad range of Nearctic and Neotropical biotic communities (Fig. 2). We present the information in Fig. 2 in order to place the borderlands within this larger context. The borderlands themselves comprise a large portion of this diverse landscape, including (1) cold temperate, warm temperate, and tropical-subtropical forests and woodlands, (2) warm temperate and tropical-subtropical scrublands, (3) cold and warm temperate grasslands, and (4) warm temperate, and tropical-subtropical desertlands (Brown et al. 2007), with valuable riparian and wetland communities embedded in each. It even contains southern examples of subalpine conifer forest at the highest montane elevations.

Climatic factors—precipitation (amount and distribution through the year), growing season length, and elevation—have some of the greatest effects on the characteristics of borderlands biotic communities. The driest portion of the borderlands region is the Gran Desierto in northwestern Sonora and the Salton Trough of southern California (annual precipitation of 39 mm) (Webster and Bahre 2001). Mean annual precipitation throughout the borderlands region varies substantially (Table 1). Lows are recorded in Mohave, Sonoran, and Chihuahuan desertscrub, and in California coastal scrub, while highs are recorded in the southeastern deciduous and evergreen forest, gulf coastal grassland, subalpine conifer forest, Tamaulipan semideciduous forest, and portions of the Great Plains grassland. Very high annual precipitation is recorded in the southernmost portions of the borderlands region in the Veracruz cloud forest (Table 1).

Annual distribution of precipitation also varies substantially throughout the borderlands region. Precipitation is spread evenly throughout the year in the Great Basin conifer woodlands. Precipitation occurs primarily in the winter in the following biotic communities: subalpine conifer forest, montane conifer forest, California coastal scrub and chaparral, California valley grassland, California portions of encinal forest and woodland, Mohave desertscrub, and southeastern deciduous and evergreen forest–balcones mixed evergreen woodland. Many borderlands biotic communities experience a majority of their precipitation during the growing season: southeastern deciduous and evergreen forest–oak-pine-hickory, most parts of encinal forest and woodland, plains, semidesert, and gulf coastal grasslands, Chihuahuan desertscrub,

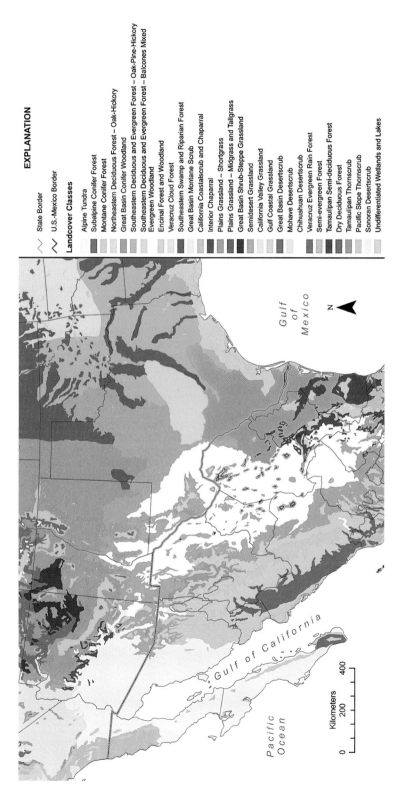

EXPLANATION

State Border

U.S.-Mexico Border

Landcover Classes

Alpine Tundra
Subalpine Conifer Forest
Montane Conifer Forest
Northeastern Deciduous Forest – Oak-Hickory
Great Basin Conifer Woodland
Southeastern Deciduous and Evergreen Forest – Oak-Pine-Hickory
Southeastern Deciduous and Evergreen Forest – Balcones Mixed Evergreen Woodland
Encinal Forest and Woodland
Veracruz Cloud Forest
Southeastern Swamp and Riparian Forest
Great Basin Montane Scrub
California Coastalscrub and Chaparral
Interior Chaparral
Plains Grassland – Shortgrass
Plains Grassland – Midgrass and Tallgrass
Great Basin Shrub-Steppe Grassland
Semidesert Grassland
California Valley Grassland
Gulf Coastal Grassland
Great Basin Desertscrub
Mohave Desertscrub
Chihuahuan Desertscrub
Veracruz Evergreen Rain Forest
Semi-evergreen Forest
Tamaulipan Semi-deciduous Forest
Dry Deciduous Forest
Tamaulipan Thornscrub
Pacific Slope Thornscrub
Sonoran Desertscrub
Undifferentiated Wetlands and Lakes

Figure 2. Biotic communities of the US-Mexico borderlands region (modified from Brown et al. 2007).

TABLE 1. Mean annual precipitation for US-Mexico borderlands biotic communities.[a]

Biotic community	Range of mean annual precipitation (mm)
Mohave desertscrub	40–255
Sonoran desertscrub	125–305
California coastal scrub and chaparral	125–760
California valley grassland	150–405
Chihuahuan desertscrub	190–305
Pacific slope thornscrub	205–635
Great Basin conifer woodland	250–560
Semidesert grassland	255–405
Plains grassland-shortgrass	300–510
Encinal evergreen woodland	305–890
Interior chaparral	380–635
Tamaulipan thornscrub	380–635
Plains grassland-midgrass and tallgrass	380–1,015
Montane conifer forest	460–760
Subalpine conifer woodland	635–1,000
Tamaulipan semi-deciduous forest	635–1015
Gulf coastal grassland	750–1,500
Southeastern deciduous and evergreen forest—balcones mixed evergreen woodland	760–1,015
Southeastern deciduous and evergreen forest—oak-pine-hickory	1,015–1,525
Veracruz cloud forest	1,900–5,080

[a] Compiled from D. Brown, pers. comm.; Brown et al. 2007, and Brown 1994.

Pacific slope thornscrub, and Veracruz cloud forest. Some of these communities average >70% of their precipitation in late spring to late summer: Tamaulipan semi-deciduous forest and Tamaulipan thornscrub. A few biotic communities experience a bimodal pattern of rainfall—interior chaparral (winter and summer monsoons with little rain in April–June) and Sonoran desertscrub (October–March and June–August); D. Brown, pers. comm.; Brown 1994).

The growing season, roughly defined as the mean number of days with temperatures >0°C (Brown 1994), varies widely in the borderlands. Extremely short growing seasons (<100 d) are found in subalpine conifer forest and montane conifer forest. Relatively short growing seasons (100–200 d) are recorded in plains grassland and Great Basin conifer woodland. Relatively long growing seasons (200–350 d) are found in encinal evergreen woodlands, all southeastern deciduous and evergreen forest communities, semidesert, California valley, and gulf coastal grasslands, coastal scrub and chaparral communities, and Mohave and Chihuahuan desertscrub. Extremely long growing seasons (>350 d) are found in the thornscrub communities, much of the Sonoran desertscrub, and Tamaulipan semi-deciduous forest; freezing temperatures are very rare in the Veracruz cloud forest (D. Brown, pers. comm.; Brown 1994).

Annual variation in precipitation is high in much of the borderlands region. The timing and amount of rainfall can have major impacts on plant and animal communities, with some extreme events such as severe drought and tropical storms and hurricanes having lasting effects (Swetnam and Betancourt 1998). Some of these communities experience rather extreme daily temperature variation; occasional severe freezes, particularly in subtropical areas, can have long-term effects on plant communities and the animals which inhabit them (Lonard and Judd 1991). The northward spread of many plants and animals over the last >100 yr (some discussed further in this volume) may be due to human-induced climate change and/or longer term climate cycles (Avise and Walker 1998, Norwine and John 2007).

In spite of the great spatial and temporal variation in precipitation levels, the great majority of the borderlands landscape is comprised of extremely arid desertscrub, thornscrub, semidesert grassland, and chaparral communities with very low annual precipitation. Much of this same landscape has a relatively long to very long growing season. The result is a region that is warm/hot and generally dry. These characteristics define the biotic communities, explain the importance of riparian and wetland areas on the landscape, and determine how this region and its flora and fauna responds to environmental and anthropogenic change.

Elevations in the borderlands range from below sea level to >2,500 m. Low elevation areas are found along the coast of the Gulf of Mexico, the Gulf of California, and the Pacific Ocean, and at the Salton Sea (69 m below sea level). The highest elevations are found in the higher mountain ranges of the borderlands region—

Serranías del Burro, Sierra Madre Oriental, Guadalupe, Sacramento, Florida, Big Hatchet, Animas, Chiricahua, Huachuca, Santa Rita, Sierra Madre Occidental, and Sierra San Pedro Mártir. Much of the borderlands falls within the so-called sky islands region (Heald 1993), a complex of forested mountain islands isolated by large expanses of desert and grassland habitats. The topographic complexity of this basin and range landscape in a region that combines temperate and tropical climates, and that is at the intersection of diverse biotic communities, makes the borderlands a region of high biological diversity and therefore conservation interest (DeBano 1995).

The biodiversity and ecological value of the borderlands region is demonstrated by the fact that it includes three Mexican biosphere reserves, five US and nine Mexican national parks, 17 US national wildlife refuges, five US national monuments, five US national forests, four US national conservation areas, >30 Mexican Áreas de Importancia para la Conservación de las Aves (AICAS), and 35 US globally Important Bird Areas (IBAs), plus a great deal of public land administered by the USDI Bureau of Land Management (BLM), US Department of Defense military installations, state parks, and state wildlife management agencies.

BIRDS IN THE BORDERLANDS

The borderlands region supports an extremely diverse breeding avian community, as well as important communities during migration and winter seasons. What makes the borderlands particularly important is the number of bird species of conservation concern found there, using a variety of measures (Table 2). The borderlands region supports 18 species, subspecies, or distinct population segments listed as Threatened or Endangered under the US Endangered Species Act and 48 species listed as Amenazada (Threatened) or En Peligro de Extinción (Endangered) under Mexican Federal Regulations—NOM-059-SEMARNAT-2001 (SEMARNAT 2002). In addition, it supports 103 species or subspecies listed by the USDI Fish and Wildlife Service (USFWS) as a Bird of Conservation Concern in at least one US borderland BCR. At the present time no Mexican equivalent exists to the US Birds of Conservation Concern list (USDI Fish and Wildlife Service 2002). However, we look forward to the availability of substantial new information regarding conservation priorities for all birds from Mexico, and conservation of landbirds at a continental perspective (Canada, US, and Mexico) from

Partners in Flight, both in the near future. Looking specifically at landbird communities, most of the region falls within the southwest avifaunal biome identified in the Partners in Flight North American Landbird Conservation Plan (Rich et al. 2004). Forty-two of the 100 national watch list species (landbirds) are found in this southwestern biome during the breeding and/or winter season, along with another 16 national stewardship species. The majority of watch list species with declining trends or high threats in this biome are riparian or grassland species; however, we lack adequate population trend information for 37 of these species of continental importance (Rich et al. 2004). The rugged, remote, hot, and arid nature of this region is one of the primary reasons for this lack of information. We hope that the information in this volume will contribute to our knowledge of some of these species of conservation concern.

We have chosen four general areas of focus for this volume—new information about bird distribution and abundance; information about population trends and ecology of riparian and wetland birds; information about population trends and ecology of grassland birds; and information about new technology applications and bird conservation planning.

Information about bird abundance and distribution in the borderlands region is particularly valuable in providing baseline data as this region faces increasing habitat loss or degradation due to agricultural and suburban/urban development, and land and water management practices. It is also of interest as we try to understand, predict, and document the effects of global climate change on avian communities and their habitats, as well as make management recommendations to address these threats. Several papers in this section present information on distribution, status, and recent changes in bird populations in the borderlands region. Brush summarizes short-term changes in the breeding avifauna in the rapidly urbanizing Lower Rio Grande Valley since the turn of the 21st century, showing that certain temperate and tropical species are increasing while others have declined. Wauer and Flippo document the changes in the breeding avifauna of Big Bend National Park over the last century, identifying recent arrivals, populations that have increased, declined, or were extirpated, as well as some species whose status is uncertain. Flesch's work provides valuable data for northern Sonora, a region with limited information about the distribution and abundance of breeding birds; he makes interesting connections between avian species richness and the number of vegetation communities present. Collins and Palacios

TABLE 2. BIRD SPECIES OF CONCERN IN THE US-MEXICO BORDERLANDS REGION (FOUND WITHIN APPROXIMATELY 325 KM OF THE BORDER AT SOME SEASON IN THEIR LIFE CYCLE—BREEDING, MIGRATION, OR WINTER). SPECIES LISTED BY THE US BIRDS OF CONSERVATION CONCERN (BCC) 2002 (USDI FISH AND WILDLIFE SERVICE 2002), THE US ENDANGERED SPECIES ACT (ESA), AND THE NORMA OFICIAL MEXICANA (NOM) (SEMARNAT 2002).

Species	USFWS and BCC[a]	ESA[b]	NOM[c]	Notes[d]
Muscovy Duck (*Cairina moschata*)			E	
Mallard (*Anas platyrhynchos*)			T*	* *A. p. diazi*
Mottled Duck (*Anas fulvigula*)			T	
Masked Duck (*Nomonyx dominicus*)			T	
Crested Guan (*Penelope purpurascens*)			T	
Great Curassow (*Crax rubra*)			T	
Northern Bobwhite (*Colinus virginianus*)		E*	E*	* *C. v. ridgewayi*
Black-footed Albatross (*Phoebastria nigripes*)	X		T	
Black-vented Shearwater (*Puffinus opisthomelas*)			E	
Leach's Storm-petrel (*Oceanodroma leucorhoa*)			E*	* *O. l. willetti*
Ashy Storm-Petrel (*Oceanodroma homochroa*)			T	
Black Storm-Petrel (*Oceanodroma melania*)			T	
Least Storm-Petrel (*Oceanodroma microsoma*)			T	
Brown Pelican (*Pelecanus occidentalis*)		E*		* all populations except Atlantic coast, Florida, Alabama
American Bittern (*Botaurus lentiginosus*)	X		T	
Reddish Egret (*Egretta rufescens*)	X			
White Ibis (*Eudocimus albus*)	X			
California Condor (*Gymnogyps californianus*)		E		
Swallow-tailed Kite (*Elanoides forficatus*)	X			
Bald Eagle (*Haliaeetus leucocephalus*)		T*	E	* recently delisted in US; but recent court order has reinstated the desert DPS in central Arizona
Northern Harrier (*Circus cyaneus*)	X			
Northern Goshawk (*Accipiter gentilis*)	X		T	
Crane Hawk (*Geranospiza caerulescens*)			T	
Common Black-Hawk (*Buteogallus anthracinus*)	X			
Harris's Hawk (*Parabuteo unicinctus*)	X			
Solitary Eagle (*Harpyhaliaetus solitarius*)			E	
Gray Hawk (*Buteo nitidus*)	X			
Swainson's Hawk (*Buteo swainsoni*)	X			
White-tailed Hawk (*Buteo albicaudatus*)	X			
Ferruginous Hawk (*Buteo regalis*)	X			
Golden Eagle (*Aguila chrysaetos*)			T	
Ornate Hawk-Eagle (*Spizaetus ornatus*)			E	
Aplomado Falcon (*Falco femoralis*)		E*	T	* *F. f. septentrionalis*
Peregrine Falcon (*Falco peregrinus*)	X	E*		* recently delisted
Prairie Falcon (*Falco mexicanus*)	X		T	
Black Rail (*Laterallus jamaicensis*)	X		E*	* *L. j. coturniculus*
Clapper Rail (*Rallus longirostris*)		E*	T**/E***	* *R. l. yumanensis, R. l. levipes* and *R. l. obsoletus* ** *R. l. yumanensis* *** *R. l. levipes*
Whooping Crane (*Grus americana*)		E	E	
American Golden-Plover (*Pluvialis dominica*)	X			
Snowy Plover (*Charadrius alexandrinus*)	X	T*		* *C. a. nivosus*
Wilson's Plover (*Charadrius wilsonia*)	X			
Piping Plover (*Charadrius melodus*)		E*/T**	E	* Great Lakes breeding population; ** all the rest
Mountain Plover (*Charadrius montanus*)	X		T	
American Oystercatcher (*Haematopus palliatus*)	X			
Black Oystercatcher (*Haematopus bachmani*)	X			
Whimbrel (*Numenius phaeopus*)	X			
Long-billed Curlew (*Numenius americanus*)	X			
Hudsonian Godwit (*Limosa haemastica*)	X			

TABLE 2. CONTINUED.

Species	USFWS and BCC[a]	ESA[b]	NOM[c]	Notes[d]
Marbled Godwit (*Limosa fedoa*)	X			
Black Turnstone (*Arenaria melanocephala*)	X			
Red Knot (*Calidris canutus*)	X			
Stilt Sandpiper (*Calidris himantopus*)	X			
Short-billed Dowitcher (*Limnodromus griseus*)	X			
Least Tern (*Sternula antillarum*)	X*	E**	E**	* *S. a. athalassos* ** *S. a. browni*
Gull-billed Tern (*Gelochelidon nilotica*)	X			
Black Tern (*Chlidonias niger*)	X			
Elegant Tern (*Thalasseus elegans*)	X			
Black Skimmer (*Rynchops niger*)	X			
Xantus's Murrelet (*Synthliboramphus hypoleucus*)	X	C	E	
Craveri's Murrelet (*Synthliboramphus craveri*)			T	
Cassin's Auklet (*Ptychoramphus aleuticus*)	X		T*	* *P. f. aleuticus*
Red-billed Pigeon (*Patagioenas flavirostris*)	X			
Green Parakeet (*Aratinga holochlora*)			E*/T**	* *A. h. brewsteri* ** rest of the species
Military Macaw (*Ara militaris*)			E	
Thick-billed Parrot (*Rhynchopsitta pachyrhyncha*)			E	
Maroon-fronted Parrot (*Rhynchopsitta terrisi*)			T	
Red-crowned Parrot (*Amazona viridigenalis*)			E	
Yellow-headed Parrot (*Amazona oratrix*)			E	
Yellow-billed Cuckoo (*Coccyzus americanus*)	X	C*		* western US DPS
Flammulated Owl (*Otus flammeolus*)	X			
Whiskered Screech-Owl (*Megascops trichopsis*)	X			
Ferruginous Pygmy-Owl (*Glaucidium brasilianum*)	X*		T*	*G. b. cactorum* recently delisted
Elf Owl (*Micrathene whitneyi*)	X			
Burrowing Owl (*Athene cunicularia*)	X			
Spotted Owl (*Strix occidentalis*)	X*	T**	T***	* *S. o. occidentalis* ** *S. o. lucida* *** entire species
Short-eared Owl (*Asio flammeus*)	X			
Black Swift (*Cypseloides niger*)	X			
Broad-billed Hummingbird (*Cynanthus latirostris*)	X			
Buff-bellied Hummingbird (*Amazilia yucatanensis*)	X			
Lucifer Hummingbird (*Calothorax lucifer*)	X			
Costa's Hummingbird (*Calypte costae*)	X			
Elegant Trogon (*Trogon elegans*)	X			
Eared Quetzal (*Euptilotis neoxenus*)			T	
Lewis's Woodpecker (*Melanerpes lewis*)	X			
Gila Woodpecker (*Melanerpes uropygialis*)	X			
Arizona Woodpecker (*Picoides arizonae*)	X			
Gilded Flicker (*Colaptes chrysoides*)	X			
Northern Beardless-Tyrannulet (*Camptostoma imberbe*)	X			
Greater Pewee (*Contopus pertinax*)	X			
Willow Flycatcher (*Empidonax traillii*)		E*		* *E. t. extimus*
Buff-breasted Flycatcher (*Empidonax fulvifrons*)	X			
Rose-throated Becard (*Pachyramphus aglaiae*)	X			
Loggerhead Shrike (*Lanius ludovicianus*)	X	E*		* *L. l. mearnsi*
Bell's Vireo (*Vireo bellii*)	X	E*	T*	* *V. b. pusillus*
Black-capped Vireo (*Vireo atricapilla*)		E	E	
Gray Vireo (*Vireo vicinior*)	X			
Island Scrub-Jay (*Aphelocoma insularis*)	X			
Clark's Nutcracker (*Nucifraga columbiana*)			E	
Verdin (*Auriparus flaviceps*)	X			
Cactus Wren (*Campylorhynchus brunneicapillus*)	X			
Sedge Wren (*Cistothorus platensis*)	X			
California Gnatcatcher (*Polioptila californica*)		T*	T	* *P. c. californica*
Bendire's Thrasher (*Toxostoma bendirei*)	X			
Curve-billed Thrasher (*Toxostoma curvirostre*)	X			

TABLE 2. CONTINUED.

Species	USFWS and BCC[a]	ESA[b]	NOM[c]	Notes[d]
Crissal Thrasher (*Toxostoma crissale*)	X			
Le Conte's Thrasher (*Toxostoma lecontei*)	X			
Sprague's Pipit (*Anthus spragueii*)	X			
Olive Warbler (*Peucedramus taeniatus*)	X			
Colima Warbler (*Vermivora crissalis*)	X			
Tropical Parula (*Parula pitiayumi*)	X			
Yellow Warbler (*Dendroica petechia*)	X*			* D. p. sonorana
Black-throated Gray Warbler (*Dendroica nigrescens*)	X			
Golden-cheeked Warbler (*Dendroica chrysoparia*)		E	T	
Grace's Warbler (*Dendroica graciae*)	X			
MacGillivray's Warbler (*Oporornis tolmiei*)			T	
Common Yellowthroat (*Geothlypis trichas*)	X*			* G. t. sinuosa
Altamira Yellowthroat (*Geothlypis flavovelata*)			T	
Red-faced Warbler (*Cardellina rubrifrons*)	X			
Spotted Towhee (*Pipilo maculatus*)	X*			* P. m. clementae
Rufous-winged Sparrow (*Aimophila carpalis*)	X			
Cassin's Sparrow (*Aimophila cassinii*)	X			
Botteri's Sparrow (*Aimophila botterii*)	X			
Worthen's Sparrow (*Spizella wortheni*)			T	
Black-chinned Sparrow (*Spizella atrogularis*)	X			
Sage Sparrow (*Amphispiza belli*)		T*		* A. b. clementae
Lark Bunting (*Calamospiza melanocorys*)	X			
Savannah Sparrow (*Passerculus sandwichensis*)			T*	* P. s. beldingi
Grasshopper Sparrow (*Ammodramus savannarum*)	X			
Baird's Sparrow (*Ammodramus bairdii*)	X			
Seaside Sparrow (*Ammodramus maritimus*)	X*			* A. m. sennetti
Song Sparrow (*Melospiza melodia*)	X*			* M. m. graminea
Harris's Sparrow (*Zonotrichia querula*)	X			
McCown's Longspur (*Calcarius mccownii*)	X			
Chestnut-collared Longspur (*Calcarius ornatus*)	X			
Pyrrhuloxia (*Cardinalis sinuatus*)	X			
Varied Bunting (*Passerina versicolor*)	X			
Painted Bunting (*Passerina ciris*)	X			
Dickcissel (*Spiza americana*)	X			
Tricolored Blackbird (*Agelaius tricolor*)	X			
Orchard Oriole (*Icterus spurius*)	X			
Hooded Oriole (*Icterus cucullatus*)	X			
Altamira Oriole (*Icterus gularis*)	X			
Audubon's Oriole (*Icterus graduacauda*)	X			
Lawrence's Goldfinch (*Carduelis lawrencei*)	X			

[a] An X in the USFWS-BCC column means that this species is listed in at least one borderlands bird conservation region and is found in the borderlands portion of that region. Note: BCC list does not include species listed as Endangered under the ESA unless it is a population or subspecies not included under the ESA that is of concern.
[b] In the ESA column, E = Endangered, T = Threatened, and C = Candidate species.
[c] In the NOM column, the two categories most similar to the ESA were selected, E = Endangered (in Spanish, P = En Peligro de Extinción), and T = Threatened (in Spanish, A = Amenazada).
[d] Provides additional information about listed subspecies or population for columns marked with an asterisk *; DPS = distinct population segment.

present information about the distribution and status of Royal Tern (*Thalasseus maximus*) in the borderlands along the Pacific coast; Royal Tern is a species listed as of moderate conservation concern in the North American Waterbird Conservation Plan (Kushlan et al. 2002).

In the arid southwestern borderlands region, where water is extremely limited, the presence of surface water and near-surface ground water provides valuable year-round habitats. Riparian woodlands support the highest diversity of landbird species of any habitat type in the region and provide critical habitat for breeding species, as well as for migrating and wintering species from other regions (Rich et al. 2004). The region also includes a wide range of aquatic habitats that support a diverse array of waterbird and shorebird species, including some high-priority species (Brown et al. 2001, Kushlan et al. 2002). Understanding the ecology and population trends of bird species using these scarce but valuable habitats in an arid landscape is critical to management and conservation. In the section on population trends and ecology of riparian and wetland birds, Villaseñor-Gómez presents a study on the importance of Sonoran riparian habitat for wintering birds; he found that riparian avian communities were different from communities in surrounding non-riparian habitats and that riparian habitat was particularly important for migratory species. Hinojosa-Huerta et al. present data on the avian community along the Colorado River, Mexico, and its habitat relationships; they found that surface water was the most important habitat feature related to avian species richness and density, and that in the breeding season, cottonwood and willow cover was also important. Hinojosa-Huerta et al., in another paper, present information about population trends of the Yuma Clapper Rail (*Rallus longirostris yumanensis*) in the Colorado River delta; this subspecies is listed as Threatened in Mexico and Endangered in the US (Table 2).

Endemic grassland bird populations have shown steeper, more consistent, and more widespread declines than any other guild of North American species (Knopf 1996). Peterjohn and Sauer (1999) found that 13 of 25 grassland bird species showed significant decreases in continental populations between 1966 and 1996, and only three species showed significant increases. The grasslands of the borderlands region support a high number of breeding species of conservation concern and provide critical wintering habitat for resident grassland birds and short-distance migrants from the northern prairies. These grasslands support the highest number of priority land-bird species with declining population trends of any southwestern habitat type (Rich et al. 2004). The section on population trends and ecology of grassland birds includes two papers about the wintering (non-breeding) ecology of grassland bird communities. Agudelo et al. present information about the responses of wintering grassland and shrubland birds to habitat fragmentation and shrub encroachment in the northern Chihuahuan Desert in New Mexico; they found that numbers of shrubs was the most consistent predictor of grassland bird abundance, with abundance being negatively correlated. Desmond et al. present a diet study of granivorous birds in the grasslands of southwestern New Mexico; they document the most important seeds in the seedbank and compare the most abundant and most preferred seeds in bird diets among species within and between sites. The section also contains a species-specific paper (Ruth) on the abundance and distribution of a subspecies of Grasshopper Sparrow (*Ammodramus savannarum ammolegus*) found only in the borderlands region; the species is a National Bird of Conservation Concern for USFWS in the Sierra Madre Occidental BCR (BCR 34) (Table 2) and the subspecies is listed as Endangered for the state of New Mexico.

The last section features two very different papers. Felix et al. present information about bird migration patterns in the borderlands region developed through the application of weather surveillance radar technology and analyses. Radar technologies are being used in many ways to address management and conservation issues related to migratory wildlife (e.g., birds, bats, insects) and new applications show great promise (Ruth 2007). Finally, Mehlman describes the conservation by design framework used by The Nature Conservancy as a model for applied bird conservation planning in the borderlands region and elsewhere. This information is particularly important in light of the challenges posed by working cooperatively across borders for international conservation. The development of cross-border conservation efforts, through both the bird conservation initiatives (Partners in Flight, Waterbird Conservation for the Americas, North American Waterfowl Management Plan, US Shorebird Conservation Plan, and the North American Bird Conservation Initiative) and regional conservation initiatives in the borderlands (e.g., the Sonoran Joint Venture, the Rio Grande Joint Venture), demonstrates the need for us to understand how best to work across biological, geographic, political, and cultural boundaries to meet our common goals of bird conservation.

ACKNOWLEDGMENTS

We thank the Cooper Ornithological Society for providing an excellent outlet for the products of this symposium. We especially want to thank our many colleagues who graciously served as peer reviewers for the chapters in this volume. We also thank USFWS, USGS, and ProNatura for contributing funds to help pay the page costs for this volume. We thank R. Felix for Fig. 1. We want to express special appreciation to D. Brown and P. Umack for providing the data for Fig. 2 as well as valuable climatic data associated with biotic communities, and to T. Fancher for creating Fig. 2. Finally, we thank C. Marti for his assistance.

CHANGES IN DISTRIBUTION AND ABUNDANCE

Brown Jay (*Cyanocorax morio*) © David J. Krueper

Studies in Avian Biology No. 37:11–19

ADDITIONS TO THE BREEDING AVIFAUNA OF THE LOWER RIO GRANDE VALLEY OF TEXAS

TIMOTHY BRUSH

Abstract. The breeding avifauna of the Lower Rio Grande Valley (LRGV) of Texas has experienced many changes during the 20th century, primarily because of declines in native habitats due to land being converted to agriculture and urban habitats. This paper summarizes changes in breeding avifauna from 2003–2007 in the area. Breeding has been confirmed for Cooper's Hawk (*Accipiter cooperii*), Eurasian Collared-Dove (*Streptopelia decaocto*), and Mangrove Yellow Warbler (*Dendroica petechia*) for the first time, and for Gray-crowned Yellowthroat (*Geothlypis poliocephala*) and Ferruginous Pygmy-Owl (*Glaucidium brasilianum*) after periods of apparent absence. Short-tailed Hawk (*Buteo brachyurus*) is a possible breeder, based on an unsuccessful, interspecific pairing with Swainson's Hawk (*Buteo swainsoni*). Red-shouldered Hawk (*Buteo lineatus*) and Rose-throated Becard (*Pachyramphus aglaiae*) are possible breeders, with territorial adults present in remnants of suitable riparian habitat. Loggerhead Shrike (*Lanius ludovicianus*) continues to expand its breeding distribution in urban areas of the LRGV. The breeding status of other previously confirmed breeders, such as Yellow-green Vireo (*Vireo flavoviridis*) and Tamaulipas Crow (*Corvus imparatus*), continues to be in flux. Continued changes are to be expected, given human population growth and habitat-related changes expected in this rapidly growing metropolitan area.

Key words: bird distribution, breeding birds, habitat changes, Lower Rio Grande Valley, riparian habitats, Texas, urban habitats.

ADICIONES A LA AVIFAUNA DE CRIANZA DEL BAJO RÍO GRANDE DE TEXAS

Resumen. La fauna avícola de crianza de la región baja del Valle del Rio Grande de Tejas ha sufrido muchos cambios durante el siglo 20 debido a la disminución de los nichos ecológicos nativos causados por la transformación de la tierra a la agricultura y al desarrollo urbano. Este artículo sumariza los cambios en la crianza de la fauna avícola durante el período 2003-2007 en la región. Se ha confirmado la crianza del halcon de Cooper (*Accipiter cooperii*), la tórtola turca (*Streptopelia decaocto*) y el chipe amarillo (*Dendroica petechia*) por vez primera. Se confirmó también crianza después de períodos de corta ausencia del buho mascarita piquigruesa (*Geothlypis poliocephala*). El halcón de cola corta (*Buteo brachyurus*) es un posible criador basado en un apareamiento no exitoso e interespecífico con el halcón Swainson (*Buteo swainsoni*). El aguililla pechirrojiza (*Buteo lineatus*) y el mosquero-cabezón degollado (*Pachyramphus aglaiae*) son posibles criadores con adultos territoriales presentes en residuos de adecuados nichos riparianos. El verdugo americano (*Lanius ludovicianus*) continua expandiendo su distribución de cria en áreas urbanas de esta región de Tejas. El estado presente de otros criadores antes confirmados tales como la cazadora (*Vireo flavoviridis*) y el cuervo de Tamaulipas (*Corvus imparatus*) continua en flujo. Se esperan cambios continuos por el crecimiento de la población humana además de cambios de nichos relacionados que se esperan en la rápida área de crecimiento urbano.

The breeding avifauna of the Lower Rio Grande Valley (LRGV) of southernmost Texas (Cameron, Hidalgo, Willacy, and Starr Counties; Fig. 1) contains a mixture of species of temperate and tropical distributions. Species at or near the northern limits of their breeding ranges include Plain Chachalaca (*Ortalis vetula*), Red-billed Pigeon (*Patagioenas flavirostris*), and Altamira Oriole (*Icterus gularis*), while species at or near their southern range limits include Swainson's Hawk (*Buteo swainsoni*), Chimney Swift (*Chaetura pelagica*), and Western Kingbird (*Tyrannus verticalis*). In addition, species typical of the US–Mexican border region, such as Black Phoebe (*Sayornis nigricans*) and Black-tailed Gnatcatcher (*Polioptila melanura*), reach their

eastern range limits in the LRGV (Oberholser 1974, Benson and Arnold 2001, Lockwood and Freeman 2004, Brush 2005).

Many bird species of the US–Mexico border region are declining as a consequence of rapidly growing human populations and associated habitat changes, while other species are increasing or extending their ranges in response to habitat types found in expanding urban and suburban landscapes (Lockwood and Freeman 2004, Brush 2005). In addition, climate change may be affecting bird distribution and abundance (Brush 2005; Table 1 for an overview of historical changes in the LRGV breeding avifauna prior to the current study period). With urban growth accelerating in recent decades in

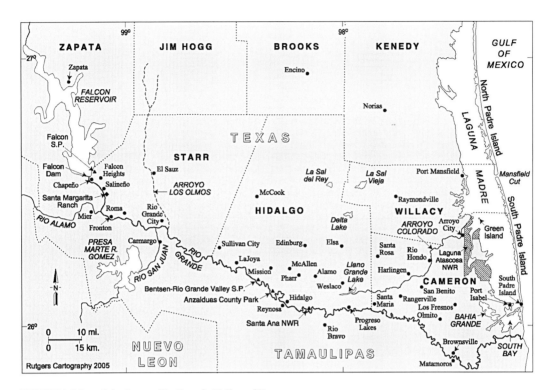

FIGURE 1. Map of the Lower Rio Grande Valley of Texas.

the LRGV, it is essential to monitor changes in breeding bird communities in order to conserve and manage them. The goal of this paper is to update the population status and/or distribution of breeding bird species in the LRGV, focusing on those species whose status changed during the past five years as well as species of conservation concern.

METHODS

From 1 January 2003–30 June 2007, I focused on confirming the presence and breeding of species which had not previously bred in the LRGV and on others that had declined or whose status was uncertain. I also obtained information from published and unpublished sources concerning the status and distribution of LRGV breeding birds. In the case of unpublished information, I assessed whether the observer had enough experience with the species and whether enough information concerning the species and evidence of nesting was presented to warrant inclusion here.

I considered breeding confirmed if the observer saw one or more of the following: nests with eggs or young; repeated visits by adults carrying food to a nest whose contents were not visible to the observer, or fledged young near

each other or to a nest and dependent on adults for food (Benson and Arnold 2001). I considered breeding probable if a pair was seen in the same area or was near a nest on at least two occasions, with at least one week between observations. I considered nesting possible if an adult was seen in the same area on at least two occasions with at least one week between observations, or if an adult showed clear territorial behavior (singing, display flights, territorial defense, nest building), or other nest-associated behaviors such as apparent incubation. Observations with no publication citation or observer's name listed are my own.

RESULTS

During 2003–2007, several species were found nesting in the LRGV for the first time. These included species whose main range is in the temperate zone, and others which are tropical in distribution, as well as more widespread species. Other species were documented re-nesting in the LRGV after a period of absence, while others failed to breed successfully.

COOPER'S HAWK (*ACCIPITER COOPERII*)

A broadly distributed breeder in the US and southern Canada, Cooper's Hawk is known to

TABLE 1. LONG-TERM CHANGES IN THE BREEDING AVIFAUNA OF THE LOWER RIO GRANDE VALLEY OF TEXAS, 1877–2002. THE DIRECTION OF THE SPECIES' MAIN BREEDING RANGE FROM THE LRGV IS SHOWN (E.G., RED-SHOULDERED HAWK IS FOUND PRIMARILY TO THE NORTH OF THE LRGV).

North	South	Uncertain
Species originally breeding regularly[a] but by 1987–2002 absent or extremely rare as breeders		
Red-shouldered Hawk	Rose-throated Becard	
(*Buteo lineatus*)	(*Pachyramphus aglaiae*)	
Common Tern	Gray-crowned Yellowthroat	
(*Sterna hirundo*)	(*Geothlypis poliocephala*)	
Blue-gray Gnatcatcher	White-collared Seedeater	
(*Polioptila caerulea*)	(*Sporophila torqueola*)	
Yellow-breasted Chat		
(*Icteria virens*)		
Summer Tanager		
(*Piranga rubra*)		
Orchard Oriole		
(*Icterus spurius*)		
Species originally absent but by 1987–2002 breeding regularly[a]		
Rock Pigeon[b]	Hook-billed Kite	Cattle Egret[b]
(*Columba livia*)	(*Chondrohierax uncinatus*)	(*Bubulcus ibis*)
Western Kingbird	Green Parakeet	Black Phoebe
(*Tyrannus verticalis*)	(*Aratinga holochlora*)	(*Sayornis nigricans*)
Purple Martin	Red-crowned Parrot	Cave Swallow
(*Progne subis*)	(*Amazona viridigenalis*)	(*Petrochelidon fulva*)
Barn Swallow	Ringed Kingfisher)	
(*Hirundo rustica*)	(*Megaceryle torquata*)	
Loggerhead Shrike	Tropical Kingbird	
(*Lanius ludovicianus*)	(*Tyrannus melancholicus*)	
European Starling[b]	Brown Jay	
(*Sturnus vulgaris*)	(*Cyanocorax morio*)	
Lesser Goldfinch	Clay-colored Robin	
(*Carduelis psaltria*)	(*Turdus grayi*)	
House Sparrow)[b]	Altamira Oriole	
(*Passer domesticus*)	(*Icterus gularis*)	

[a] Regular breeding indicates confirmed breeding in more than one location for more than one year (modified from Brush 2005).
[b] Exotic species, not native to North America.

nest in Brooks and Kenedy Counties, immediately north of the LRGV (Benson and Arnold 2001; G. A. Proudfoot, pers. comm.). It is now a confirmed breeder in the LRGV. The first known LRGV nesting was at Bentsen-Rio Grande Valley State Park (hereafter, Bentsen) in 2003 (Brush 2005). Single displaying adults were seen at Sabal Palm Grove, near Brownsville, in 2003 (W. S. Clark, pers. comm.) and at Bentsen on 29 May 2007 (M. Gustafson, pers. comm.). Single adults were observed giving alarm calls at Santa Ana National Wildlife Refuge (hereafter, Santa Ana) in 2005 (W. S. Clark, pers. comm.) and in May 2007. In April–June 2007, a pair produced two young at a nest in Alamo, Hidalgo Co., ca. 11 km north of Santa Ana (K. Hackland, pers. comm., photos).

RED-SHOULDERED HAWK (*BUTEO LINEATUS*)

Broadly distributed in the eastern half of the US as far as the eastern two thirds of Texas, Red-

shouldered Hawk was once a fairly common species in the LRGV in summer, with confirmed breeding records in Cameron and Hidalgo Counties (Oberholser 1974). Declining riparian habitat has impacted this species negatively and it is now only a possible breeder in the LRGV. There are no recent nesting records since successful (1994) and unsuccessful (1995) nests at Santa Ana (Brush and Cantu 1998, Brush 2005). Recently, two adults were observed in the same tree at Santa Ana on 22 December 2006, and one adult and two juveniles were seen flying together in southwestern Cameron County, on 13 March 2005. Those observations were likely of wintering (non-breeding) birds. An adult was seen at a nest (status unknown) ca. 1 km downstream from Salineño, Starr County, on 20 February 2005 (S. G. Monk, pers. comm.). Because nesting activity may begin in early March (Brush 2005), the nest might have been active at that time. More recently, an adult was seen at Santa Ana on 16 June 2007.

SHORT-TAILED HAWK (*BUTEO BRACHYURUS*)

Short-tailed Hawk, a widespread tropical species, was originally absent from the US–Mexico border region. It has expanded northward into the border area, with first records for Texas (LRGV) in 1989, Nuevo León in 1996, and Chihuahua and New Mexico in 2005 (Williams et al. 2007). Short-tailed Hawk was first seen in central Texas (Edwards Plateau) in 1995 (Lockwood and Freeman 2004, Williams et al. 2007). This species is now a possible breeder in the LRGV. Individuals have been observed during the summer in the LRGV, e.g., 6 June–2 July 1996 at Santa Ana. Birds have been seen during spring migration, e.g., 12 April 2003 at Sabal Palm Grove (Lockwood 2004), and 14 April 2007 at Bentsen (W. S. Clark, pers. comm.). They have also been seen during other summers; e.g. 20 June–20 July 2003 and 20 June–4 July 2004 at Santa Ana (Lockwood 2004, 2005) and a light-morph individual at Sabal Palm Grove from 31 March–27 May 2004. The last-mentioned bird paired with a Swainson's Hawk and nested unsuccessfully (Lockwood 2005).

EURASIAN COLLARED-DOVE (*STREPTOPELIA DECAOCTO*)

Eurasian Collared-Dove was introduced to the Bahamas in the mid-1970s, became established in Florida by the late 1980s, and subsequently spread rapidly across the southern US (Romagosa 2002). The species was first noted in the LRGV in 1999 (Brush 2005), and was first noted on an LRGV Breeding Bird Survey (BBS) route in 2003, when eight birds were reported in northeastern Cameron County (Sauer et al. 2006). Eurasian Collared-Dove is now a confirmed breeder in the LRGV. Various observers have noticed birds in display flights, entering possible nesting trees, or showing other signs of nesting. For example, on 3 June 2007, an adult chased a male Great-tailed Grackle (*Quiscalus mexicanus*) from a school campus in western Edinburg, Hidalgo County, but no nest was found. On 26 May 2007, two juveniles were seen in urban habitat on South Padre Island. Those birds remained in dense foliage and, when approached to within 5 m, flew only 20 m away, suggesting recent fledging. On 8 June 2007 at a public park in western Edinburg, a male, which had been vocalizing regularly from the top of a light pole, descended to near ground level and fed one full-grown juvenile by regurgitation. One other vocalizing male was present at the same time.

FERRUGINOUS PYGMY-OWL (*GLAUCIDIUM BRASILIANUM*)

Primarily a tropical species, reaching the US only in southern Arizona and southern Texas, Ferruginous Pygmy-Owl once occurred in woodlands throughout the LRGV. By the mid-20th century, Davis (1966, 1974) determined it to be rare, probably due to extensive habitat loss. This species was not reported from Santa Ana or Bentsen between the 1960s and the early 2000s, but birds were reported regularly from Starr County and the oak-mesquite savannahs and woodlands in Kenedy and Brooks Counties. immediately north of the LRGV (Lockwood and Freeman 2004). Ferruginous Pygmy-Owl is now a confirmed breeder in the LRGV, after >40 yr of uncertain status. After one pygmy-owl was seen in 1994 on a ranch in northeastern Hidalgo County, a nest-box study was begun there in 1995 (G. A. Proudfoot, pers. comm.). From 1999–2006, many broods were raised in nest-boxes, and 163 pygmy-owls have been banded at the ranch (G. A. Proudfoot, unpubl. data and here). Ferruginous Pygmy-Owls were re-discovered at Bentsen in September 2002, by Charles and Louise Gambill (Brush 2005). As of April-May 2007, J. S. Rose (pers. comm.) estimated two territorial pairs at Bentsen, although nesting has not been confirmed there.

BUFF-BELLIED HUMMINGBIRD (*AMAZILIA YUCATANENSIS*)

A tropical species whose range extends into southern Texas, Buff-bellied Hummingbird is a confirmed breeder in the LRGV, nesting regularly from Santa Ana and the Edinburg-McAllen area eastward (Brush 2005). It occurs only in moister woodlands with tropical sage (*Salvia coccinea*) or Turk's cap (*Malvaviscus drummondii*), or in urban areas with natural or artificial nectar sources (Brush 2005). However, Buff-bellied Hummingbird appears to be expanding its breeding distribution westward in the LRGV. A nest was completed by 15 April 2007 at Bentsen, a location historically lacking suitable nectar sources until tropical sage and Turk's cap were planted around the new park headquarters in 2004. Eggs were incubated for about 2 wk until the nest was depredated (M. Gustafson, pers. comm.).

ROSE-THROATED BECARD (*PACHYRAMPHUS AGLAIAE*)

Rose-throated Becard, a tropical species with breeding records only in southern Arizona and southern Texas, was historically a confirmed but rare breeder in the LRGV. Always considered rare (Davis 1966, 1974), Rose-throated Becards nested successfully in the LRGV in the 1940s, 1960s, and 1970s (Brush 2005). However all known recent nesting attempts in the 1990s and the early 2000s have been unsuccessful (Brush 2000, 2005), and the species is currently considered only a possible breeder in the LRGV. A female nested unsuccessfully at Santa Ana in 2003 (observed 9 March–28 June; Lockwood 2004) and 2006 (observed 20 May–22 June; Lockwood 2007). John C. Arvin saw a female at Santa Margarita Ranch, Starr County, on 6 June 2004 (Lockwood 2005), in a county where the species has never been known to nest. With continued declines in tall riparian forest and isolation from existing populations in Nuevo León and Tamaulipas (Brush 2005), re-establishment of a breeding population is unlikely.

LOGGERHEAD SHRIKE (*LANIUS LUDOVICIANUS*)

The historical status of the widespread Loggerhead Shrike in the LRGV has been debated, with some short-term visitors (Sennett 1878, Griscom and Crosby 1926) assuming that it bred, while resident ornithologists and those carefully examining seasonal distribution of specimen records pointed out the lack of breeding-season records (Davis 1974, Phillips 1986). Although declining in the second half of the 20th century in much of the US (Cade and Woods 1997), Loggerhead Shrikes expanded their range south into the LRGV within the past 25 yr. The species has been a confirmed breeder since 1988 (Brush 2005). The first nest was near Alamo, Hidalgo County, and more recently nests have been found throughout southern Hidalgo County. A total of 15 nests were found in Edinburg, McAllen, Mission, Weslaco, and Mercedes during 2005–2007. In Cameron County, a pair of shrikes was seen in April 2004 and March–April 2005, ca. 6 km north of Harlingen, Cameron Co. (C. Watenpool, pers. comm.). Pairs were seen at four additional locations in Harlingen in 2005 (W. S. Clark and P. Wade, pers. comm.), the easternmost suspected breeding sites in the LRGV.

All pairs or nests have been seen in urban habitats such as golf courses, city parks, school yards, and office parks. In most cases, the birds forage regularly over regularly mown grass lawns or infrequently cut grass of vacant city lots. They tend to avoid foraging in dense, tall grass, or residential areas with dense vegetation. On 22 May 2007, an adult was seen in an agricultural area with scattered houses, between Edinburg and Delta Lake, but no nests or pairs have been found in agricultural areas, native grasslands, or open wooded habitats.

In the LRGV, eight of nine BBS sightings of Loggerhead Shrikes were recorded since 1991, indicating their period of establishment (Sauer et al. 2006).

YELLOW-GREEN VIREO (*VIREO FLAVOVIRIDIS*)

A widely distributed tropical species, Yellow-green Vireo was confirmed breeding in the LRGV in 1943 (Davis 1945) but has been considered a rare breeder since then. The most recent known nesting was at Laguna Atascosa National Wildlife Refuge (NWR) in 1988 (Brush 2005). It is now considered a possible breeder in the LRGV. Birds are seen annually in small numbers in riparian remnants and wooded residential areas of southern Hidalgo and Cameron Counties. For example, there has been a singing male on the same territory in Brownsville during the summers of 2004–2007 (M. Gustafson, pers. comm.). Birds are most regularly seen at Sabal Palm Grove, where a maximum of three were observed together from 7 June–17 August 2004, suggesting possible nesting (Lockwood 2005). Additional field work may reveal a small number of nests in areas where birds are most consistently seen.

BROWN JAY (*CYANOCORAX MORIO*)

Although a few Brown Jays were observed in the LRGV between 1890 and 1910, the species began to establish itself as a breeding species in the 1970s. The first nest of this tropical species in the United States was found in 1974, between Salineño and Roma, Starr County. Using riparian forests, Brown Jays soon spread upstream to Falcon Dam and downstream to Roma (Brush 2005). No additional nests were found until 9 May 1996, when Marty Bray and I found a female apparently incubating, accompanied by one other adult and two other birds of uncertain age. That nest was depredated by 25 May 1996 (Brush 2005).

The largest single-day count during the mid-1990s was of 17 birds that Marty Bray and I counted on 20 August 1994, as we canoed between Chapeño and Fronton. J. C. Arvin (pers. comm.) estimated an LRGV population of about 100 individuals during that period. During the late 1990s and early 2000s, a very severe drought period for the LRGV and the surrounding region, Brown Jays were seen in much smaller numbers consisting of two flocks of <10 individuals total, only at or near the feeding stations at Chapeño and Salineño (Brush 2005, Lockwood 2007). J. Puschock (pers. comm.) reported an adult carrying a stick across the Rio Grande at Chapeño on 20 or 21

July 2003, but no nests were found during 2003–2007. Although additional field work is needed, Brown Jay is currently only a possible breeder in the LRGV. Given its apparent isolation from the closest known population along the Sierra Madre Oriental from Monterrey, Nuevo León, south into Tamaulipas, there must be concern over the future of the LRGV Brown Jays.

TAMAULIPAS CROW (*CORVUS IMPARATUS*)

Tamaulipas Crow, endemic to northeastern Mexico, invaded the LRGV in 1968 (Oberholser 1974). During 1968–1971, hundreds to thousands of birds were observed in the Brownsville area, and it was confirmed as a breeder in 1989, when four nests were found east of Brownsville (Brush 2005). The species was regular in small numbers at the Brownsville Municipal Landfill through most of the 1990s, but nests were neither sought nor found. Tamaulipas Crows were less regularly seen at the landfill in the late 1990s and early 2000s, but observers found a few nests in eastern Brownsville during that period (Lockwood and Freeman 2004, Brush 2005). Today this species remains a confirmed nester in very small numbers. For example, two adults and two juveniles were seen in Brownsville from early May to late July 2004, but no nest was reported (Lockwood 2005). J. C. Arvin and D. Benn (pers. comm.) saw six pairs building nests in Brownsville on 27 March 2005, and at least 16 birds (including adults and juveniles) were seen in the same area from late March–late July 2005 (Lockwood 2006). In 2007, only one nest was found in Brownsville (B. Buchanan and J. Odgers, pers. comm.). The Tamaulipas Crows nesting in Brownsville may be isolated from the main population center of southern Tamaulipas (J. C. Arvin, pers. comm.), so any possible losses in the LRGV population due to extreme weather or other causes would be difficult to replace.

BLUE-GRAY GNATCATCHER (*POLIOPTILA CAERULEA*)

Widespread across most of the US and the Mexican Highlands, the breeding status of Blue-gray Gnatcatcher in the LRGV has long been unclear (Oberholser 1974, Phillips 1991). In the late 1870s, the species nested in Hidalgo County, but Blue-gray Gnatcatchers were never a common nesting species (Oberholser 1974, Brush 2005). The most recent active nest was reported in 1921 near Port Isabel (Oberholser, unpubl. data). Davis (1974) stated that there were no definite June records and that it was not a breeder. Currently, the species is a very rare summer resident and possible breeder in the

LRGV. A singing male was observed at Estero Llano Grande State Park near Weslaco, on 24 June 2006 (R. Zamora, pers. comm.). Daniel Jones saw a pair at La Sal del Rey, Lower Rio Grande Valley NWR on 20 May 2007, but the pair could not be relocated on 22 May. Early fall migrants, sometimes seen in late June or early July, confuse the breeding status of local birds. Additionally, the species is a common winter resident and migrant throughout the region (Phillips 1991, Brush 2005).

YELLOW WARBLER (*DENDROICA PETECHIA*)

The Mangrove Yellow Warbler (presumably *D. p. oraria*; Parkes and Dickerman 1967) was first recorded in the Port Isabel area, Cameron County, in 1978 and again in 1990 (Lockwood and Freeman 2004). These were the first records of the Mexican subspecies, characterized by a completely chestnut head in the adult male, in the United States (Lowther et al. 1999). This subspecies appears to be expanding northward from southeastern Tamaulipas. One seen near Port Isabel 1 December 2003–1 March 2004 (S. Colley, pers. comm.), and an adult male at the mouth of the Rio Grande (Boca Chica area) 17 April–5 May 2004 (Lockwood 2005), preceded a major invasion of the species. About 30 were seen near Port Isabel, from August–December 2004 (Lockwood 2006).

Yellow Warbler is now a confirmed breeder for the LRGV. At least one fledgling was fed by an adult male near Port Isabel on 14 May 2007 (J. Bax and S. Colley, pers. comm.). A nest with one egg was found in the same area on 28 May 2007, and five eggs were counted in that nest on 5 June 2007 (S. Colley, pers. comm.). All birds have occurred on tidal flats dominated by black mangrove (*Avicennia germinans*), which has re-established itself throughout much of the Lower Laguna Madre area since the severe freezes of 1983 and 1989. Black mangrove is generally 2–3 m tall and usually grows in strips less than 200 m wide in its Texas range (Tunnell and Judd 2002), but this narrow band of habitat is still usable by Mangrove Yellow Warblers.

GRAY-CROWNED YELLOWTHROAT (*GEOTHLYPIS POLIOCEPHALA*)

In the late 1800s, Gray-crowned Yellowthroat, a tropical species, was commonly encountered by ornithologists in the LRGV. It bred at Hidalgo (1880) and near Port Isabel (1921), and >34 specimens were taken in the Brownsville area from 1890–1894 (Oberholser 1974; Oberholser, unpubl. data; Lorenz et al. 2006). This, the only breeding population in the United States, disappeared in the early 20th century, possibly due to loss of wetlands or associated habitats. Subsequently, the Gray-crowned Yellowthroat was recorded very rarely in Cameron Co. until 1988, when the species was rediscovered at Sabal Palm Grove (Lockwood and Freeman 2004). A probable breeding pair was found in northwestern Webb Co. in 1997 (Woodin et al. 1998), a few territorial males were observed in 1999 and 2000 at Santa Ana (Brush 2005), and a male was observed at Sabal Palm Grove from 8 February–12 August 2004. One to two individuals were recorded there from 8 December 2004–30 June 2005 (Lockwood 2006).

Today, the Gray-crowned Yellowthroat can again be considered a confirmed breeder in the LRGV. On 25 June 2005, a nest with four recent hatchlings was discovered at the Sabal Palm Grove, and the male was banded on 29 June (Lorenz et al. 2006). Although the nest had been depredated when re-checked on 30 June 2005, 1–2 individuals continued to be seen in the area through 17 May 2007 (J. Paz, pers. comm.). The grass-dominated fields with scattered small woody plants, which the birds used at Sabal Palm Grove, are similar to those used in Tamaulipas (Brush 2005). The birds breeding recently in the LRGV are likely of the northeastern Mexican-LRGV subspecies, *G. p. ralphi*, but no in-hand examination has been carried out to confirm this.

SUMMER TANAGER (*PIRANGA RUBRA*)

Widespread across the southern United States and also occurring in north-central Mexico, Summer Tanager vanished as a breeding species from the LRGV in the early 1970s as riparian forest deteriorated due to lack of flooding and was lost due to clearing for agriculture (Oberholser 1974, Brush 2005). However, the species may be making a modest comeback and is again a confirmed breeder in the LRGV. A completed nest with a few female breast feathers was found ca. 5 km southwest of Mission in 1999 (Brush 2005). On 8 July 2006 a pair fed at least two fledglings on a ranch in northeastern Hidalgo Co. (K. Hunke, pers. comm.), and two males were seen in the same location on 12 May 2007. The species remains common in live oak (*Quercus virginiana*) forest patches and strips of tall riparian forest 30–190 km north of the LRGV (Lockwood and Freeman 2004).

WHITE-COLLARED SEEDEATER (*SPOROPHILA TORQUEOLA*)

The White-collared Seedeater, a widespread tropical species, was once considered common

in wetlands and moist grassy areas along the Rio Grande and resacas (oxbow lakes) in the LRGV (Davis 1966, Oberholser 1974). It then declined, becoming uncommon in the 1960s and extremely rare in the 1970s (Davis 1966, 1974; Oberholser 1974). Reasons for the decline are poorly understood, since weedy habitat remains widespread in the LRGV. Extensive pesticide application to the greatly expanded cotton acreage and increased cowbird numbers may have been important (Oberholser 1974). Seedeaters still breed in Zapata and Webb Counties immediately upstream of the LRGV (Woodin et al. 1999, Lockwood and Freeman 2004). A singing male was observed in moist resaca-edge habitat at Santa Ana NWR on 18 May 2007, but there has been no evidence of recolonization of the LRGV. It is therefore considered only a possible breeder in the LRGV.

HOUSE FINCH (*CARPODACUS MEXICANUS*)

Common and widespread across much of North America and most of Mexico, the House Finch is a very rare winter resident in South Texas south of Laredo and Rockport, including the LRGV (Lockwood and Freeman 2004). The species is absent from the coastal plain of eastern Mexico (Howell and Webb 1995). A singing male was seen at Roma, Starr County, on 21 April 2007, and two pairs were observed regularly at the University of Texas-Texas Southmost College campus, Brownsville, for at least 2 wk in May 2007 (P. Wade pers. comm., photos of two males from those pairs taken on 17 May 2007). It is not known why House Finches, which are well-adapted to both urban and rural areas, have been slow to colonize the LRGV, but based on the recent observations, they are now probable breeders. Incidentally, a singing male in Ciudad Mante, southwestern Tamaulipas, 29 May 2007, may indicate an attempted range expansion in Tamaulipas as well.

DISCUSSION

Establishment or recolonization of several avian species has occurred in the LRGV in recent years. For species such as Gray-crowned Yellowthroat and House Finch, the first step in recolonization or colonization seems to be winter residency by small numbers of individuals (Brush 2005). The probable source of colonists for tropical species is eastern Mexico (Tamaulipas and southern Nuevo León), while temperate or US–Mexican border species may spread downstream along the Rio Grande or directly south through South Texas toward the LRGV. Summer Tanager and Ferruginous

Pygmy-Owl probably spread south from the remaining oak forests immediately north of the LRGV (Proudfoot and Johnson 2000, Lockwood and Freeman 2004).

Species such as Mangrove Yellow Warbler, that became established for the first time as breeders may have taken advantage of habitat expansion or recovery, such as the re-establishment of black mangrove since severe freezes of 1983 and 1989, which killed or severely stunted this frost-sensitive species (Lonard and Judd 1991, Tunnell and Judd 2002). Presumably, the warblers spread north from their nearest known breeding range in southeastern Tamaulipas (Howell and Webb 1995), but it is not known whether the species also occurs in northeastern Tamaulipas. Another opportunistic and rapidly expanding tropical species, the Clay-colored Robin (*Turdus grayi*), established itself in the late 1990s in riparian forest and expanding urban forests and became widespread in the LRGV and upstream to Laredo (Brush 2005).

Breeding distributions of well-established species like Buff-Bellied Hummingbird may be dependent upon management practices such as planting native nectar sources. For Red-shouldered Hawk and Rose-throated Becard, which depend on tall riparian forest near water, habitat management has proven more difficult. Water is often in short supply or cannot be delivered to desiccated forests, with resultant loss of lush riparian forests and associated wetlands along many stretches of the lower Rio Grande. A pilot flooding project in a riparian forest patch at Santa Ana enhanced tree survival and reproduction, but was on too small a scale to help those avian species (Brush 2005)

For tropical species which are at the northern edge of their breeding range, such as Tamaulipas Crow and Brown Jay, isolation from other breeding populations may be contributing to their decline. Both Tamaulipas Crows and Brown Jays are now very rare or absent in northern Tamaulipas (J. C. Arvin, pers. comm.). Although there have been no obvious changes in their preferred LRGV habitats, any impacts of drought might be more difficult for a small population to recover from.

For some species, such as White-collared Seedeater, the reasons for population declines and failure to recolonize historically-occupied habitats remain unclear. Plant species thought to provide suitable habitat, such as giant reed (*Arundo donax*), common reed (*Phragmites australis*), and shorter grasses are common in the LRGV. However, perhaps the area is too fragmented to allow recolonization, or some other unknown, crucial habitat feature is missing (Eitniear 1997, 2004).

Preference for or tolerance of urban habitats has aided Loggerhead Shrikes and Eurasian Collared-Doves in their establishment in the LRGV. The apparently successful colonization of Loggerhead Shrikes is noteworthy, given the species' decline in much of the US and Canada. The urban habitats used in the LRGV resemble the savannah or parkland habitat often used by shrikes elsewhere. Boal et al. (2003) also noted urban nesting by shrikes in Tucson, Arizona. In a semiarid climate such as within the LRGV, use of irrigated habitats may ensure a more reliable food source. If shrikes are in fact better adapted to wetter coastal habitats, they may be able to establish themselves in coastal Tamaulipas, as some recent observations suggest (Wauer 1998, Ramírez-Albores et al. 2007). Eurasian Collared-Doves were at first limited to grain elevators, where seed abundance is greatest, but they have since spread into other urban habitats as they have begun breeding. The species has spread south throughout the lowlands of Tamaulipas in the early 2000s (T. Brush, unpubl. data), mainly in agricultural areas.

Some predictions can be made about future breeding status and distribution of new additions to the LRGV avifauna. Although some species appear well established, others may be susceptible to extreme weather events. For examples, future severe freezes could have considerable impact on the Mangrove Yellow Warbler, which breeds in freeze-sensitive black mangrove habitat. The future status of other species that are spreading north, such as Short-tailed Hawks, are largely unpredictable, due to uncertainties about their habitat and foraging requirements. If current climatic and habitat trends continue, several urban-tolerant tropical species, such as Blue-gray Tanager (*Thraupis episcopus*) and Social Flycatcher (*Myiozetetes similis*), both of which bred in southern Nuevo León in 2007 (Gómez de Silva 2007), may eventually be added to the LRGV breeding avifauna. Several other species have moved northward in eastern Mexico in the past decade, such as Ivory-billed Woodcreeper (*Xiphorhynchus flavigaster*) and Scrub Euphonia (*Euphonia affinis*; Garza-Torres et al. 2003; Brush, in press). Species such as the last two, dependent on high-quality riparian or other moist forests will probably have a harder time colonizing than urban-adapted species. Continual change should be expected in the LRGV's avifauna, given population growth and related habitat changes expected in this rapidly growing metropolitan area on the US–Mexican border.

ACKNOWLEDGMENTS

The University of Texas-Pan American provided space for electronic and physical storage of breeding records. I thank the many field observers whose observations, often made under challenging conditions, are cited in this paper. Thanks to Glenn A. Proudfoot for providing unpublished data on Ferruginous Pygmy-Owls and for other suggestions. Marc Woodin and Mary Gustafson provided useful comments on an earlier version. Luis Materon provided the resumen.

Studies in Avian Biology No. 37:20–27

AVIFAUNAL CHANGES IN BIG BEND NATIONAL PARK, TEXAS

Roland H. Wauer and Mark Flippo

Abstract. Population changes in the breeding avifauna of the Big Bend National Park from 1901 through 2006 were recorded for 24 species. They include recent arrivals, increasing, declining or extirpated, apparently stable species, and species of uncertain status. Recent arrivals include Black-crowned Night-Heron (*Nycticorax nycticorax*), Eurasian Collared-Dove (*Streptopelia decaocto*), Golden-fronted Woodpecker (*Melanerpes aurifrons*), Dusky-capped Flycatcher (*Myiarchus tuberculifer*), Cave Swallow (*Petrochelidon fulva*), Carolina Wren (*Thryothorus ludovicianus*), and Lucy's Warbler (*Vermivora luciae*). Increasing species include Mallard (*Anas platyrchynchos*), Green Heron (*Butorides virescens*), Gray Hawk (*Buteo nitida*), Common Black-Hawk (*Buteogallus anthracinus*), Lucifer Hummingbird (*Calopthorax lucifer*), Green Kingfisher (*Chloroceryle americana*), Painted Redstart (*Myioborus pictus*), Great-tailed Grackle (*Quiscalus mexicanus*), and Bronzed Cowbird (*Molothrus aeneus*). Declining or extirpated species include Gambel's Quail (*Callipepla gambelii*), Montezuma Quail (*Cyrtonyx montezumae*), Harris's Hawk (*Parabuteo unicinctus*), Golden Eagle (*Aquila chrysaetos*), Prairie Falcon (*Falco mexicanus*), Yellow Warbler (*Dendroica petechia*), and Hooded Oriole (*Icterus cucullatus*). Apparently stable species include Peregrine Falcon (*Falco peregrinus*), Loggerhead Shrike (*Lanius ludovicianus*), Bell's Vireo (*Vireo bellii*), Black-capped Vireo (*Vireo atricapilla*), and Colima Warbler (*Vermivora crissalis*). Uncertain status applies only to Aplomado Falcon (*Falco femoralis*).

Key words: avifaunal declines, avifaunal increases, Big Bend National Park, breeding avifauna, new arrivals, stable species, west Texas.

CAMBIOS A LA AVEFAUNA DEL PARQUE NACIONAL BIG BEND, TEXAS

Resumen. Desde 1901 hasta 2006 ha registrado cambios en la población de 24 especies de aves que anidan en el parque nacional Big Bend. Categorías para ellos incluyen recién llegado, aumentado, diminuido o extinguido, especies aparentemente en estado estable, y finalmente, en estado incierto. Especies recién llegados incluyen *Nycticorax nycticorax*, *Streptopelia decaocto*, *Melanerpes aurifrons*, *Myiarchus tuberculifer*, *Petrochelidon fulva*, *Thryothorus ludovicianus*), y *Vermivora luciae*. Especies con población aumentado incluyen pato de *Anas platyrchynchos*, *Butorides virescens*, *Buteo nitida*, *Buteogallus anthracinus*, *Calopthorax lucifer*, *Chloroceryle americana*, *Myioborus pictus*, *Quiscalus mexicanus*, y *Molothrus aeneus*. Especies diminuidos o extinguidos incluyen *Callipepla gambelii*, *Cyrtonyx montezumae*, *Parabuteo unicinctus*, (*Aquila chrysaetos*, *Falco mexicanus*, *Dendroica petechia*, y *Icterus cucullatus*. Especies aparentemente en estado estable incluyen *Falco peregrinus*, *Lanius ludovicianus*, *Vireo bellii*, *Vireo atricapilla*, y *Vermivora crissalis*. La categoría de especies en estado incierto aplica únicamente al *Falco femoralis*.

The Big Bend region of western Texas includes a great variety of habitats, including desertscrub and grassland at lower elevations and woodlands dominated by oaks (*Quercus* spp.) and pines (*Pinus* spp.) at higher elevations. Emory Peak, the highest point, is 2,385 m above sea level. The region is best known for supporting the only US breeding population of Colima Warbler (*Vermivora crissalis*) but also contains a great variety of resident and migratory species, including many species characteristic of the US–Mexico border region (Wauer 1973, 1996; Lockwood and Freeman 2004). Much land is currently protected within Big Bend National Park, and the remainder is in private or public ownership.

The earliest ornithological study in the Big Bend region occurred when the United States Biological Survey visited in 1901 (Wauer 1996). During May, June, and July of that year, Harry C. Oberholser, Vernon Bailey, and Louis Agassiz Fuertes conducted extensive field work throughout the area. Oberholser (1902) summarized their more important findings, Fuertes (1903) published on the Montezuma Quail (*Cyrtonyx montezumae*), and Bailey (1905) reported on the expedition's overall findings.

This early period of activity was followed by one in which expeditions to this remote section of the United States were discouraged due to unrest along the border associated with the Mexican Revolution. In 1928, Josselyn Van Tyne, accompanied by F. M. and H. T. Gaige, surveyed the bird life from Alpine to the summit of Emory Peak between 8 June and 7 August. Significant findings of that expedition included the first specimen of Colima Warbler for the US and only the twelfth known specimen of this species. Van Tyne returned in 1932, and reported his successful search for nesting Colima Warblers

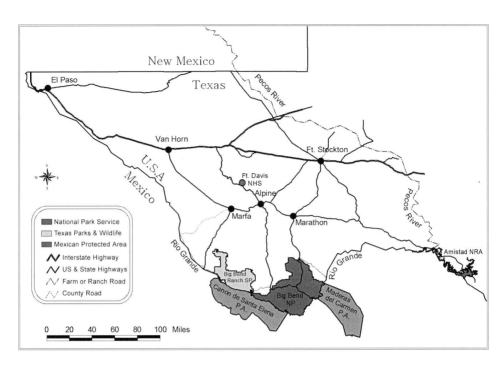

FIGURE 1. Map of Big Bend National Park, Texas, and the surrounding areas of the United States and Mexico.

(Van Tyne 1936). By this time, sufficient information on the bird life of the area was available to permit a comprehensive analysis of the avifauna (Van Tyne and Sutton 1937) in which a total of 215 species of birds was reported.

Big Bend National Park (BBNP) was established in southern Brewster County, Texas, in 1944 (Fig. 1), and National Park Service (NPS) employees began to record their bird observations. Harold Brodrick, the first park naturalist, maintained excellent bird records. Brodrick (1960) listed 236 species for BBNP. C. Phillip Allen and Anne LeSassier, who added several important records, revised Brodrick's checklist (Brodrick et al. 1966), increasing it to 241 species. Since then, revised park checklists have appeared every 5-10 yr; an upcoming edition currently features 409 confirmed species and 41 hypothetical species (R. H. Wauer and M. Flippo, unpubl. data).

The following list includes only breeding bird species whose status has changed, since records have been available. They are described as recent arrivals or as increasing, declining or extirpated species, and species of uncertain status. Our report is based upon data obtained from the historic and contemporary literature and field work by the authors. Unless otherwise cited, historic records are assumed to be from Wauer (1973, 1996), and new records summarized by

the authors from unpublished bird records submitted to Big Bend National Park.

RESULTS

MALLARD (*ANAS PLATYRHYNCHOS*)

Status: *increasing*. Although the Mallard has been considered to be only a winter resident in the Big Bend region, the subspecies known as Mexican Duck (*A. p. diazi*), is a fairly common year-round resident in aquatic habitats within and adjacent to BBNP and its abundance has increased in recent years. Intergrades between *A. p. platyrhynchos and A. p. diazi* are found occasionally.

GAMBEL'S QUAIL (*CALLIPEPLA GAMBELII*)

Status: *declining*. Wauer (1973) reported it to be an extremely rare resident in the Big Bend lowlands, with recent (since 1966) sightings at Maverick, the Old Ranch, Dugout Wells, and along the River Road. Oberholser (1974) considered it a fairly common resident along the Rio Grande from El Paso County south to upper Big Bend in Presidio County and rare to Big Bend National Park (nesting unconfirmed) and Terrell County (nesting doubtful). There have been no further reports for BBNP.

MONTEZUMA QUAIL (*CYRTONYX MONTEZUMAE*)

Status: *declining with possible limited recovery*. Van Tyne and Sutton (1937) reported that as early as 1933 this species seemed to be on the decline in BBNP. Local hunters and ranchers testified unanimously to the great decrease in the numbers of this quail in recent years in even remote areas. No adequate explanation of this decrease was offered but surely overgrazing, which now prevails in nearly every part of the country, must be an important contributing factor. Albers and Gehlbach (1990) found that Montezuma Quail in the Edwards Plateau disappeared when 40–50% of the tall grass was removed from an area. No BBNP records occurred for Montezuma Quail after the early 1940s. In January 1973, Wauer released 26 birds captured near Nogales, Arizona, into suitable habitat in the Pine Canyon area of the Chisos Mountains. In May 1973, five individuals were found there, along with two other birds in upper Boot Canyon. Since the 1973 release there were only scattered reports from the 1980s into the early 2000s.

In May 2003, Flippo and Dan Leavitt reported a probable calling male in upper Green Gulch. This report was followed by several other unconfirmed observations in 2004 and early 2005. On 28 May 2005, Sylvestre Sorola, David Holdermann, and Raymond Skiles confirmed the species' presence when they observed and video-taped two or three males on the South Rim of the Chisos (Holdermann et al. 2007). Subsequent visitor reports from the same area indicated that the quail remained through the summer of 2005.

The numerous reports of Montezuma Quail from 2003 through 2005, after so many years, raise the question of where they came from. Possible scenarios include: (1) the introduced birds and their progeny persisted in low density until detected, (2) surplus birds from a population in Mexico's Maderas del Carmen, approximately 80 km to the southeast, somehow found their way across the desert into adequate habitat in the Chisos Mountains, or (3) the quail have always been there but were overlooked because of their secretive nature and perhaps low density, in spite of the uncountable hours by birders and researchers in suitable habitat throughout the same areas.

Montezuma Quail is a rare and declining species in Texas (Shackelford and Lockwood 2000). Extant populations in the Davis Mountains, in intervening ranges with suitable habitat, and in the Maderas del Carmen range of Mexico are highly isolated and discontinuous.

GREEN HERON (*BUTORIDES VIRESCENS*)

Status: *increasing*. Nesting records anywhere along the Rio Grande corridor from El Paso downstream through the Big Bend region were reported only occasionally during the 1930s (Oberholser 1974). That status did not change, at least for BBNP (Wauer 1996), through the 1990s. However, the Green Heron is now a permanent resident in the park, and an uncommon nester at Rio Grande Village in southeastern BBNP. Efforts underway to restore permanent wetland areas near Rio Grande Village may enhance that population.

BLACK-CROWNED NIGHT-HERON (*NYCTICORAX NYCTICORAX*)

Status: *recent arrival*. Previously, it had been considered only as a rare spring migrant; casual in summer, fall, and winter in the park (Wauer 1996). Increased sightings of birds year-round starting in the 1990s, included juveniles in late summer and early fall at Rio Grande Village, suggest breeding.

COMMON BLACK-HAWK (*BUTEOGALLUS ANTHRACINUS*)

Status: *increasing*. Although this species has nested in the Davis Mountains in the northern edge of the Big Bend Country at least since 1940, nesting was not recorded in the BBNP area until 1979 (Wauer 1996). Nesting has occurred almost every year since then, including a nest in Rio Grande Village, which has been utilized every summer by black-hawks for the past decade. Shackelford and Lockwood (2000) consider it a rare and declining bird in Texas, although there is also a small population along the Devil's River in central Val Verde County (Lockwood and Freeman 2004), and one–two pairs nest in the Concho Valley near San Angelo (M. W. Lockwood, pers. comm.). A pair nested at 1927 m in the Davis Mountains in 2000, indicating some expansion from lowland canyons into higher elevations (Bryan and Karges 2001), but no such upward expansion has been seen in BBNP.

HARRIS'S HAWK (*PARABUTEO UNICINCTUS*)

Status: *declining or extirpated*. Considered a rare summer and winter visitor and migrant, there have been no documented nesting records within BBNP since 1964 (Wauer 1996). It does occur to the northeast, especially east of Sanderson, Texas, and to the west of the park in central and northern Presidio County.

GRAY HAWK (*BUTEO NITIDA*)

Status: increasing. Prior to 1988, when nesting was discovered in BBNP (Wauer 1996), its US nesting range was thought to be the Lower Rio Grande Valley of Texas, southwestern New Mexico, and southeastern Arizona (Oberholser 1974, Phillips et al. 1964). Since 1988 one–two pairs have nested almost every year along the floodplain at Cottonwood Campground and Rio Grande Village. Beyond BBNP, Gray Hawks colonized the Davis Mountains in 1995 and now several pairs are known to nest in that area. Within BBNP it is considered uncommon in spring, summer, and fall and has over-wintered once at Cottonwood Campground. In addition, a Gray Hawk paired with a Red-shouldered Hawk (*B. lineatus*) was found nesting near Cottonwood Campground in 1988; the one hatchling did not survive. Shackelford and Lockwood (2000) include Gray Hawk in their list of rare and declining Texas birds.

GOLDEN EAGLE (*AQUILA CHRYSAETOS*)

Status: declining or extirpated. Wauer (1996) reported that at least five pairs of Golden Eagles occurred in BBNP during the summer, and he listed several breeding records from the Chisos Mountains. It was then considered an uncommon summer resident. However, valid reports have become increasingly scarce over the past 5 yr or so. The last possible breeding pair in BBNP was seen in the Dead Horse Mountains on 28 May 1985 (Wauer 1996), but it was not known if the birds remained together or nested.

APLOMADO FALCON (*FALCO FEMORALIS*)

Status: uncertain. Although the species was once present on the yucca (*Yucca* spp.)-studded grasslands in the Marfa-Valentine-Sierra Blanca region, eastward to BBNP and the Pecos River valley, no verified records exist from the early 1950s to the early 1990s. In 1992, one individual was seen near Valentine, Jeff Davis County (Wauer 1996). Recent reintroduction efforts have been underway north of the park in the Marfa grasslands in northeastern Presidio County and in the Marathon Basin area of northern Brewster County (http://www.peregrinefund.org/press_full.asp?id=9&category=Aplomado%20Falcon). The Aplomado Falcon is listed as a rare and declining Texas bird by Shackelford and Lockwood (2000). On 28 March 2007, BBNP visitors John and Char Ester photographed a banded Aplomado Falcon on an ocotillo (*Fouquieria splendens*) approximately 11 km southeast of Panther Junction. Peregrine Fund

representatives with the West Texas restoration project identified the falcon as a female released in 2004 18 km east of Marathon, Texas. No further observations of this or other Aplomados have been documented in the park.

PEREGRINE FALCON (*FALCO PEREGRINUS*)

Status: apparently stable. On 25 August 1999, the Peregrine Falcon was officially removed from the US Endangered species list. Texas, however, still lists the Peregrine Falcon as Endangered. Of the fewer than 20 known breeding pairs in the state, most occur in the Big Bend Region. With delisting, federal funding for annual surveys of the Big Bend Peregrine population diminished, and for the last five years (2002–2007) the NPS has only conducted limited surveys at four known nesting sites. As far as is known, the population remains stable within BBNP.

PRAIRIE FALCON (*FALCO MEXICANUS*)

Status: declining or extirpated. Wauer (1996) listed a number of nesting sites within BBNP at least through 1995. There have been no recent nesting records for the park, although there was a nesting pair just west of BBNP on Hen Egg Mountain near Study Butte as recently as 2006.

EURASIAN COLLARED-DOVE (*STREPTOPELIA DECAOCTO*)

Status: recent arrival. The first verified reports of this rapidly expanding exotic species in BBNP occurred in April and May 2001 (Sexton 2001). Since spring 2004 they have been reported from numerous locations throughout the Big Bend region. Breeding populations have become established at Study Butte, Terlingua, Lajitas, Redford, Presidio, Marathon, and Alpine. M. W. Lockwood (pers. comm.) estimates the Alpine population at more than 5,000 individuals. Breeding was first confirmed in BBNP at Rio Grande Village in 2006.

LUCIFER HUMMINGBIRD (*CALOTHORAX LUCIFER*)

Status: increasing. The first record of this hummingbird for the US was in 1901 by the U.S. Biological Survey (Bailey 1905), and it was considered a vagrant until the first US nest was discovered near Terlingua in July 1962 (Pulich and Pulich 1963). Since then it has become fairly common in BBNP; P. Scott (pers. comm.) located 24 nests between Panther Junction and the Chisos Basin during May and June 1982. M. W. Lockwood (pers. comm.) has found male and female Lucifers, but no nests, during the breeding season in both the Christmas (just north of BBNP) and Chinati Mountains (west of BBNP in Presidio County).

GREEN KINGFISHER (*CHLOROCERYLE AMERICANA*)

Status: *increasing.* In BBNP, no records existed until 1966, but it has been reported every year since then, primarily as a fall–winter visitor. No nesting has been recorded within the park, but a few records are known primarily from along the Rio Grande west of the park. East of BBNP, Green Kingfishers are common along the Devils River, Val Verde County, and Independence Creek, Terrill County, and they also occur along the lower Pecos River (J. Karges, pers. comm.), so future establishment of the species in BBNP is possible.

GOLDEN-FRONTED WOODPECKER (*MELANERPES AURIFRONS*)

Status: *recent arrival.* The status of this bird has changed dramatically since the mid-1970s, when it was considered a rare vagrant to BBNP (Wauer 1969). By the mid-1980s it had become a locally common year-round resident in cottonwood canopy habitat at Rio Grande Village and Cottonwood Campground. Wandering individuals occasionally appear at Panther Junction (grasslands) and Dugout Wells (desert oasis) in the spring. West of BBNP, Golden-fronted Woodpeckers are present along the Rio Grande upstream to Presidio, including wooded tributaries in Big Bend Ranch State Park. They also occur north of BBNP along Calamity Creek and at Post County Park, near Marathon, northern Brewster County

DUSKY-CAPPED FLYCATCHER (*MYIARCHUS TUBERCULIFER*)

Status: *recent arrival.* A very rare species in Texas, this small *Myiarchus* of the oak-pine woodlands has been a casual visitor to the park since 1937 (Van Tyne and Sutton 1937, Wauer 1996). In the spring of 2000, a pair nested on the lower Laguna Meadow Trail, approximately 3 km from the Chisos Basin (Lockwood 2002). On 9 May, the pair was photographed carrying nesting material to a cavity in a large oak. Later, on 23 June, two adults were photographed carrying insects into the nest. The next day at least two nestlings were heard calling from the cavity. Finally, an adult and two fledglings were seen on 27 June. This was the first confirmed nesting of this species in Texas. In subsequent years (2001, 2003, 2004, 2007) pairs of Dusky-

capped Flycatchers have been observed higher up in the Boot Canyon drainage where nesting was probable, but not confirmed. A pair was seen in the Davis Mountains in June 1991 (Peterson et al. 1991), and the species has since become a low-density but regular nester there (M. W. Lockwood, pers. comm.).

TROPICAL KINGBIRD (*TYRANNUS MELANCHOLICUS*)

Status: *recent arrival.* First documented in BBNP in June 1996 at Cottonwood Campground, a pair was subsequently found nest-building there. The nest failed after a late-summer thunderstorm. Since the initial discovery, 1–3 pairs of Tropical Kingbirds have nested every year at the same location. Nesting also has been confirmed once at Rio Grande Village (2002), and once (1999) at Post County Park (Lockwood and Freeman 2004). The species was removed from the Texas Ornithological Society review list in 1999 based on the establishment of a permanent population in the lower Rio Grande Valley, in southernmost Texas (Brush 2005).

LOGGERHEAD SHRIKE (*LANIUS LUDOVICIANUS*)

Status: *apparently stable.* Although declines have been noted elsewhere, particularly in the northeast and upper midwestern US, Loggerhead Shrike populations in the Big Bend Region seem to be stable, although its status is uncertain due to lack of targeted study. At BBNP it is a common to fairly common bird of the open desert during the winter and uncommon during the breeding season.

BELL'S VIREO (*VIREO BELLII*)

Status: *apparently stable.* Although this species is listed as a rare and declining species in Texas (Shackelford and Lockwood 2000), no appreciable change has been detected in its status in BBNP. It is an abundant summer resident on the Rio Grande floodplain and can also be found in smaller numbers nesting in dense brushy habitat from the Chisos Basin out into the lower desert along dry arroyos with suitable shrubby thickets.

BLACK-CAPPED VIREO (*VIREO ATRICAPILLA*)

Status: *apparently stable.* A US Endangered species, its status in BBNP has remained stable. It is at the western edge of its range and is considered an uncommon summer resident. Surveys have been conducted annually in May since 1986. From a high count of 36 individuals found in 1995, subsequent surveys noted a decline in the population through the late 1990s to a low of only 10 individuals in 2001. Researchers have attributed this decline to extreme drought periods. The population rebounded by 2004 to a total of 28–31 individuals, 23–25 of which were adult birds (Maresh 2004). The most recent survey (2006) reported 25-27 individuals, 23-25 of which were adults (Troy 2006). This small population is scattered in and around the Chisos Mountains in areas of transitional deciduous shrubland (dominated by gray oak, [*Quercus grisea*], and evergreen sumac, [*Rhus virens*]) between lower desert scrub and higher pine-oak-juniper woodland. Core areas include Juniper Canyon, Green Gulch, Oak Creek Canyon, and the Upper Chisos Basin (Panther Pass to Chisos Basin campground).

CAVE SWALLOW (*PETROCHELIDON FULVA*)

Status: *recent arrival*. This species was not recorded in BBNP prior to 1969, when a nesting colony was discovered on Mariscal Mountain, in the southern section of BBNP (Wauer and Davis 1972). Since then they have been reported sporadically within the park, and the species has expanded its range throughout much of Texas (Lockwood and Freeman 2004).

CAROLINA WREN (*THRYOTHORUS LUDOVICIANUS*)

Status: *recent arrival*. This eastern wren first appeared at Rio Grande Village during the 1990s, and has since been recorded on numerous occasions along the floodplain near the eastern edge of the park as well as at a number of locations some distance from the river. Locations include higher elevations in the Chisos Mountains such as Boot Canyon. Although there are no known nesting records, there is little doubt that it is an established resident. There are also sightings west of BBNP, upstream to Lajitas.

COLIMA WARBLER (*VERMIVORA CRISSALIS*)

Status: *apparently stable*. This Mexican montane species reaches the northern edge of its breeding range in the Chisos Mountains, BBNP. Because it is found nowhere else in the US, surveys have been conducted about every 5 yr, from 1967 through 2006. The surveys provided sufficient evidence that the Big Bend population was remaining stable. In the Davis Mountains, several Colima Warblers, as well as individuals which were intermediate in appearance between Colima Warbler and Virginia's Warbler (*Vermivora virginiae*) in 2005 and 2006. This has prompted speculation of a hybrid

swarm (Lockwood et al. 2006; M.W. Lockwood, pers. comm.) but needs further study.

LUCY'S WARBLER (*VERMIVORA LUCIAE*)

Status: *recent arrival*. Although this southwestern warbler has long been a breeding bird along the floodplain below El Paso in extreme western Texas (Oberholser 1974), reports from farther east increased during the 1970s and 1980s. These included nesting near Candelaria, Presidio County, in 1979, and the first nest at Cottonwood Campground in 1986 (Wauer 1996). Nesting in mesquite bosques upstream from Cottonwood Campground to the mouth of Santa Elena Canyon, BBNP, has become an annual occurrence.

YELLOW WARBLER (*DENDROICA PETECHIA*)

Status: *declining or extirpated*. Although Van Tyne and Sutton (1937) found this species nesting along the floodplain in the eastern portion of BBNP during the 1930s, no known nesting has occurred since. It is likely that this species has been extirpated from the park and elsewhere along the Rio Grande in Texas.

PAINTED REDSTART (*MYIOBORUS PICTUS*)

Status: *increasing*. This species was first reported from the Chisos Mountains in 1928 (Van Tyne and Sutton (1937), and Brandt (1940) first recorded it nesting there in 1937. Since then it has been reported sporadically in spring. Since 2001, one–three pairs have nested annually in the Boot Canyon drainage.

GREAT-TAILED GRACKLE (*QUISCALUS MEXICANUS*)

Status: *increasing*. This species has greatly expanded its range in Texas during the last few decades, facilitated by urban and agricultural development. It was well established in the El Paso Valley by the 1930s and became established along the Pecos River by the 1950s (Oberholser 1974). Reports from BBNP, especially along the Rio Grande floodplain at Rio Grande Village and Cottonwood Campground, have increased. Although a sizable population exists in nearby Lajitas, we have no evidence of nesting in BBNP.

BRONZED COWBIRD (*MOLOTHRUS AENEUS*)

Status: *increasing*. Prior to the 1960s, when it was first recorded at BBNP (Wauer 1996), the Bronzed Cowbird's Texas range was limited to south Texas (Oberholser 1974). Since then it has expanded its range significantly throughout much of Texas, including the Big Bend region (Robbins and Easterla 1981, Kostecke et al. 2004). Bronzed Cowbirds are now locally common along the riparian corridor of the Rio Grande, especially at Rio Grande Village and Cottonwood Campground, and occasionally are found away from the river at higher elevations (Panther Junction and Terlingua) in suburban settings.

HOODED ORIOLE (*ICTERUS CUCULLATUS*)

Status: declining. Prior to the arrival of Bronzed Cowbirds in BBNP, Hooded Orioles were a fairy common summer resident at Rio Grande Village and the adjacent floodplain (Wauer 1973). Populations declined during the ensuing 20 yr. By 1996, numerous reports of Bronzed Cowbird parasitism were noted, and the Hooded Oriole was listed as uncommon (Wauer 1996). A few breeding pairs persist at Rio Grande Village and Cottonwood Campground.

DISCUSSION

Over the last 100 yr, several notable changes have occurred in the breeding avifauna in the Big Bend region of Texas, encompassing BBNP. Using BBNP as the baseline, at least eight species have arrived and nested since the 1960s, nine other species have increased in number or frequency, and the population of at least five breeding species have either declined or disappeared from the park altogether.

Recent arrivals include Black-crowned Night-Heron, Eurasian Collared-Dove, Golden-fronted Woodpecker, Dusky-capped Flycatcher, Tropical Kingbird, Cave Swallow, Carolina Wren, and Lucy's Warbler. Of these, three—Golden-fronted Woodpecker, Tropical Kingbird, and Carolina Wren—are of eastern affinity, apparently having moved westward along the Rio Grande corridor. Two—Dusky-capped Flycatcher and Cave Swallow—are of southern affinity, and Lucy's Warbler is of western affinity. Climate change could be a factor causing expansion of species mentioned as being of southern or eastern affinity above (Brush 2005), although it is difficult to determine exclusive or even primary causes for changes in distribution. Although the Rio Grande pathway almost certainly has been important for Black-crowned Night-Heron, Eurasian Collared-Dove has evidently spread from city to city across Texas after their accidental introduction to the Bahamas.

Increasing populations include those of Mallard (Mexican Duck subspecies), Green Heron, Montezuma Quail, Gray Hawk, Common Black-Hawk, Lucifer Hummingbird, Green Kingfisher, Painted Redstart, and Great-tailed Grackle. Possible reasons for these increases in the last few decades are only conjecture. However, especially for those that use riparian habitat—Mexican Duck, Green Heron, Gray Hawk, Common Black-Hawk, and Green Kingfisher—that area within the well-protected park has remained stable over the years while riparian zones to the south in Mexico, as well as outside the park in south Texas, have been negatively affected, especially by grazing. Also, increased reports along the Rio Grande for such species as Green Heron may be due to increased observers, using the river for recreation.

Different species may be affected by various factors. It is possible that long-term drought conditions, that probably increase the spread of lechuguilla (*Agave lechuguilla*), on which Lucifer Hummingbirds nest, may have more of a positive effect than generally expected. The Painted Redstart is a common nesting species of the Maderas del Carmen montane forest (Wauer and Ligon 1977), and may have spread from there, without any apparent habitat- or climate-related cause. Montezuma Quail recovery was discussed above. Great-tailed Grackle numbers have increased dramatically throughout the Big Bend region, Texas, and northward into the Great Plains (Dinsmore and Dinsmore 1993), presumably due to its success in human-modified habitats.

Declining or extirpated species include Gambel's Quail, Harris's Hawk, Golden Eagle, Prairie Falcon, Yellow Warbler, and Hooded Oriole. In addition, the status of the Aplomado Falcon is uncertain because of unreliable early documentation. Three raptors—Harris's Hawk, Golden Eagle, and Prairie Falcon—have experienced a general decline throughout much of their range (Wauer 1996, Lockwood and Freeman 2004). Drought conditions that have created serious shortages of prey, including Gambel's Quail, are the most likely reason for raptor declines. For Yellow Warbler and Hooded Oriole, cowbird parasitism may be the principal cause of their decline or extirpation. Nesting Yellow Warblers may have been impacted by Brown-headed Cowbirds, although they may always have been peripheral in BBNP. Hooded Oriole declines were evident only after the Bronzed Cowbird moved into the Big Bend area in 1969 (Wauer 1969), and the species is known to be heavily parasitized by that species (Brush 2005, Ellison and Sealy 2007). Also, invasion by giant cane (*Arundo donax*) and tamarisk (*Tamarix* sp.) has substantially altered the woodland composition and structure of the riparian corridor.

Several species may nest in BBNP, but because they are known only from sporadic observations during the nesting season, cannot yet be considered as confirmed breeders. These are Cooper's Hawk (*Accipiter cooperii*), Swainson's Hawk (*Buteo swainsonii*), Cassin's Kingbird (*Tyrannus vociferans*), Scissor-tailed Flycatcher (*Tyrannus forficatus*), Warbling Vireo (*Vireo gilvus*), Chihuahuan Raven (*Corvus cryptoleucus*), and Rufous-capped Warbler (*Basileuterus rufifrons*).

Several species which merit comment because they seem to be declining or of conservation concern in other portions of their range but are apparently stable in BBNP and vicinity. These include Peregrine Falcon, Loggerhead Shrike, Bell's Vireo (*Vireo bellii*), Black-capped Vireo (*Vireo atricapilla*), and Colima Warbler. Although populations of some of these species, such as the endangered Black-capped Vireo and, to a lesser extent, peregrines and Colima Warblers, have received some monitoring over the years, a distinct need exists to assess each of the species discussed above. All the avifauna within the national park is fully protected, and therefore constitutes an important baseline for long-term understanding of our changing environment.

ACKNOWLEDGMENTS

We thank the dozens of ornithologists and birders who, for more than 100 yr, have provided considerable data on the avifauna of the Texas Big Bend Region; the majority of their published materials are referenced in the section on ornithological history. In addition, Jim Paton and Mark Lockwood, and an anonymous reviewer read the manuscript and made several helpful suggestions. Any incorrect assumptions or other errors are the fault of the authors.

Studies in Avian Biology No. 37:28–45

DISTRIBUTION AND STATUS OF BREEDING LANDBIRDS IN NORTHERN SONORA MEXICO

Aaron D. Flesch

Abstract. Northern Sonora, Mexico is dominated by steep elevation and rainfall gradients and a variety of vegetation communities with affinity to the Sonoran, Madrean, Sinaloan, and Chihuahuan biogeographic provinces. Despite high environmental diversity and moderate accessibility, current information on distribution and abundance of breeding landbirds is limited throughout much of this vast region. Between 2000 and 2007, I surveyed landbirds in northern Sonora in four of the six primary watersheds that occur within 125 km of the US. I detected 161 species of landbirds that I presumed were breeding (59% confirmed) and four additional species that were possibly breeding during 568 site visits to 306 localities. I did not detect seven species that had been presumed to breed in the past, six of which likely still occur, or 10 species that I suspect may breed locally or irregularly in the study area. Based on probabilistic methods, I estimate that as many as 178 species of land-birds likely breed in the study area. Species richness within each of 16 secondary watershed regions increased as the number of major vegetation communities that were present increased, and presence of broadleaf riparian woodland, Madrean evergreen woodland, and Madrean montane conifer forest had the greatest influence on richness. Geographic ranges of many species that I observed were much larger than that suggested by previous studies likely as a result of increased effort. Evidence for some species however, suggested that distributions have either expanded or contracted, likely as a result of major changes in vegetation and perhaps climate change. Although some populations await discovery, my findings suggest that northern Sonora supports higher richness of breeding landbirds than any other region of similar area in the borderlands of northern Mexico.

Key Words: borderlands, climate change, distribution, distributional change, landbirds, Mexico, Sonora, transboundary conservation, US-Mexico border.

DISTRIBUCIÓN Y ESTADO DE AVES TERRESTRES REPRODUCTIVAS EN EL NORTE DE SONORA, MÉXICO

Resumen. El norte de Sonora, México esta dominado por un marcado gradiente altitudinal y de precipitación pluvial, así como por una variedad de comunidades vegetales con afinidad a las provincias biogeográficas Sonorense, Madreano, Sinaloense y Chihuahuense. A pesar de la alta diversidad ambiental y cierta accesibilidad, la información actual de distribución y abundancia de aves terrestres reproductivas es limitada en gran parte de esta vasta región. Entre 2000 y 2007, realicé monitoreos de aves terrestres en el norte de Sonora, en cuatro de las seis principales cuencas que se ubican a 125 km o menos, de los Estados Unidos. Detecté 161 especies de aves terrestres que asumí estaban reproduciéndose (59% confirmadas), y cuatro especies adicionales que posiblemente estaban reproduciéndose durante 568 visitas a 306 localidades. No detecté siete especies que se presumían en el pasado como reproductoras, seis de las cuales es probable que todavía ocurran, como tampoco 10 especies que sospecho se reproducen localmente o irregularmente dentro del área. Basado en métodos probabilísticos estimé que hasta 178 especies de aves terrestres probablemente se reproducen en el área de estudio. La riqueza de especies dentro de cada una de las 16 subcuencas incremento en la medida en que aumentaba el número de comunidades vegetales, y la presencia de bosques ribereños de hojas anchas, bosques siempre verdes Madreanos y bosques montanos de coníferas Madreanos tuvieron la mayor influencia en la riqueza. Los rangos geográficos de muchas especies que observé fueron mucho más grandes que lo sugerido por estudios previos, muy probablemente como resultado de un esfuerzo mayor. Sin embargo la evidencia para algunas especies, sugiere que ha habido expansión o contracción de sus distribuciones, probablemente como resultado de cambios mayores en la vegetación y quizás por cambios climáticos. Aunque algunas poblaciones esperan ser descubiertas, mis hallazgos sugieren que el norte de Sonora soporta mayor riqueza de aves terrestres reproductivas que cualquier otra región de área similar, en las tierras fronterizas del norte de México.

Information on the status, distribution, and habitat needs of wildlife are essential for efficient conservation and management. In regions where little information is available and rapid environmental changes are anticipated, detailed information may be required to ensure that populations are identified, managed, and conserved before they are significantly altered or lost. Efforts to identify and manage wildlife populations may be especially challenging near international boundaries because ownership, management objectives, and national priorities often vary and development pressure and security concerns are often high. Despite these challenges, cooperation among neighboring nations can help achieve conservation objectives in trans-boundary landscapes (Mittermeier et al. 2005, Plumptre et al. 2007).

At approximately 600 km in length, the international boundary between the state of Arizona in the US and the state of Sonora in Mexico bisects a region of exceptional diversity. Spanning nearly a 10-fold range of annual rainfall, this region extends from mountains at the northern edge of the Sierra Madre Occidental west to the delta of the Río Colorado and supports both highland vegetation communities of oaks (*Quercus* sp.) and pines (*Pinus* sp.) and vast lowlands of Sonoran and Chihuahuan desertscrub and grassland (Brown 1982). Complex elevation and moisture gradients and convergence of several major biogeographic provinces foster high regional diversity and result in the distributional limits of both Neotropical and Nearctic species of plants and animals (Halffter 1987, Howell and Webb 1995, Turner et al. 1995, Escalante et al. 2004).

Large areas of the Sonora-Arizona borderlands are managed with explicit conservation directives by the Mexican and US federal governments (Cartron et al. 2005, Felger et al. 2007), yet a number of environmental concerns exist (Liverman et al. 1999, Goodwin 2000). Although human population densities are low in many areas of northern Sonora, groundwater use and urban growth are increasing, significant areas of riparian vegetation have been degraded or lost, and security concerns have culminated in ongoing development along much of the international border (Cartron et al. 2005, Búrquez and Martínez-Yrízar 2007, Cohn 2007). These and other factors may threaten long-term conservation objectives unless their effects are understood and information on the distribution and status of plant and wildlife populations are known and monitored. Information on bird communities may be especially valuable because relative to other vertebrates birds are often good indicators of specific environmental conditions upon which they depend (Canterbury et al. 2000, Bryce et al 2002) and because birds are relatively easy to detect and survey (Ralph and Scott 1981, Bibby et al. 2000)

Ornithological investigations in Sonora began well over a century ago and continue to this day (Stephens 1885, Moore 1938, van Rossem 1945, Marshall 1957, Short 1974, Russell and Monson 1998, Rojas-Soto et al. 2002, Villaseñor 2006). Despite these efforts, vast portions of northern Sonora remained little studied by the early 1950s (Phillips and Amadon 1952) after which additional work occurred. Marshall

(1957) provided detailed information in pine-oak woodlands in many of the higher mountains in northeast Sonora. Russell and Monson (1998) synthesized information from previous studies and collections from throughout Sonora that they supplemented with field work in some regions of northern Sonora. Since these efforts, Hinojosa-Huerta et al. (2007) summarized status and provided additional records of birds in the lower Colorado River Valley and adjacent areas of extreme western Sonora, Flesch and Hahn (2005) described bird communities in several little-known mountain ranges west of the region visited by Marshall (1957), and Villaseñor (2006) reported on wintering birds at several widely scattered localities. Despite these efforts, the large size of northern Sonora, limited accessibility, and high environmental diversity have precluded a detailed assessment of distribution and status of breeding landbirds.

To provide current information on landbirds in the borderlands of northern Sonora, I surveyed much of the region between 2000 and 2007. Herein I summarize information on distribution and status of breeding landbirds, assess recent distributional changes, and describe patterns of species richness across the region.

METHODS

STUDY AREA

I defined northern Sonora as the area within 125 km of the international boundary with the US. Several major watersheds traverse this region and many originate near the international boundary and flow in a north-south direction (Fig. 1). In northeastern Sonora, the Río Yaqui begins in extreme southeast Arizona and southwest New Mexico and flows south through Sonora toward the Gulf of California. To the west in the Gila watershed, the Ríos San Pedro and Santa Cruz originate in mountains near the border, traverse small portions of Sonora, then flow north into Arizona. To the south, the adjacent Río Sonora, and its tributaries the Ríos Bacanuchi and San Miguel, flow south from mountains within 70 km of the border. Farther west in the Concepción watershed, the Río Altar and Arroyo Sasabe, drain small areas of south-central Arizona and the Río Magdalena and Arroyo Plomo originate immediately south of the border. These and several other tributaries of the Río Concepción flow south before converging and flowing west toward the Gulf of California. In the more arid west, the Río Sonoyta and its tributary the Arroyo Vamori drain a region immediately along the border and empty into the sands of the Gran Desierto

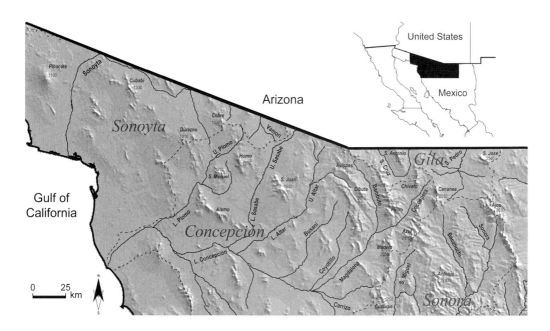

FIGURE 1. Map of study area in northern Sonora Mexico indicating boundaries of primary watersheds (dashed line) and major drainages and mountain ranges. The maximum elevation of each mountain range is in meters. Elevations are based on data from Instituto Nacional de Estadística, Geografía e Informática and my own measurements using a GPS. The small portion of the Yaqui watershed to the east was not considered nor were areas >125 km from the international boundary with the US.

de Altar. Still west is the Río Colorado that drains much of the southwestern US.

In this study, I considered the Sonora, Gila, Concepción, and Sonoyta watersheds that together cover approximately 70% of northern Sonora and excluded the extreme western portion of the Sonoyta watershed which is predominately sand dunes. I did not consider the Yaqui watershed where field work is not yet complete or the much smaller Río Colorado watershed which has been described elsewhere (Hinojosa-Huerta et al. 2007). To describe distribution of breeding landbirds, I subdivided these four primary watersheds into 16 secondary watershed regions (Table 1) by combining some nearby drainages or subdividing long drainages into upper and lower sections.

Vegetation communities in the region included large expanses of Sonoran desertscrub, semi-desert and plains grassland, and smaller areas of Chihuahuan desertscrub, subtropical thornscrub, and montane forest and woodland. In the west, desertscrub of the Lower Colorado River Valley subdivision of the Sonoran Desert was dominant throughout much of the lower Concepción and Sonoyta watersheds and was replaced by desertscrub of the Arizona Upland subdivision at higher elevation. Savannah

dominated the Plains of Sonora subdivision and occurred only in the extreme south-central Concepción watershed (Shreve 1951), whereas to the east, Chihuahuan desertscrub occurred only in the lower San Pedro watershed. In the extreme south, Sinaloan thornscrub occurred locally on slopes in the Coyotillo-Magdalena-Carrizo watersheds and was widespread only in the southern portion of the San Miguel and especially in the Bacanuchi-Sonora watersheds. Semi-desert grassland occurred at elevations above desertscrub in north-central Sonora west to the upper Plomo and Vamori watersheds and more open expanses of plains grassland occurred in the San Pedro and in the upper Santa Cruz and Sonora watersheds. Above grasslands, Madrean evergreen woodland was dominated by oaks at low elevation and by oaks and pines at high elevation; isolated stands of oak woodland occurred in mountains as far west as the upper Sasabe (Sierra San Juan) and upper Plomo (Sierra el Humo) watersheds. Woodland transitioned to Madrean montane conifer forest at high elevations in the Sierras el Pinito, Azul, Cananea (Elenita and Mariquita), los Ajos, and to the east in the Yaqui watershed. These forests were dominated by pine and rarely by Douglas fir (*Pseudostuga menziesii*) or white fir

TABLE 1. SURVEY EFFORT AND SPECIES RICHNESS OF BREEDING LANDBIRDS IN FOUR PRIMARY AND 16 SECONDARY WATERSHED REGIONS IN NORTHERN SONORA, MEXICO 2000–2007. SITE TOTALS INCLUDE TRANSECT AND INCIDENTAL SURVEYS. OBSERVED SPECIES RICHNESS IS THE TOTAL NUMBER OF SPECIES DETECTED IN EACH REGION DURING THE STUDY WHEREAS HISTORICAL RICHNESS INDICATES ADDITIONAL SPECIES THAT WERE NOTED BY RUSSELL AND MONSON (1998) OR BY MARSHALL (1957) BUT WERE NOT OBSERVED DURING THE STUDY. ESTIMATED SPECIES RICHNESS WAS CALCULATED USING THE JACKKNIFE ESTIMATOR (BURNHAM AND OVERTON 1979) AND OBSERVED SPECIES ABUNDANCE DISTRIBUTIONS IN EACH PRIMARY WATERSHED AND FOR THE ENTIRE STUDY AREA. BREEDING SPECIES ARE THOSE PRESUMED AND CONFIRMED BREEDING. ALL DATA ARE BASED ON OBSERVATIONS OBTAINED WITHIN 125 KM OF THE INTERNATIONAL BOUNDARY WITH THE US.

Primary watershed Watershed region	Effort				Breeding species richness					
	Transects	Transect visits	Sites	Site visits	Observed	Historical	Total observed	Estimated $\hat{N}$	SE	95% CI
Sonoyta	31	66	48	85	82	6	88	88	3.5	81.2–94.8
Lower	19	31	28	40	68	5	73			
Vamori	12	35	20	45	70	3	73			
Concepción	113	286	197	408	150	4	154	156	3.5	149.2–162.8
Lower	18	18	24	24	51	14	65			
Plomo Lower	11	13	14	16	53	6	59			
Plomo Upper	11	47	15	52	83	0	83			
Sasabe Lower	3	6	6	12	49	2	51			
Sasabe Upper	9	38	26	57	90	2	92			
Altar Lower	13	32	17	46	89	0	89			
Altar Upper	10	44	25	67	113	3	116			
Busani	7	22	12	31	73	0	73			
Coyotillo-Magdalena-Carrizo	21	54	44	87	106	3	109			
Cocospera-Bambuto	10	12	14	16	128	6	134			
Gila	6	15	18	27	106	14	120	113	3.7	105.7–119.8
Santa Cruz	3	3	7	7	79	16	95			
San Pedro	3	12	11	20	91	10	101			
Sonora	20	28	43	48	134	14	148	142	4.0	134.2–148.8
San Miguel Upper	18	20	26	31	98	5	103			
Bacanuchi-Sonora Upper	8	8	17	17	120	24	144			
All regions	176	395	306	568	161	6	167	166	3.2	159.7–172.3

(*Abies concolor*) that were restricted to the highest elevations and mainly on east- and north-facing slopes in the Yaqui watershed. Broadleaf riparian woodland and gallery forest occurred along valley bottoms and in canyons within several other vegetation communities and were dominated by willows (*Salix* sp.), Fremont cottonwood (*Populus fremontii*), and velvet ash (*Fraxinus velutina*) at low elevation and by Arizona sycamore (*Platanus wrightii*), Arizona walnut (*Juglans major*), and bigtooth maple (*Acer grandidentata*) at high elevation.

SITE SELECTION

I used three methods to select sites for surveys: (1) random placement of survey transects, (2) non-random placement of survey transects, and (3) incidental observations. Random sampling provided inference to large portions of the study area whereas non-random sampling allowed the flexibility needed to efficiently locate and survey important environments that had low landscape coverage and otherwise low probability of being sampled.

To randomize placement of transects, I generated a random sample of coordinates at elevations ≤1,200 m that I stratified by major vegetation community and allocated in proportion to the coverage of each community. At each point, I established one transect along the closest drainage that was >2 m wide and within 1 km of a road in each of four possible topographic formations (valley bottoms, lower bajadas, upper bajadas, and mountain canyons) that occurred within 20 km of each point. Selection was constrained to low and moderate elevations because most transects were initially established for surveys of Ferruginous Pygmy-Owls (*Glaucidium brasilianum*; Flesch 2003).

To expand coverage across a broader range of elevations, I selected another sample of transects non-randomly. I placed transects along drainages and occasionally on slopes or trails in riparian areas, large canyons, montane woodland and forest, grassland, and focused in areas that were not adequately covered by random transects or where I suspected the occurrence of rare species with specialized habitat requirements. I selected locations for incidental observations opportunistically by noting observations while scouting, traveling between transects, in camp, and at times of day that were not efficient for transect surveys.

FIELD SURVEYS

I surveyed from February 2000 to June 2007 and focused during the breeding season between mid-February and late August of each year. I visited some transects only once and visited others up to 11 times depending on timing of initial surveys, accessibility, interest, and the location of other efforts (Flesch and Hahn 2005; Flesch and Steidl 2006, 2007). I prioritized transects for secondary surveys when initial surveys occurred before the anticipated arrival of migratory species and in areas where I suspected occurrence of rare species.

Each transect consisted of a linear search area approximately 1–6 km in length. To survey transects, I walked linear routes that typically followed drainages and temporarily walked in perpendicular directions to investigate bird activity or areas of interest. I recorded all species of birds that I detected during surveys, estimated numbers of individuals or pairs, noted any evidence of breeding, and walked at variable speeds depending on the amount of bird activity and complexity of the terrain. I often noted only presence and breeding behavior of common species so that I could focus on detecting and estimating abundance of less common species and traverse larger areas during morning. I surveyed during mornings but noted observations at other times of day or night. To rouse birds and augment visual and aural detection probabilities, I often mimicked or broadcast recorded territorial calls of pygmy-owls during surveys, which is similar to the method used by Marshall (1957). Along most transects that I selected randomly, I broadcast calls of Ferruginous Pygmy-Owl at 350–600 m intervals while simultaneously surveying for that species (Flesch 2003). Along transects that I selected non-randomly, I mimicked or broadcasted calls of pygmy-owls at less systematic intervals. At night I broadcasted conspecific vocalizations to elicit responses from nocturnal species on an opportunistic basis. I focused incidental observations on species that were uncommon, rare or of interest, and recorded the number of individuals detected and any evidence of breeding.

ANALYSES

To describe status within each region, I estimated relative abundance by dividing the number of transects where a species was present by the total number of transects visited during the breeding season. I used these estimates and incidental observations to classify relative abundance as common (frequently encountered as individuals, pairs, or small groups), fairly common (a few individuals or pairs detected), uncommon (present but may not be found in a day or two of field observations), and rare (present but rarely detected and often restricted to localized area), as defined by Russell and Monson (1998: 15). Species that were locally common but restricted to environments with low coverage were often considered uncommon. I presumed breeding was occurring if individuals were singing, paired, territorial, or exhibiting other circumstantial evidence of breeding when birds were in typical breeding habitat during the breeding season. For raptors, I presumed breeding was occurring if adults were present in typical breeding habitat during the breeding season. I used more rigorous standards for species that were in atypical breeding habitat by presuming breeding was occurring only when a territorial pair, courtship, or other behaviors indicative of breeding were observed. I did not presume breeding of migratory species unless observations occurred outside periods when populations typically migrate. To confirm breeding, I used criteria of the North American Ornithological Atlas Committee (1990). To define breeding habitat, distribution, and migration and wintering periods, I supplemented my observations with data from northern Sonora (van Rossem 1945, Marshall 1957, Russell and Monson 1998), adjacent portions of southern Arizona (Monson and Phillips 1981, Rosenberg and Witzeman 1998 and 1999, Rosenberg 2001, Corman and Wise-Gervais 2005), and other relevant literature (Poole 2005). I then compared my findings with information from these sources to assess potential changes in status or distribution.

I calculated observed species richness by summing all species that I presumed or confirmed to be breeding during the study within each region and calculated cumulative observed species richness by including species that I did not detect but that had been either presumed or confirmed breeding in the past (Marshall 1957, Russell and Monson 1998). Because all species are not detected perfectly during surveys, I estimated species richness ($\hat{N}$) based on the abundance distribution I observed and a limiting form of the jackknife estimator (Burnham and Overton 1979) calculated by program SPECRICH (J. E. Hines, available at http://www.mbr-pwrc.usgs.gov/software.html). To assess the range of likely values for each estimate, I calculated 95% confidence intervals. I did not estimate species richness at the scale of watershed regions because sample sizes in some regions were small.

To assess the influence of large-scale geographic and environmental factors on cumulative observed species richness, I used linear regression. As explanatory variables, I calculated the geographic position of each watershed region by estimating latitudinal and longitudinal centers and an index of environmental diversity equaled to the number of major vegetation communities present within each region and considered broadleaf riparian woodland as a community. To determine vegetation communities that had the greatest influence on species richness, I used multiple linear regression with stepwise selection (P < 0.25 to enter, P < 0.10 to stay). To evaluate adequacy of sampling, I assessed whether observed species richness and the number of species that were at least presumed to breed in the past but not detected during the study varied with effort (site visits).

RESULTS

Effort

I completed 395 surveys along 176 transects, 70% of which I located randomly, and 173 incidental surveys at 130 additional localities (Table 1). Number of surveys per transect averaged 2.7 ± 0.1 (± SE) with 54% of transects visited ≥two times and 27% of transects visited ≥four times. All effort combined yielded 568 site visits to 306 sites, 92% of which were between 11 February and 31 August and 54% were in May or June. I personally completed 77% of site visits, six observers each completed 3–5%, and an additional four observers completed the remaining 3% of visits all of which were incidental observations.

Number of transects and total effort (site visits) were approximately proportional to the size of primary watersheds (Table 1, Fig. 1). In the Concepción watershed, most effort was in the Altar (28%), Coyotillo-Magdalena-Carrizo (21%), Sasabe (17%), and Plomo (17%) watersheds and least effort was in the Busani (8%), lower Concepción (6%), and Cocospera-Bambuto (4%). Effort was higher in Arizona upland desertscrub (45%) and semi-desert grasslands (36%) than in Madrean evergreen woodland (6%). Effort was low in Lower Colorado River Valley (3%) and Chihuahuan (1%) desertscrub, plains grassland (3%), Sinaloan thornscrub (3%), and in Madrean montane conifer forest (1%), communities that covered much smaller portions of the study area. Effort in broadleaf riparian woodland totaled 15% and most of these sites were in semi-desert grassland (44%), Arizona Upland desertscrub (25%), plains grassland (9%), Sinaloan thornscrub (9%), and Madrean evergreen woodland (9%).

I visited virtually all major vegetation communities that occurred in lowlands within each watershed region and only some that occurred in highlands. At high elevations, I surveyed portions of the Sierras los Ajos (Bacanuchi-Sonora), el Pinito and Cananea (Cocospera-Bambuto), Cucurpe (San Miguel and Coyotillo-Magdalena-Carrizo), las Avispas (Upper Altar), San Juan (Upper Sasabe), el Humo (Upper Plomo), el Cobre (Vamori), and el Durazno (Lower Sonoyta) (Fig. 1). Difficult access and time contraints prevented surveys at upper elevations in the San Pedro (Sierra San Jose), Santa Cruz (northeast Sierras el Pinito and San Antonio), Coyotillo-Magdalena-Carrizo (Sierra la Madera), Busani (south of Sierra las Avispas), Lower Sonoyta (Sierra Cubabi), and Lower Concepción (Sierra el Alamo) watersheds and in areas above 1,300 m in the Sierra Azul (Cocospera-Bambuto and San Miguel), 1,200 m in the Sierra San Antonio (San Miguel and Bacanuchi-Sonora), and 1,600 m in the Sierra el Chivato (Santa Cruz).

SPECIES RICHNESS

I observed 66 species of landbirds that I presumed were breeding and another 95 species that I confirmed breeding. Four species (Wild Turkey [*Meleagris gallopavo*], Osprey [*Pandion haliaetus*], Fan-tailed Warbler [*Euthlypis lachrymosa*], Western Meadowlark, [*Sturnella neglecta*]) possibly bred but evidence was not sufficient to presume so. I did not detect seven species that had been at least presumed to breed in the past; five were associated with high-elevation forests (Flammulated Owl [*Otus flammeolus*], Blue-throated Hummingbird [*Lampornis clemenciae*], Magnificent Hummingbird [*Eugenes fulgens*], Pygmy Nuthatch [*Sitta pygmaea*], and Red-faced Warbler [*Cardellina rubrifrons*]), one with low desert (Le Conte's Thrasher [*Toxostoma lecontei*]), and one with grassland (Northern Bobwhite [*Colinus virginianus*]) (Tables 1 and 2). I estimate that 171 ± 3.7 species of landbirds at least possibly breed (upper bound of 95% CI = 178) and that 166 ± 3.2 species at least presumably breed (upper bound of 95% CI = 172) in the study area.

Within primary watersheds, species richness was high in the Concepción and Sonora, and low in the Sonoyta watersheds. Estimates of species richness within each primary watershed were similar to observed values (Table 1); observed richness averaged 5.6 ± 0.6% lower than that estimated and cumulative observed richness differed from that estimated by only 2.9 ± 1.4%.

Cumulative observed richness increased by an average of 15 ± 2 species with each additional vegetation community present in a region (t_{14} = 6.58, P < 0.001; Fig. 2). Although richness also

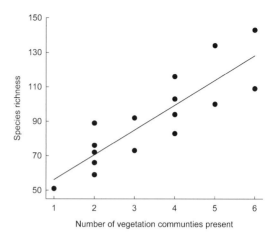

FIGURE 2. Association between species richness and the number of major vegetation communities present within each of 16 watershed regions in northern Sonora, Mexico. Richness equaled the number of landbird species that were presumed or confirmed breeding during the study plus species that I did not detect but that had been presumed or confirmed breeding in the past. Richness increased by 15 ± 2 species with each additional vegetation community (t_{14} = 6.58, P < 0.001).

increased from west to east (estimate ± SE = 3 ± 1 species/10 km, t_{14} = 4.04, P = 0.001), once the effect of vegetation was considered, richness did not vary with longitude (t_{13} = 1.21, P = 0.25). Presence of broadleaf riparian woodland, Madrean evergreen woodland, and Madrean montane conifer forest (t_{12} ≤ 2.29, P ≤ 0.04) influenced species richness more than presence of other vegetation communities (t_{11} ≤ 1.61, P ≥ 0.14); when any of these communities were present, richness averaged at least 40 ± 9 species greater than in regions where these communities were absent.

Observed species richness did not vary with effort (t_{14} = 0.50, P = 0.63), yet the number of species that were at least presumed to breed in the past but not observed during the study decreased as effort increased (t_{14} = 2.20, P = 0.04). On average, observed richness was 7 ± 2% lower than cumulative observed richness and differences were greatest in the lower Concepción (21%), Santa Cruz (17%), and Bacanuchi-Sonora (17%) watersheds (Tables 1 and 2).

DISTRIBUTION AND STATUS

I detected six species of breeding landbirds that had not been observed previously in the study area and many others that had been observed at few localities. Of species that had not been observed previously, Short-tailed Hawk

TABLE 2. DISTRIBUTION AND STATUS OF BREEDING LANDBIRDS IN FOUR PRIMARY AND 16 SECONDARY WATERSHED REGIONS IN NORTHERN SONORA, MEXICO 2000–2007. DATA ARE BASED ON OBSERVATIONS OBTAINED WITHIN 125 KM OF THE INTERNATIONAL BOUNDARY WITH THE UNITED STATES. SPECIES STATUS IS NOTED AS RARE (R), UNCOMMON (U), FAIRLY COMMON (F), OR COMMON (C). SPECIES THAT WERE NOT NOTED IN RUSSELL AND MONSON (1998) OR BY MARSHALL (1957) BUT THAT WERE NOT OBSERVED DURING THE STUDY ARE NOTED WITH AN ASTERISK AND STATUS WAS ASSESSED BASED ON PAST DESCRIPTIONS AND THE AMOUNT OF HABITAT THAT WAS AVAILABLE DURING THE STUDY. SPECIES FOR WHICH INSUFFICIENT EVIDENCE WAS OBTAINED TO PRESUME BREEDING ARE NOTED WITH A QUESTION MARK. WATERSHEDS ARE LISTED FROM WEST TO EAST.

	Sonoyta			Concepción									Gila		Sonora	
	Sonoyta	Vamori	Lower	Plomo Lower	Plomo Upper	Sasabe Lower	Sasabe Upper	Altar Lower	Altar Upper	Busani	Coyotillo Magdalena	Cocospera-Bambuto	Santa Cruz	San Pedro	San Miguel	Bacanuchi-Sonora
Galliformes																
Wild Turkey (*Meleagris gallopavo*)												?				?*
Scaled Quail (*Callipepla squamata*)	R				R		R				R*			U		
Elegant Quail (*Callipepla douglasii*)											R				U	U*
Gambel's Quail (*Callipepla gambelii*)	C	C	C	C	C	C	C	C	C	C	C	C	C	C	C	C
Northern Bobwhite (*Colinus virginianus*)							U*		R			U		U		
Montezuma Quail (*Cyrtonyx montezumae*)		R*					R		R			U	U	U	R	R
Ciconiiformes																
Black Vulture (*Coragyps atratus*)	U	U	F	U	U	F	U	F	U	U	U	U	U*		U	U
Turkey Vulture (*Cathartes aura*)	C	C	C	C	C	C	C	C	C	C	C	C	C	C	C	C
Falconiformes																
Osprey (*Pandion haliaetus*)	?															
White-tailed Kite (*Elanus leucurus*)										R		?*		R		
Sharp-shinned Hawk (*Accipiter striatus*)															R*	R
Cooper's Hawk (*Accipiter cooperii*)		R			R	R		R	U		R	U		U		R
Northern Goshawk (*Accipiter gentilis*)														R		
Common Black-Hawk (*Buteogallus anthracinus*)									R*		R	R	R		R	R*
Harris's Hawk (*Parabuteo unicinctus*)	F	R	U	U	F	U	R	F		F	U	F	U	U	F	F
Gray Hawk (*Buteo nitida*)		?			?	U	R	U	F	U	F	R	F	F	F	R
Short-tailed Hawk (*Buteo brachyurus*)			R*													
Swainson's Hawk (*Buteo swainsoni*)		R		R	F		U	U	U	U	U	R	U	U	U	
Zone-tailed Hawk (*Buteo albonotatus*)	U	U	R	F	F		U	U	U	U	U	U	R	R	R	R*
Red-tailed Hawk (*Buteo jamaicensis*)	F	F	U	U	F	U	F	U	F	U	U	F	U	F	U	U
Golden Eagle (*Aquila chrysaetos*)	R	R	R		R			R	R			R	R	R	R	R
Crested Caracara (*Caracara cheriway*)	U	F	U	U	U	U	F	U	U	U	U				R	
American Kestrel (*Falco sparverius*)	U	U	U	U	U	U	U	U	U	U	U	U	U	F	U	U
Peregrine Falcon (*Falco peregrinus*)	R	R	R		R			R	R	R	R	R	R		R	U
Prairie Falcon (*Falco mexicanus*)					R					?						R*
Columbiformes																
Rock Pigeon (*Columba livia*)	F	R	F	R	R	F	U	F	R	F	F	U	R	U	R	R
Band-tailed Pigeon (*Patagioenas fasciata*)								R	R*			R	R*	R	R*	R
Eurasian Collared-Dove (*Streptopelia decaocto*)	R						R				U			R		
White-winged Dove (*Zenaida asiatica*)	C	C	C	C	C	C	C	C	C	C	C	C	C	C	C	C
Mourning Dove (*Zenaida macroura*)	C	C	C	C	C	C	C	C	C	C	C	C	C	C	C	C

TABLE 2. CONTINUED.

	Sonoyta					Concepción							Gila		Sonora	
	Sonoyta	Vamori	Lower	Plomo Lower	Plomo Upper	Sasabe Lower	Sasabe Upper	Altar Lower	Altar Upper	Busani	Coyotillo Magdalena	Cocospera-Bambuto	Santa Cruz	San Pedro	San Miguel	Bacanuchi-Sonora
Inca Dove (*Columbina inca*)	U	R	C	U	R	C	U	C	U	U	U	C	U	U	U	U
Common Ground-Dove (*Columbina passerina*)	R	R	R	U	R	R	U	U	U	U	C	C	C	C	C	C
White-tipped Dove (*Leptotila verreauxi*)										R	R				R	U
Cuculiformes																
Yellow-billed Cuckoo (*Coccyzus americanus*)	R*	R	R*		R	R	R	U	U	U	U	U	U	U	U	U
Greater Roadrunner (*Geococcyx californianus*)	U	U	U		F	U	F	F	F	F	F	F	U	F	F	U
Strigiformes																
Barn Owl (*Tyto alba*)	R				R	R*			R	R	R	R			R	
Flammulated Owl (*Otus flammeolus*)					R	R*						R				R*
Western Screech-Owl (*Megascops kennicottii*)	U	U		F	F	F	F	F	F	U	F	F	F	F	F	F
Whiskered Screech-Owl (*Megascops trichopsis*)					R	R			R			F	R*		U	U
Great Horned Owl (*Bubo virginianus*)	C	C	C	C	C	C	C	C	C	C	C	C	R*	C	C	U
Northern Pygmy-Owl (*Glaucidium gnoma*)												R	R	C		R
Ferruginous Pygmy-Owl (*Glaucidium brasilianum*)	R	U	R	U	U	U	U	U	U	U	U	U	U		U	R*
Burrowing Owl (*Athene cunicularia*)													R	R		
Elf Owl (*Micrathene whitneyi*)	C	C	U	U	C	C	C	C	C	C	C	C	U	U	U	U
Spotted Owl (*Strix occidentalis*)												R	R	R*		R*
Caprimulgiformes																
Lesser Nighthawk (*Chordeiles acutipennis*)	U	C	U	F	C	F	C	C	C	C	C		U	U	F	F
Common Nighthawk (*Chordeiles minor*)														C		U*
Common Poorwill (*Phalaenoptilus nuttallii*)	U	U	R	R	F	U	U	U	F	U	F	U	U	U	U	U
Buff-collared Nightjar (*Caprimulgus ridgwayi*)					R	R			U		U	U			U	
Whip-poor-will (*Caprimulgus vociferus*)									R			R	R*			R
Apodiformes																
White-throated Swift (*Aeronautes saxatalis*)	R				R				R	R	R	R		R	R	R
Broad-billed Hummingbird (*Cynanthus latirostris*)		R	R	R	R	R			F	F	C	C			C	C
Violet-crowned Hummingbird (*Amazilia violiceps*)						R					R	R			U	R
Blue-throated Hummingbird (*Lampornis clemenciae*)																R*
Magnificent Hummingbird (*Eugenes fulgens*)																R*
Black-chinned Hummingbird (*Archilochus alexandri*)					R	R		R	R				U*	U		R
Anna's Hummingbird (*Calypte anna*)		?			R	R					R		R			R*
Costa's Hummingbird (*Calypte costae*)	C	C	C	C	C	C	?	C	U	U	U	R			U*	U*
Broad-tailed Hummingbird (*Selasphorus platycercus*)	U	U										R				R

TABLE 2. CONTINUED.

	Sonoyta			Concepción									Gila		Sonora	
	Sonoyta	Vamori	Lower	Plomo Lower	Plomo Upper	Sasabe Lower	Sasabe Upper	Altar Lower	Altar Upper	Busani	Coyotillo-Magdalena	Cocospera-Bambuto	Santa Cruz	San Pedro	San Miguel	Bacanuchi-Sonora
Trogoniformes																
Elegant Trogon (*Trogon elegans*)									R		R	R	R	R	U	U
Coraciformes																
Green Kingfisher (*Chloroceryle americana*)			R	R				R	R		R	R			R	R
Piciformes																
Acorn Woodpecker (*Melanerpes formicivorus*)	C	C			?		?		R			U	U	U	U	U
Gila Woodpecker (*Melanerpes uropygialis*)	C	C	C	C	C	C	C	C	C	C	C	U	C	C	C	C
Ladder-backed Woodpecker (*Picoides scalaris*)	F	F	F	C	F	F	F	F	F	F	F	F	F	F	F	F
Hairy Woodpecker (*Picoides villosus*)												R				R
Arizona Woodpecker (*Picoides arizonae*)				R	R		R	R	R			U	R			U
Northern Flicker (*Colaptes auratus*)				R	?		?	R	R			U	U	C	R	U
Gilded Flicker (*Colaptes chrysoides*)	C	C	C	C	C	C	C	C	C	C	C	U			U	U
Passeriformes																
Northern Beardless-Tyrannulet (*Camptostoma imberbe*)				R	R		U	U	U	R	U	U	U		U	U
Greater Pewee (*Contopus pertinax*)												R	R*	R*		R
Western Wood-Pewee (*Contopus sordidulus*)							R	R	U		U	F	F	F	U	F
Buff-breasted Flycatcher (*Empidonax fulvifrons*)												R				R
Cordilleran Flycatcher (*Empidonax occidentalis*)												R				R
Black Phoebe (*Sayornis nigricans*)	R						R	R	U		U	U	U	F	F	F
Say's Phoebe (*Sayornis saya*)	U	R*		U			R	R	U		U	U	U*	U*	R	U*
Vermilion Flycatcher (*Pyrocephalus rubinus*)	R	R*	U		R		U	U	F	U	C	F	C	C	C	F
Dusky-capped Flycatcher (*Myiarchus tuberculifer*)					R		R	R	U		U	U	U	C	U	U
Ash-throated Flycatcher (*Myiarchus cinerascens*)	C	C	C	C	C	C	C	C	C	C	C	C	C	C	C	C
Nutting's Flycatcher (*Myiarchus nuttingi*)											R	R			R	R*
Brown-crested Flycatcher (*Myiarchus tyrannulus*)	C	C	F	F	C	F	F	C	C	C	C	C	U	F	C	U
Sulphur-bellied Flycatcher (*Myiodynastes luteiventris*)									R		R	R	R*		U	R
Tropical Kingbird (*Tyrannus melancholicus*)								U	U		U	R			U	R
Cassin's Kingbird (*Tyrannus vociferans*)		R*	R				R	U	U	R	U	U	F	F	F	U
Thick-billed Kingbird (*Tyrannus crassirostris*)	R	R	R				R	R	U		U	U	R		U	U
Western Kingbird (*Tyrannus verticalis*)	R*	R	R				R	R	R	U	R	U	U	F	U	U*
Rose-throated Becard (*Pachyramphus aglaiae*)								R	R		R	R	R		R	R
Loggerhead Shrike (*Lanius ludovicianus*)	R	R	R*			R	R	R	R	R	R	R	R	U	R	U
Bell's Vireo (*Vireo bellii*)	U	U	R*			R	U	U	U	U	U	U	U	U	U	U
Plumbeous Vireo (*Vireo plumbeus*)												R				R
Hutton's Vireo (*Vireo huttoni*)							R		R		R	U	U	R*	R	R
Steller's Jay (*Cyanocitta stelleri*)												R	R*	R*		R

TABLE 2. CONTINUED.

	Sonoyta			Concepción									Gila		Sonora	
	Sonoyta	Vamori	Lower	Plomo Lower	Plomo Upper	Sasabe Lower	Sasabe Upper	Altar Lower	Altar Upper	Busani	Coyotillo Magdalena	Coccospera-Bambuto	Santa Cruz	San Pedro	San Miguel	Bacanuchi-Sonora
Western Scrub-Jay (*Aphelocoma californica*)					R		R		R			R*	R	R*	R	R*
Mexican Jay (*Aphelocoma ultramarina*)												F	F	U	U	U
Chihuahuan Raven (*Corvus cryptoleucus*)		F	?	F	U	U	F	?	R	?	?	F	?	F	?	F
Common Raven (*Corvus corax*)	F	F	F		F	F	F	F	F	F	F	F	F	F	F	F
Horned Lark (*Eremophila alpestris*)	U*	R*	R*						F	R	F		U*	C		
Purple Martin (*Progne subis*)	U	U	U*	U	F	U	U	F	F	F	U	R			R	
Violet-green Swallow (*Tachycineta thalassina*)	R			R										?		
Northern Rough-winged Swallow (*Stelgidopteryx serripennis*)	R		R*				R		R		R		U	U	R	R
Cliff Swallow (*Petrochelidon pyrrhonota*)	R*		R*					R	R	R*	R	R*		R*	R	R
Barn Swallow (*Hirundo rustica*)	U	U	U			U		U		U	U		U	U	U	U
Bridled Titmouse (*Baeolophus wollweberi*)			U	U	U		R		U		R	U	U	U	U	U
Verdin (*Auriparus flaviceps*)	C	C	C	C	R	C	C	C	R	C	C	U	C	C	C	C
Bushtit (*Psaltriparus minimus*)					C		R		C	C	C	F	U	F		
White-breasted Nuthatch (*Sitta carolinensis*)					R				R			U	F	F		U
Pygmy Nuthatch (*Sitta pygmaea*)									R			R*		R*		
Brown Creeper (*Certhia americana*)												R		R*		R
Cactus Wren (*Campylorhynchus brunneicapillus*)	C	C	C	C	C	C	C	C	C	C	C	F		R	C	U
Rock Wren (*Salpinctes obsoletus*)	?	R			R	R*	R	R	R		U	U		U	U	U
Canyon Wren (*Catherpes mexicanus*)	R	R	R*	R	U		U	R	U		U	F	U		F	F
Sinaloa Wren (*Thryothorus sinaloa*)											R	R	U		R*	R
Happy Wren (*Thryothorus felix*)											R					R
Bewick's Wren (*Thryomanes bewickii*)	?	R	R	R	U		F	F	F	U	F	C	C	C	C	C
House Wren (*Troglodytes aedon*)												R				R
Blue-gray Gnatcatcher (*Polioptila caerulea*)	C	C	C	C	C	C	C	C	C	C	C	R		?		R
Black-tailed Gnatcatcher (*Polioptila melanura*)												R			F	U*
Black-capped Gnatcatcher (*Polioptila nigriceps*)												U			U	U*
Eastern Bluebird (*Sialia sialis*)												R	R	R		
American Robin (*Turdus migratorius*)												R	R*			R
Northern Mockingbird (*Mimus polyglottos*)	U	U	U	U	U		U	F	F	U	U	R	F	C		U
Bendire's Thrasher (*Toxostoma bendirei*)		R	U*	R*				R	R	R	U	R*			F	
Curve-billed Thrasher (*Toxostoma curvirostre*)	C	C	C	C	C	C	C	C	C	U	F	F	U*	F		U
Crissal Thrasher (*Toxostoma crissale*)	U	U	R*	R	U	U	U	F	U	U	U	R		R	C	U
Le Conte's Thrasher (*Toxostoma lecontei*)	U*														U	R*
European Starling (*Sturnus vulgaris*)	R							R	R	U	R	R*	R*	R	R*	R
Phainopepla (*Phainopepla nitens*)	C	U	F	U	C	U	C	C	C		F	F	C	C	C	F
Olive Warbler (*Peucedramus taeniatus*)					R							R				R*
Lucy's Warbler (*Vermivora luciae*)	F	F	R	R	C	U	C	C	C	C	C	C	C	C	C	C

Table 2. Continued.

	Sonoyta					Concepción							Gila		Sonora	
	Sonoyta	Vamori	Lower	Plomo Lower	Plomo Upper	Sasabe Lower	Sasabe Upper	Altar Lower	Altar Upper	Busani	Coyotillo Magdalena	Cocospera-Bambuto	Santa Cruz	San Pedro	San Miguel	Bacanuchi-Sonora
Yellow Warbler (*Dendroica petechia*)								U	R		R	U	U	C	U	U
Black-throated Gray Warbler (*Dendroica nigrescens*)											R	R				R
Grace's Warbler (*Dendroica graciae*)											R	R				R
Common Yellowthroat (*Geothlypis trichas*)								U			R	R		F	R	R*
Red-faced Warbler (*Cardellina rubrifrons*)																R*
Painted Redstart (*Myioborus pictus*)				R*					R		R	R	R*			R
Fan-tailed Warbler (*Euthlypis lachrymosa*)											?					
Rufous-capped Warbler (*Basileuterus rufifrons*)									R		R	R				R*
Yellow-breasted Chat (*Icteria virens*)	R	R		R*	R		R	U	U	R	U	U	U	R	U	U
Hepatic Tanager (*Piranga flava*)						R	R	R	R			U	U		R	U
Summer Tanager (*Piranga rubra*)						R	R	R	U		U	U	U	F	F	U
Spotted Towhee (*Pipilo maculatus*)						R	R	R	R			U	U			U
Canyon Towhee (*Pipilo fuscus*)	C	C	C	C	C		C	C	C	C	C	C	C		C	C
Abert's Towhee (*Pipilo aberti*)													U	U		
Rufous-winged Sparrow (*Aimophila carpalis*)	R	U	R	R	U	R	U	R	U	R	U	U	R	R	R	R
Cassin's Sparrow (*Aimophila cassinii*)		U		R*	R		U	R	U	R	U	U	F	C	R*	U
Botteri's Sparrow (*Aimophila botterii*)		R								R			U	C	R*	U
Rufous-crowned Sparrow (*Aimophila ruficeps*)	R*	R*		R	R		R	F	F		U	F	F	F	U	F
Five-striped Sparrow (*Aimophila quinquestriata*)							R	U	U		U	U	U		U	U
Lark Sparrow (*Chondestes grammacus*)									R*				U	F		
Black-throated Sparrow (*Amphispiza bilineata*)	C	C	C	C	C	C	F	C	F	F	C	C	U	U	F	U
Savannah Sparrow (*Passerculus sandwichensis*)	R*															
Grasshopper Sparrow (*Ammodramus savannarum*)													C	C		
Song Sparrow (*Melospiza melodia*)	R							U		R	U	U	F	C	U	U
Yellow-eyed Junco (*Junco phaeonotus*)											R	R	R*	R*	R*	R
Northern Cardinal (*Cardinalis cardinalis*)	U	U		U	F	U		U	U		U	U	U	U	F	U
Pyrrhuloxia (*Cardinalis sinuatus*)	R	U		R	U	R		F	R	R	U	R*	U*	R*	R	R
Black-headed Grosbeak (*Pheucticus melanocephalus*)					R		R		R			U	R	R	R	R
Blue Grosbeak (*Passerina caerulea*)	R	R	R*	U*	U		U	U	F	F	F	F	R	F	R	F
Indigo Bunting (*Passerina cyanea*)									R	R	R	R				
Varied Bunting (*Passerina versicolor*)	R	R	R*	R	F	F		F	F	F	F	F			F	
Red-winged Blackbird (*Agelaius phoeniceus*)				R*				R	R	R	R*	R*				
Eastern Meadowlark (*Sturnella magna*)														U		U
Western Meadowlark (*Sturnella neglecta*)	?												U	F		
Great-tailed Grackle (*Quiscalus mexicanus*)	R	F	R	R				U	U	F	F	U	U	F	U	U

TABLE 2. CONTINUED.

	Sonoyta			Concepción										Gila		Sonora	
	Sonoyta	Vamori	Lower	Plomo Lower	Plomo Upper	Sasabe Lower	Sasabe Upper	Altar Lower	Altar Upper	Busani	Coyotillo Magdalena	Cocospera Bambuto		Santa Cruz	San Pedro	San Miguel	Bacanuchi Sonora
Bronzed Cowbird (Molothrus aeneus)								R	F	R	R	R		R*	R	U	R
Brown-headed Cowbird (Molothrus ater)	U	U	U	U	U		U	F	F	F	F	U		F	F	F	F
Hooded Oriole (Icterus cucullatus)	U	U	R	R	U	U		U	R	U	U	R		U	U	F	U
Streak-backed Oriole (Icterus pustulatus)						?					R	R					R*
Bullock's Oriole (Icterus bullockii)		R		R	R	U	R	R	U		U	?		U	F	?	
Scott's Oriole (Icterus parisorum)	U	U	R	R	U	R	U	R	U	C	U	F		U	U	U	U
House Finch (Carpodacus mexicanus)	C	C	C	C	C	C	C	C	C		C	C		C	C	U	U
Lesser Goldfinch (Carduelis psaltria)	R	R	R	R*			U	F	C	F	F	F		F	C	U	U
House Sparrow (Passer domesticus)	U		U	U	U	U	U	U	U	U	U	U		U	U	U	U

(Buteo brachyurus), Eurasian Collared-Dove (Streptopelia decaocto), Violet-green Swallow (Tachycineta thalassina), and Happy Wren (Thryothorus felix) were presumed breeding in at least two watershed regions, and Fan-tailed Warbler and Western Meadowlark were possibly breeding in one. Of species that had been observed previously at only a single locality, I presumed breeding by Cordilleran Flycatcher (Empidonax occidentalis) in one additional watershed region, White-tailed Kite (Elanus leucurus), White-tipped Dove (Leptotila verreauxi), and Nutting's Flycatcher (Myiarchus nuttingi) in two, Sinaloa Wren (Thryothorus sinaloa) and Rufous-capped Warbler (Basileuterus rufifrons) in three, Thick-billed Kingbird (Tyrannus crassirostris) in four, and Five-striped Sparrow (Aimophila quinquestriata) in five additional watershed regions. Of species that had been observed previously at only two localities, I presumed breeding by Elegant Quail (Callipepla douglasii) in one, Streak-backed Oriole (Icterus pustulatus) in three, and Buff-collared Nightjar (Caprimulgus ridgwayi) in four additional regions (Table 2). All of these species were rare or uncommon.

Breeding distribution of many species was much broader than that suggested by previous studies. For example, I detected several species that typically breed in riparian woodlands including Gray Hawk (Buteo nitida), Yellow Warbler (Dendroica petechia), and Summer Tanager (Piranga rubra) at numerous localities in the Altar, Santa Cruz, and San Pedro watersheds where they had either not been documented or had been presumed to breed at only single localities. Similarly, I detected several species that typically breed in oak woodlands including Whiskered Screech-Owl (Megascops trichopsis), Hutton's Vireo (Vireo huttoni), and Hepatic Tanager (Piranga flava) in the upper Altar and upper Sasabe watersheds which is west of areas where they had been presumed to breed; Northern Flicker (Colaptes auratus), Arizona Woodpecker (Picoides arizonae), and Dusky-capped Flycatcher (Myiarchus tuberculifer) occurred still farther west in oak woodlands in the upper Plomo watershed. I detected species that typically breed in grasslands including Swainson's Hawk (Buteo swainsoni) and Botteri's Sparrow (Aimophila botterii) west to the Vamori watershed and Cassin's Sparrow (Aimophila cassinii) west to the upper Plomo watershed. American Kestrel (Falco sparverius), Brown-crested Flycatcher (Myiarchus tyrannulus), Bell's Vireo (Vireo bellii), and Lucy's Warbler (Vermivora luciae) were at least presumed breeding in all 16 watershed regions despite lack of previous records in many of these regions.

Distribution and abundance varied widely among watersheds. Scaled Quail (*Callipepla squamata*), Botteri's Sparrow, Grasshopper Sparrow (*Ammodramus savannarum*), and Eastern Meadowlark (*Sternella magna*) were restricted mainly to the San Pedro and occasionally the Santa Cruz and Vamori watersheds; Scaled Quail occurred locally west to the upper Plomo watershed. White-tipped Dove and Nutting's Flycatcher were restricted to the Bacanuchi-Sonora, San Miguel, and Coyotillo-Magdalena-Carrizo watershed regions, whereas Sinaloa Wren and Black-capped Gnatcatcher (*Polioptila nigriceps*) occurred in these and the Cocospera-Bambuto watershed. I observed Happy Wren at only single localities in both the Bacanuchi-Sonora and Coyotillo-Magdalena-Carrizo watersheds. Sharp-shinned Hawk (*Accipiter striatus*), Northern Goshawk (*Accipiter gentilis*), and Broad-tailed Hummingbird (*Selasphorus platycercus*) presumably bred only in the Sierra los Ajos (Bacanuchi-Sonora watershed); Cordilleran Flycatcher, Buff-breasted Flycatcher (*Empidonax fulvifrons*), and Plumbeous Vireo (*Vireo plumbeus*) occurred in the Sierra los Ajos and to the west in one–two mountain ranges in the Cocospera-Bambuto watershed.

DISCUSSION

SPECIES RICHNESS

Northern Sonora, Mexico supports a wide range of environments and a rich and varied avifauna. Between 2000 and 2007, I recorded 161 species of landbirds that I at least presumed were breeding in the Sonoyta, Concepción, Gila, and Sonora watersheds within 125 km of the international boundary with the US. Including seven additional species that had been recorded previously, 168 species of landbirds have been at least presumed to breed in the region, and all except Northern (Masked) Bobwhite likely still occur. In comparison to estimates from neighboring Arizona between 1993 and 2000 (Corman and Wise-Gervais 2005), northern Sonora supports approximately 35% fewer species of breeding landbirds in an area approximately one-tenth the size and with 45% less elevation range; including additional species in the adjacent northern Yaqui watershed lowers this estimate to at most 31% (Marshall 1957, Russell and Monson 1998; A. D. Flesch, unpubl. data). Although estimates are not available for other regions of northern Mexico, large-scale patterns of bird distribution (Howell and Webb 1995) suggests that northern Sonora supports higher richness of breeding landbirds than any other region of similar area in the borderlands of northern Mexico.

Using probabilistic methods, I estimated that as many as 178 species of landbirds likely breed in the study area. Information from Sonora (Russell and Monson 1998; A. D. Flesch, unpubl. data) and neighboring southern Arizona (Corman and Wise-Gervais 2005), combined with vegetation associations that I observed, suggest 10 additional species may breed locally or irregularly in the study area (Ruddy Ground Dove [*Columbina talpacoti*], Long-eared Owl [*Asio otus*], White-eared Hummingbird [*Hylocharis leucotis*], Berylline Hummingbird [*Amazilia beryllina*], Lucifer Hummingbird [*Calothorax lucifer*] Flame-colored Tanager [*Piranga bidentata*], Chipping Sparrow [*Spizella passerina*], Black-chinned Sparrow [*Spizella atrogularis*], Red Crossbill [*Loxia curvirostra*] and Pine Siskin [*Carduelis pinus*]). Rusty Sparrow (*Aimophila rufescens*) was once detected just south of the study area (Thayer and Bangs 1906) and could also breed locally in the Bacanuchi-Sonora region. Although I obtained evidence that Hermit Thrush (*Catharus guttatus*) and Western Tanager (*Piranga ludoviciana*) breed in mixed-conifer forest just east of the Yaqui-Sonora divide (A. D. Flesch, unpubl. data), in Sonora these species and possibly Warbling Vireo (*Vireo gilvus*) are likely restricted to the upper Yaqui watershed. Breeding species that have been observed combined with those I expect may occur suggest estimates of species richness that I calculated are accurate.

Not surprisingly, species richness increased markedly with the number of major vegetation communities that were present in a region. As such, regions in the east that had broader elevation ranges and therefore greater environmental diversity had higher richness. Presence of broad-leaf riparian woodland, Madrean evergreen woodland, and Madrean montane conifer forest had the greatest influence on species richness indicating that these vegetation communities supported more species with specialized requirements than other communities in the region. In contrast, although richness was also high in regions with Sinaloan thornscrub, this community likely had less of an overall effect on richness because many species that are associated with thornscrub, such as Buff-collared Nightjar, Black-capped Gnatcatcher, and Five-striped Sparrow, also occurred away from thornscrub in dense desertscrub and woodland.

DISTRIBUTION PATTERNS

Bird species that occurred in desertscrub were universally more common and widespread than species that were typically associated with grassland, thornscrub, oak woodland, or conifer forest. Species that were found predominantly in oak woodland, grassland, and broadleaf riparian woodland were typically rare and had much narrower and more fragmented distributions. Species associated with conifer forest were rarest and were largely restricted to high elevations in the Sierra los Ajos, Cananea, Pinito, and as described by Marshall (1957), in the Sierra Azul. Grassland species were especially rare in the west with some species reaching the western edge of their distribution on the east sides of the Sierras el Humo and el Cobre. Grassland species were more abundant and widespread in the upper Santa Cruz and especially in the upper San Pedro watersheds where plains grassland with high levels of horizontal and vertical vegetation cover still persist. Breeding populations of species that occurred only in broadleaf riparian woodland did not occur west of the Río Altar and were largely restricted to the Ríos Altar, Bambuto, Magdalena, and portions of other major valley bottoms to the east.

Northern Sonora supports the westernmost and northernmost patches of some vegetation communities and these patterns have important implications for bird distribution. Isolated stands of oak woodland in the Sierra el Humo for example, are the westernmost Madrean evergreen woodland in the Madrean Sky Islands, mountains that form the northern and western extensions of Sierra Madre Occidental (Marshall 1957, Warshall 1995). As such, populations of birds that are associated with oak woodland in the Sierra Madre Occidental, such as Arizona Woodpecker, reach the western edge of their global distribution in the Sierra el Humo (Flesch and Hahn 2005). Similarly, oak woodland in the nearby Sierra San Juan supported several additional species of birds that I did not detect to the west in the Sierra el Humo, including Whiskered Screech-Owl, which reach the northwestern edge of their global distribution here and in the neighboring Baboquivari Mountains of Arizona (Phillips et al. 1964). Species typically associated with Neotropical environments such as Elegant Quail, White-tipped Dove, Nutting's Flycatcher, and Sinaloa Wren were restricted mainly to three or four watersheds in the more humid south-central and southeast portions of the study area. The northernmost patches of Sinaloan thornscrub that had similar structure and composition to that found further south occurred in and northeast of the Sierra Cucurpe and at low to moderate elevations in the Bacanuchi-Sonora region and these were the only regions where I observed Happy Wren.

CHANGES IN DISTRIBUTION AND STATUS

Patterns of animal distribution represent a complex response to a range of factors including the arrangement and size of resource patches, physiological tolerances, and biotic interactions that vary in space and time (Andrewartha and Birch 1954, MacArthur 1972, Brown 1995). In northern Sonora, my observations indicate that a wide range of species are distributed across much larger areas than suggested by previous studies. Determining whether these patterns are due to actual changes in bird distribution or limited effort during past studies is difficult because few data on localities where species were undetected are available and because there are few historical accounts of vegetation conditions and change in Sonora.

Limited fieldwork in many regions of northern Sonora likely explains the wider patterns of distribution that I observed of a broad range of species. Russell and Monson (1998) for example, cited just four records of Brown-crested Flycatcher west of the Río Bambuto, north of the Río Concepción, and east of the Río Sonoyta, yet this species and its habitat are common or fairly common in all 11 watershed regions in this vast region. Distribution of other widespread migratory species such as Bell's Vireo and Lucy's Warbler were also understated, yet this pattern was somewhat less evident for resident species, suggesting that survey effort during the breeding season had been limited. Similarly, many rare species that occurred in isolated or otherwise disjunct vegetation communities had also gone undetected. If Phillips and Amadon (1952) or Russell and Monson (1998) had visited oak woodlands in the Sierra San Juan and Sierra el Humo during the breeding season rather than in fall, they probably would have detected many of the same species that I recorded. Previous fieldwork seems to have been most limited in the San Pedro, Altar, Busani, Sasabe, Vamori, and Plomo watersheds where many breeding species had not been previously documented.

Where known, patterns of vegetation change in northern Sonora have been complex and variable (Bahre and Hutchinson 2001, Turner et al. 2003), and these changes have likely influenced bird distribution. In high-elevation pine forests in the Cocospera-Bambuto watershed for example, presence of Cordilleran Flycatcher, Buff-breasted Flycatcher, and Plumbeous Vireo in mountain ranges where they were not observed by Marshall (1957) is likely attributable to recovery of these forests following extensive logging that occurred just prior to Marshall's visits. In contrast, although presence of species that are associated with oak woodland in the Sierras San

Juan and el Humo could also be related to vegetation change, evidence suggests distribution of these woodlands has been largely stable in the region during recent times (Bahre and Minnich 2001) despite some recession at lower elevations (Turner et al. 2003).

In vegetation communities that are typically more dynamic, such as broadleaf riparian woodland (Webb et al. 2007), attributing changes in bird distribution to vegetation change is more difficult. In the San Pedro Valley for example, many riparian species such as Gray Hawk, Yellow Warbler, and Summer Tanager may not have been widely documented because gallery forests were once rare or absent. In 1892 and 1893, Mearns (1907) observed only scattered broadleaf trees along the Río San Pedro at the international boundary, and gallery forests of cottonwood and willow did not develop until the 1960s and especially in the late 1970s and 1980s (Webb et al. 2007).

In the Altar Valley, however, where most species of riparian birds had been described only in the extreme upper watershed at Rancho la Arizona (van Rossem 1931), broadleaf riparian woodland has likely been present for some time. Nentvig et al. (1980) for example, described presence of permanent surface water along many portions of the Río Altar in 1764 and Shreve (1951) noted that virgin mesquite woodlands persisted near Tubutama into the 1950s despite elimination from virtually all other major valley bottoms in the Sonoran Desert at that time. Therefore, despite only recent description of breeding bird communities in the cottonwood-willow forests along the Río Altar, these communities have likely been present for some time.

Although lack of previous effort and vegetation change may explain why I observed much broader patterns of distribution for some species, distribution and abundance of many of these same species may in fact be much more limited than in the past. Along the Río Altar, for example, completion of the Cuauhtémoc Dam and Reservoir (Presa Cuauhtémoc) in 1950 diverted surface water and likely contributed to increased vegetation clearing for agriculture, degradation of gallery forests, and subsequent declines in distribution and abundance of birds associated with these forests. Early descriptions of birds and vegetation along the lower Río Concepción are available (Stephens 1885, Neff 1947, Phillips and Amadon 1952). Undoubtedly, complete elimination of the once extensive mesquite woodland near Pitiquito and Caborca caused the local extirpation of many species of birds and in part, explains why I failed to detect 21% of species that had been at least presumed

to breed in this region in the past. Similarly, although I found small, localized populations of some grassland birds south and west of Sasabe, these species were likely much more abundant and widespread before these grasslands were largely degraded or lost (Brown 1900, 1904; Bahre 1991, Turner et al. 2003), as suggested by Stephens' (1885) observation of the now extirpated Northern Bobwhite.

More widespread distributions of some species are likely the results of range expansion that has occurred largely independent of major changes in vegetation. Comparing my findings with previous observation from Sonora (Russell and Monson 1998) and the southwestern US suggests recent range expansions of the following species: White-tailed Kite (Monson and Phillips 1981, Gatz et al. 1985), Short-tailed Hawk (Corman and Wise-Gervais 2005, Williams et al. 2007), Buff-collared Nightjar (Bowers and Dunning 1997), Thick-billed Kingbird (Phillips 1968, Monson and Phillips 1981), Sinaloa Wren (Russell and Monson 1998), Rufous-capped Warbler (Rosenberg and Witzeman 1999), Five-striped Sparrow (Groschupf 1994), and Streak-backed Oriole (Corman and Monson 1995, Corman and Wise-Gervais 2005). Eurasian Collared-Dove rapidly expanded across much of North America since arriving in Florida in the early 1980s (Romagosa and McEneaney 1999) and recent arrival in Sonora since at least 2004 (Gómez de Silva 2004) is not surprising. Although I found Zone-tailed Hawk (*Buteo albonotatus*) to be much more common and widespread in western Sonora than had been described previously, its presence in western Arizona since at least 1939 (Phillips et al. 1964) suggests distribution has been largely static in this region despite recent expansion to the north (Johnson 1994, Corman and Wise-Gervais 2005). In contrast, although I also found Gray Hawk at many new localities, especially in the west and at somewhat higher elevations, this species has likely expanded its range due to vegetation change and other factors. Gray Hawk were not documented along the Río San Pedro until 1963 (Phillips et al. 1964) and have recently expanded into central Arizona (Corman and Wise-Gervais 2005).

Most species that I found to be more widely distributed or present for the first time in northern Sonora have likely expanded their geographic ranges from more tropical regions to the south (e.g., Short-tailed Hawk, White-tipped Dove, Buff-collared Nightjar, Thick-billed Kingbird, Sinaloa Wren, Happy Wren, and Rufous-capped Warbler). Although wider occurrence of some of these species could be attributable to increased effort, this seems unlikely, because many of these same species have recently occurred for the first time or become regular summer residents in southern Arizona where effort has been much more extensive (Monson and Phillips 1981, Rosenberg and Witzeman 1999, Corman and Wise-Gervais 2005). These patterns and those in other areas of western North America (Johnson 1994) and southern Texas (Brush 2005) suggest some southern species are expanding northward possibly in response to changing resource distributions resulting from climate change and a widening of tropical atmospheric circulations during recent decades (Seidel et al. 2008). Although poleward shifts in species distributions in response to climate change have been observed on nearly every continent (Parmesan and Yohe 2003, Root et al. 2003, Parmesan 2006), time and additional study are required to further elucidate these trends in northern Mexico.

EFFORT—PAST, PRESENT, AND FUTURE

Although my coverage was extensive, it was limited in some regions. After comparing my findings with those of previous studies, I failed to detect an average of 7% of all species that had been at least presumed to breed in a watershed region, and this quantity varied with effort (Tables 1 and 2). Although some species that I failed to detect may no longer occur, more effort especially at high elevations would have produced additional data, particularly in the Santa Cruz, Bacanuchi-Sonora, San Pedro, and San Miguel watershed regions. Upper elevations in several mountain ranges in northern Sonora have likely never been visited by ornithologists including the Sierras San Antonio, San Jose, el Chivato, la Madera, Cucurpe, Cubabi, el Alamo, and San Manuel. Aside from my efforts, bird observations at upper elevations in the Sierras el Pinito, Cananea, and los Ajos had not been reported for over five decades (Marshall 1957) and other lower yet regionally significant mountains such as the Sierras San Juan and el Humo had not been visited during the breeding season. Additional effort in these and other areas of northern Sonora will yield new and valuable information especially when the adjoining Yaqui watershed is considered.

Despite more than a century of ornithological work in northern Sonora, Mexico (van Rossem 1945, Russell and Monson 1998) status and distribution of many species had remained little known in some regions. This is in sharp contrast to neighboring portions of Arizona where a great deal of historical (Swarth 1914, Brandt 1951, Phillips et al. 1964) and recent (Monson and Phillips 1981, Rosenberg and Witzeman 1998 and 1999, Rosenberg 2001, Corman and Wise-Gervais 2005) information is available. Availability of biological information in many areas of northern Sonora should increase as accessibility is improved and as interest in the diversity, uniqueness, and preservation of this region is enhanced.

CONSERVATION AND THREATS

Information on distribution and abundance of wildlife is essential for conservation. Without these data, conservation priorities may be misguided and important populations may be lost or degraded before they can be managed and protected. Prospects for conserving, managing, and enhancing populations of landbirds in northern Sonora are promising because human population densities throughout much of the region are low and because vast areas of natural vegetation remain relatively intact and unfragmented (Stoleson et al. 2005, Felger et al. 2007). Further, recent federal laws in Mexico have created a system that could aid landowners in conservation and sustainable use of wildlife especially once these programs are improved and additional resources are provided (Valdez et al. 2006, Weber et al. 2006, Sisk et al. 2007). In recent years there has also been an increase in activity by private conservation organizations in northern Sonora. These efforts have been led by Biodiversidad y Desarrollo Armónico, Naturalia, and The Nature Conservancy in northeast Sonora, by Pronatura in northwest Sonora, and assisted by partnerships with public agencies through organizations such as Sonoran Joint Venture. When enhanced by data on distribution, status, and habitat needs of landbirds, these efforts can produce valuable results.

Despite good prospects for conservation, significant threats exist. Loss and degradation of riparian areas due to agriculture, unsustainable grazing practices, and excessive groundwater pumping are having a profound influence on the structure and function of these systems. Cottonwood forests along the Río Magdalena between Magdalena de Kino and Santa Ana have been steadily declining for some time and no longer occur more than a few kilometers below Magdalena de Kino (A. D. Flesch, pers. obs.). Riparian forests throughout much of the Santa Cruz Valley have been highly degraded and although conditions are generally better in the San Pedro Valley, regeneration of broadleaf trees is limited in many areas. Riparian forest along the Río Altar is also declining locally above Tubutama and especially near Saríc where quantity of surface water declined greatly between 2000 and 2007. Other significant threats to landbirds in northern Sonora include over-grazing and degradation of grasslands, limited regeneration of important nest-cavity substrates such large trees and saguaros (*Carnegiea gigantea*), excessive fuel-wood cutting, and urbanization on a local scale (Flesch 2003, Búrquez and Martínez-Yrízar 2007). Grazing intensity in northern Sonora is generally much higher than in adjacent Arizona (Balling 1988), and if better managed could reduce the ecological costs and enhance the economic benefits of this nearly ubiquitous land use.

Cross-border partnerships between government and non-governmental organizations, scientists, and private citizens have the potential to optimize conservation, management, and restoration efforts in the borderlands. This need for coordination is emphasized by the ecological connections we share across the border and our joint stake in conserving natural resources for future generations. The international border is a political, not a biological boundary and as such, persistence of many populations depends on the actions and priorities of our two nations.

ACKNOWLEDGMENTS

I am grateful to my field assistants. They include Sky Jacobs, Greg Greene, Elliott Swarthout, and Glenn Johnson who surveyed transects and Gabriel Valencia Ortega, Andrés Villareal Lizárraga, Shawn Lowery, Jeremy Russell, Jon Green, and Robert Hunt who contributed incidental observations. I thank Sky Jacobs, Mac Hudson, and Lisa Hahn for companionship in the field. For logistical support in Sonora, I thank Eduardo Lopez Saavedra of Biodiversidad y Desarrollo Armónico, Jaqueline Garcia Hernandez of Centro de Investigacion en Alimentacion y Desarrollo, and Elvira Rojero Diaz and the staff of the Ajos-Bavispe Reserve, Comisión Nacional de Áreas Naturales Protegidas. I thank Bob Steidl for administrative support and Juan Carlos Bravo and Gerardo Carreón Arroyo for Spanish translation. Indirect financial support was provided by of the USDI Fish and Wildlife Service, National Park Service, and Arizona Department of Transportation. Direct financial support was provided by Sonoran Joint Venture, T&E, Inc., and mainly through personal contributions. I thank Glenn Johnson, Stephen Russell, and two anonymous reviewers for comments on earlier versions of the manuscript. Finally, I thank the people and landowners of northern Sonora for welcoming us on their lands. This effort is dedicated to the memory of Benjamin M. Chameides who inspired me to explore.

Studies in Avian Biology No. 37:46–51

THE DISTRIBUTION AND STATUS OF ROYAL TERNS ON THE PACIFIC COAST OF SOUTHERN CALIFORNIA AND BAJA CALIFORNIA, MEXICO

Charles T. Collins and Eduardo Palacios

Abstract. In the early part of the 1900s non-breeding Royal Terns (*Thalasseus maximus*) were commonly found on the California coast, particularly in winter. By the 1950s their numbers had declined, along with populations of the Pacific sardine (*Sardinops sagax*). Today they are resident on the southern California coast and have bred there since 1959. The current breeding population is nearly 140 pairs and slowly increasing. On the Pacific coast of Baja California, Mexico, Royal Terns are also permanent residents and have bred in coastal wetlands since at least 1926. The recent breeding population in the Laguna San Ignacio and Laguna Ojo de Liebre wetland systems is between 1,300 and 3,500 pairs. Continued protection of colony sites from human disturbance and terrestrial predators, particularly in southern California, seem to be the most important factors for the continued increase in Royal Tern populations in this portion of their extensive range.

Key Words: Baja California, breeding distribution, California, Mexico, population size, *Thalasseus maximus*.

DISTRIBUCIÓN Y STATUS DE LA GOLONDRINA MARINA REAL EN LA COSTA DEL PACIFICO DEL SUR DE CALIFORNIA Y BAJA CALIFORNIA, MEXICO

Resumen. A principios de los 1900s, los individuos no reproductivos de golondrinas marinas reales (*Thalasseus maximus*) eran comunes en la costa de California, particularmente en invierno. Hacia los 1950s sus números habían disminuido, junto con las poblaciones de la sardina Monterrey (*Sardinops sagax*). Ahora son residentes en la costa del sur de California y han anidado ahí desde 1959. La población reproductiva actual es 140 parejas pero esta aumentando gradualmente. En la costa del Pacífico de la península de Baja California, México, las golondrinas marinas reales también son residentes permanentes y se reproducen en lagunas costeras desde por lo menos 1926. La población reproductiva actual en los complejos lagunares de Laguna Ojo de Liebre y Laguna San Ignacio es de alrededor de 1,300–3,500 parejas. La protección continua de las colonias contra el disturbio humano y los depredadores terrestres, especialmente en el sur de California, parecen ser los factores más importantes para el aumento continuo de las poblaciones de la golondrina marina real en esta porción de su extenso intervalo de distribución.

The Royal Tern (*Thalasseus maximus*) is one of the most widespread of the seven species of crested terns. It is a common summer resident on the Atlantic and Gulf coasts of North America and resident in the Gulf of California and also breeds in coastal west Africa (Buckley and Buckley 2002). Royal Terns nest in dense clusters at colony sites (Buckley and Buckley 1977) in coastal locations where they forage on schooling fish in the marine environment (Buckley and Buckley 1972, 1974, 2002; Erwin 1977). Colony sizes range from only a few individuals intermixed with Sandwich (*Thalasseus sandvicensis*) or Elegant Terns (*Thalasseus elegans*) to colonies of 17,000 pairs (Buckley and Buckley 2002, Velarde et al. 2005, Mellink et al. 2007). Overall population trends are poorly known, with declines in some areas (Buckley and Buckley 2002). On a world-wide basis its population status is considered to be of moderate concern (Kushlan et al. 2002). Here we review the history, current status, diet, and conservation of Royal Terns in the California Current system of southern California and the west coast of the Baja California peninsula. The status of Royal Terns in the Gulf of California has been reviewed elsewhere (Velarde et al. 2005, Mellink et al. 2007) and is not part of this analysis.

ROYAL TERNS IN BAJA CALIFORNIA

In Baja California, Royal Terns have long been considered to be fairly common to common on both coasts of the peninsula (Grinnell 1928, Wilbur 1987). The first documentation of their breeding on the Pacific side was in 1926 (Bancroft 1927a) at Scammons Lagoon (hereafter Laguna Ojo de Liebre) and again there in 1927 (Bancroft 1927b). Although records exist of Royal Terns along the coast of Baja California from Cabo San Lucas north to the Coronados

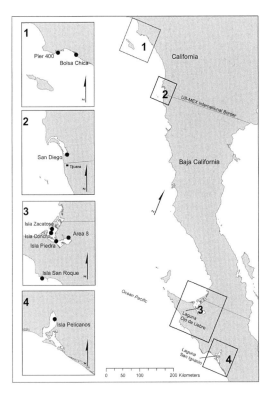

FIGURE 1. Locations of breeding colonies of Royal Terns on the Pacific coast of southern California and Baja California, Mexico.

Islands near the California border, in nearly all seasons (Grinnell 1928, Wilbur 1987), no further mention of breeding was made until 1946, when they were again reported breeding at Laguna Ojo de Liebre (Kenyon 1947).

In the early 1990s, Royal Terns were reported to be present in several coastal estuaries of Baja California and breeding in both the Laguna Ojo de Liebre and Laguna San Ignacio complexes (Massey and Palacios 1994). In Laguna Ojo de Liebre, Royal Terns have nested at four sites (Fig. 1). The oldest colony, on Isla Concha, first mentioned by Bancroft (1927a), has been utilized, perhaps regularly, up to 2007 (Table 1). Kenyon's report of 150 nests included terns nesting on both Isla Concha and on nearby Isla Zacatosa (K. W. Kenyon, unpubl. data). No Royal Tern nests were found on Isla Piedra in 1998 (Castellanos et al. 2001). However, by 2002 all Royal Terns had shifted their nesting from Isla Concha 16 km south to Isla Piedra with 1,845–3,500 nests having been reported between 2002 and 2005 with an estimated 1300 in 2007 (Table 1).

A fourth nesting site is on an islet in area 8 of the Guerrero Negro saltworks (Fig. 1). Royal Terns were first reported nesting at this site in 1992 (Massey and Palacios 1994). It has been utilized regularly from 2003–2007 (Table 1). Since 1998 the number of Royal Terns breeding at the several sites in Laguna Ojo de Liebre has averaged 2,406 pairs (range 1,330–3,500).

In Laguna San Ignacio (Fig. 1), up to 350 pairs of Royal Terns have nested on Isla Pelícanos in recent years (Table 1). None were observed there in 1989 (Danemann and Guzman 1992) but 350 pairs were found nesting there in 1992 (Massey and Palacios 1994), 100 pairs (60 on nests) in 1998 (D. W. Anderson, unpubl. data), at least 200 pairs (150 on nests) in 1999 (D. W. Anderson, unpubl. data), and ca. 350 in 2004 (R. Mayoral, pers. comm.). Caspian Terns (*Hydroprogne caspia*) first colonized this site in the mid-1980s and were joined by Royal Terns in 1992. The earlier report of Royal Terns nesting there (Everett and Anderson 1991) was based on a misidentification of the nesting Caspian Terns (Palacios and Mellink 1993). No terns of either species were found nesting at this site in 2006 (G. Danemann, pers comm.) with predation by coyotes (*Canis latrans*) thought to be the cause of desertion.

The nest site in Laguna San Ignacio is on an island largely divided into two sections by a tidal channel. This has been alternatively referred to as a single island, Isla Ballena (Danemann and Guzman 1992) or Islas Pelícano (Tejas et al. 1991). It has also been considered as two separate islands, Islas Ballenas, on some maps of the area (Crumpton 1991, 1997; Automobile Club of Southern California 1998, Baja Almanac Publishers 2003), in which case the northern of the two islands has also been called Isla Garzas and the southern island, the site of the Caspian and Royal Tern colonies, Isla Pelícanos (Crumpton 1991). We prefer the latter terminology and have adopted it here (Table 1).

Bancroft (1927a) also stated that Royal Terns were breeders on [Isla] San Roque and other islands to the south of Laguna Ojo de Liebre. No other documentation was presented. This report was subsequently mentioned, without further elaboration, by Grinnell (1928), Wilbur (1987) and Everett and Anderson (1991). Royal Terns have not bred on Isla San Roque for many years (Wolf 2002) presumably due to predation by feral cats (*Felis catus*). The recent eradication of these cats from Isla San Roque (Wolf et al. 2006) may encourage Royal Terns to again breed on this island.

In Baja California, it is hard to detect any trends in Royal Tern numbers because the reporting has been, until recent years, rather uneven with large information gaps in important time

TABLE 1. Number of nesting pairs of Royal Terns at Baja California, Mexico, colonies. See text for description of colony sites.

Site	Year	Number of pairs	Source [a]
Laguna Ojo de Liebre			
Isla Concha (27°49′48″N, 114°14′06″W)			
	1926	present	1
	1927	present	2
	1946	150	3
	1980	400	4
	1992	400	5
	1998	2,762	4
	2007	30	16
Isla Piedra (27°42′18″N, 114°19′06″W)			
	2002	3,500	6
	2003	2,500	7
	2004	2,500	8
	2005	1,845	9
	2007	1,300	16
Guerrero Negro, area 8 (27°42′18″N, 113°58′07″W)			
	1975	0	10
	1992	100	5
	1996	99	11
	2002	0	6
	2003	42	7
	2004	400	8
	2005	135	9
	2007	100	16
Laguna San Ignacio			
Isla Pelícanos (26°55′N, 113°09′W)			
	1989	0	12
	1992	350	5
	1998	100	13
	1999	200	13
	2004	ca 350	14
	2006	0	15
	2007	20	16

[a] 1—Bancroft (1927a); 2—Bancroft (1927b); 3—Kenyon (1947, unpubl. data); 4—Castellanos et al. (2001); 5—Massey and Palacios (1994); 6—E. Palacios, E. Amador, and M. García (unpubl. data); 7—E. Palacios and E. Mellink (unpubl. data); 8—E. Amador (pers. comm.); 9—E. Palacios, E. Amador, and M. García (unpubl. data); 10—M. Evans (pers comm.); 11—Danemann and Carmona (2000); 12—Danemann and Guzman (1992); 13—D. W. Anderson (pers. comm.); 14—R. Mayoral (pers. comm.); 15—G. Danemann (pers. comm.), 16—E. Palacios (pers. obs.).

periods. The number of Royal Terns breeding in Laguna Ojo de Liebre had increased in recent years but decreased in 2007. They colonized Laguna San Ignacio in 1992, but were extirpated from Isla San Roque and suffered breeding failure at Laguna San Ignacio in 2006.

ROYAL TERNS IN SOUTHERN CALIFORNIA

Royal Tern populations in California were substantially larger in the past, particularly in winter, when they ranged north to Tomales Bay, Marin County (Grinnell and Miller 1944). In the early part of the 1900s Royal Terns were the commonest large tern in coastal southern California (Unitt 1984) but this was followed by a sharp decline in their numbers, particularly after 1950 (Cogswell 1977); they are now rare in northern California (Stallcup 1990, Small 1994, Roberson 2002) and no breeding records exist for Royal Terns in northern California.

In southern California Royal Terns are commonly found in small numbers during the winter along the coast and throughout the Channel Islands (Howell 1917, Garrett and Dunn 1981, Small 1994) but are less common during the summer (Howell 1917, Unitt 1984, 2004. Wilbur (1987) suggested that there was a northward movement from further south in Baja California in the fall and winter although no direct evidence supports this. Royal Terns were first reported breeding in southern California in 1959 in south San Diego Bay (Gallop and Bailey 1960, Unitt 1984) but not subsequently until 1980 and 1982 at the same location (Schaffner 1985, Unitt 2004).

More recently, Royal Terns have also nested within the large clusters of Elegant Terns in the colonies at the Bolsa Chica State Ecological Reserve in Orange County beginning in 1988 (Collins et al. 1991) and Pier 400 in the Port of Los Angeles, Los Angeles County beginning in

1998 (K. Keane, pers. comm.). Since 1988, Royal Terns have bred annually at one or more of the following three man-made nesting sites (Fig. 1). In San Diego, Royal, Elegant, and Caspian Terns nest on the dikes of the salt evaporation ponds located in southern San Diego Bay. At Bolsa Chica they occupy one of two 1.7 ha sand islands established in 1978 as a nesting place for the endangered California Least Tern (*Sternula antillarum browni*; Collins et al. 1991). The Pier 400 site is one part of a newly established 40 ha sand-fill area of the Port of Los Angles most of which is now fully developed as one of the busiest container cargo terminals on the west coast. The number of pairs of Royal Terns nesting at these sites has increased from <10 during 1988–1990 to >60 in 2005 and about 140 in 2007 (Table 2). This appears to be related largely to a high adult survival rate (>95%, Collins and Doherty 2006).

INTERCOLONY MOVEMENT

The Royal Terns of the Pacific coast of Mexico (including Baja California) and southern California have been included in a single geographical region (Buckley and Buckley 2002) but the interaction between more distant nesting sites in the Gulf of California and those on the Pacific coast has not been examined. As also true for Elegant Terns (Collins 2006) substantial year to year movement of Royal Terns occurs among the three southern California colonies as indicated by band sightings (Collins and Doherty, 2006). However, to date, no Royal Terns banded as chicks in southern California have been recovered in any of the colonies in either Baja California or the Gulf of California. The converse is also true. One color-banded Royal Tern, banded in Santa Maria Bay, Sinaloa,

Mexico in 2003, was observed and the band read, in Seal Beach, Orange County, California on 13 March 2005 among a newly arrived group of migrant Elegant Terns (C. T. Collins, unpubl. data); it was not seen subsequently at a local breeding colony.

Movement between colonies in Mexico and the colonies in southern California seems to be minimal based on existing data. This suggests that the Royal Terns in southern California form a distinct, albeit small, metapopulation separate from those in coastal western Baja California and the Gulf of California. The amount of interchange between colonies in the Gulf of California and colonies on the Pacific coast of Baja California is currently unknown.

NESTING ASSOCIATES OF ROYAL TERNS

It may be more than coincidental that in all of the Pacific coast colonies Royal and Elegant Terns are nesting in association with Caspian Terns (Bancroft 1927a; Unitt 1984, 2004; Collins et al. 1991, Massey and Palacios 1994, K. Keane, pers. comm.). Schaffner (1985) suggested that the less aggressive crested terns, including both Royal and Elegant Terns, require the presence of other more aggressive larids, such as Caspian Terns, for protection from potential predators. The colonization by Royal Terns of several of the sites considered here (Guerrero Negro area 8, Isla Pelicanos, San Diego, Bolsa Chica and Pier 400) was similarly preceded by the utilization of these sites by Caspian Terns. Thus, on the Pacific coast, prior establishment of a Caspian Tern colony may be both a social attraction and an anti-predator prerequisite for Royal and Elegant Terns to utilize new breeding sites. Other examples of such nesting associations would include Black Skimmers (*Rynchops niger*) nesting among the more aggressive Common Terns (*Sterna hirundo*) on the Atlantic coast as previously suggested by Erwin (1979).

FOOD AND FORAGING

The food of Royal Terns is predominantly fish, augmented by crustaceans, particularly shrimp (Buckley and Buckley 2002). Most foraging is in nearshore ocean waters with minimal utilization of bays, estuaries and tidal lagoons. The exact species composition of fish taken varies extensively from colony to colony (Buckley and Buckley 2002). In California, the mid-century decline of Royal Terns seemed to coincide with the decline in their major prey item, the Pacific sardine (*Sardinops sagax*; MacCall 1979, Schaffner 1985). Although sardine populations are now slowly increasing, currently the

TABLE 2. NUMBER OF NESTING PAIRS OF ROYAL TERNS IN SOUTHERN CALIFORNIA COLONIES. SEE TEXT FOR DESCRIPTION OF COLONY SITES.[a]

Year	San Diego	Bolsa Chica	Pier 400
1997	2	12	0
1998	0	0	17
1999	36	8	0
2000	2	0	0
2001	3	18	1
2002	1–3	1	5
2003	28–31	3	5
2004	38	2	10
2005	52	11	0
2006	35	ca 15	0
2007	109	30	0

[a] San Diego— R. Patton (pers. comm.); Bolsa Chica—C. T. Collins (unpubl. data); Pier 400—C. T.Collins and K. Keane (unpubl. data). Coordinates: San Diego—32°35'56"N, 117°06'02"W; Bolsa Chica—33°41'44"N, 118°02'46"W; Pier 400—33°43'06"N, 118°14'52"W.

principal food item of both Royal and Elegant Terns foraging in the coastal waters is the northern anchovy (*Engraulis mordax*; Horn et al. 1994, 1996). The availability of this fish in the colder California Current waters can be greatly reduced by the warm-water incursions of recurring El Niño events. This in turn, would expectedly have short-term impacts on the nesting success and population recruitment of Royal Terns in both southern California and Baja California. Several studies have documented such El Niño impacts on a variety of other seabirds in the California current system (Massey et al. 1992, Anderson et al. 1999, Hyrenbach and Veit 2003).

CONSERVATION CONCERNS

The availability of secure nesting areas is an important component of conservation programs for a number of nesting seabirds on the Pacific coast of southern California and Baja California. On the Atlantic coast, human intrusions and terrestrial predators are significant causes of breeding failures in Royal Terns (Buckley and Buckley 2002). All current Royal Tern colonies in Baja California are on sites inside a protected area, the El Vizcaino Biosphere Reserve which will limit, to some extent, human intrusions. Isla Concha, Isla Piedra, and Isla Pelícanos are naturally occurring island sites in core areas of the reserve. The islet in area 8 at Guerrero Negro is also a natural site, although located within a hypersaline cell of the saltworks. Normal environmental changes (e.g., wind and wave erosion of sand and shell nesting islands such as Isla Concha) may cause abandonment of some sites and colonization of new ones, such as Isla Piedra, within this wetland system. Predation may also play a role and seems to have recently caused the failure of the terns nesting in Laguna San Ignacio. Isla Piedra is also accessible to land predators, especially coyotes. In the late 1970s and early 1980s, coyotes frequently invaded Islas Piedra and Alambre and caused the abandonment of large waterbird colonies (Castellanos et al. 2001). Royal Terns were, at that time, still nesting on Isla Concha and were not impacted. Currently, no active management activities exist, including terrestrial predator control, which would benefit nesting egrets, gulls and terns at these sites in the reserve.

In southern California, two of the three Royal Tern nesting sites are in state or federally protected areas. Bolsa Chica is a state ecological reserve and the salt pond dikes in south San Diego Bay are part of the South San Diego Bay Unit of the San Diego National Wildlife Refuge. Only at Pier 400 is a nesting site in jeopardy. The portion of this site utilized by the larger terns is immediately adjacent to a 6 ha area being managed for the endangered California Least Tern. In 2005 a nocturnal predation event at Pier 400 caused the Royal, Elegant, and Caspian Terns starting to nest there (eggs had been laid) to immediately abandon the site and largely relocate to Bolsa Chica. After its abandonment in 2005 much weedy vegetation grew up on the Pier 400 site. In 2006 and 2007 this site was not cleared of vegetation as had been done prior to previous nesting seasons. As result none of these larger terns nested there (K. Keane, pers. comm.). This portion of the Pier 400 site may soon be used for Port of Los Angeles activities and thus become permanently unavailable for future Royal Tern nesting. The adjacent portion utilized by California Least Terns will, however, remain as a protected and managed nesting site.

An extensive renovation of the Bolsa Chica wetlands, completed in 2006, included a new tidal basin and ocean entrance as well as an enlarged area for nesting terns and Black Skimmers. The degree of utilization of this new nesting area, as well as the increased foraging zone immediately adjacent to it, remains to be seen.

Despite its extensive geographic range, many populations of Royal Terns remain conspicuously unstudied (Buckley and Buckley 2002). The available data for the overall Atlantic coast populations suggest that the number of breeding pairs there is holding constant although a 33% decline occurred in North Carolina during 1988–1990 (Buckley and Buckley 2002). Smaller populations and those near the periphery of the species' range, as those examined here, would likely be more sensitive to environmental changes as indicated by range contraction or expansion. They would also be prone to larger inter-annual fluctuations in colony size and a greater risk of local extirpation. However, the current protection afforded Royal Tern nesting sites in both southern California and Baja California bodes well for further increases in these two populations in the near future.

ACKNOWLEDGMENTS

We are indebted to the many field observers and colony monitors who have provided data on colony sizes: E. Amador, D. W. Anderson, G. Danemann, M. U. Evans, R. Mayoral and R. Patton. Permission to conduct studies at Bolsa Chica State Ecological Reserve was granted by the California Department of Fish and Game. Kathy Keane and the Port of Los Angeles made observations at Pier 400 possible. We thank the two reviewers who provided helpful comments on the organization and content of the manuscript. Our particular thanks to Jose M. Beltran for producing Figure 1.

POPULATION TRENDS AND ECOLOGY
OF RIPARIAN AND WETLAND BIRDS

Green Kingfisher (*Chloroceryle americana*) © David J. Krueper

Studies in Avian Biology No. 37:53–68

HABITAT USE OF WINTERING BIRD COMMUNITIES IN SONORA, MEXICO: THE IMPORTANCE OF RIPARIAN HABITATS

José Fernando Villaseñor-Gómez

Abstract. Riparian systems are dynamic and diverse despite their limited areal extent. They are especially important for breeding bird communities in southwestern US and are highly used as migratory corridors; however, their importance for wintering birds has not been assessed systematically. Information from 1,816 standard 10-min point counts was gathered at 85 locations in the State of Sonora, Mexico from sea level to 2,175 m during January and February 2004–2006. I detected 253 bird species across 14 vegetation types, including nine categories of riparian vegetation. Eighty percent of total species were detected in riparian habitats, and 72% were detected in non-riparian habitats. The mean number of species and individuals detected per count were significantly higher in riparian habitats than in non-riparian habitats for migratory species, but not for residents. A hierarchical classification analysis showed that riparian bird communities are different from those in non-riparian communities, and they contribute 22% of the species that comprise the regional avifauna, which is more than any other habitat type.

Key Words: habitat use, Mexico, neotropical migrant birds, riparian, Sonora, wintering.

USO DE HABITAT DE COMUNIDADES DE AVES INVERNANTES EN SONORA, MEXICO: IMPORTANCIA DE LOS HABITATS RIPARIOS

Resumen. Los sistemas riparios son dinámicos y diversos a pesar de su limitada cobertura espacial. Son especialmente importantes para las comunidades de aves que se reproducen en el Suroeste de los Estados Unidos y son usados extensamente como corredores migratorios; sin embargo, su importancia para las aves invernantes no se ha determinado de forma sistemática. Información de 1,816 conteos estándar de 10-minutos se obtuvo en 85 localidades en el Estado de Sonora, México, desde el nivel del mar hasta 2,175m durante Enero-Febrero de 2004–2006. Detecté 243 especies en 14 tipos de vegetación, incluyendo nueve categorías de vegetación riparia. Ochenta por ciento de las especies fueron registradas en hábitats riparios y 72% en hábitats no-riparios. El número promedio de especies e individuos detectados por conteo fue significativamente mayor en hábitats riparios que en no-riparios para las especies migratorias, pero no para las residentes. Un análisis de clasificación jerárquica mostró que las comunidades de aves riparias son diferentes a las comunidades de sitios no-riparios, y contribuyen con 22% de las especies que conforman la avifauna regional, la mayor contribución entre los hábitats estudiados.

Riparian habitats are dynamic and generally more biologically diverse than surrounding uplands, especially in arid regions (Hunt 1985). This faunal diversity is due to the presence of water, high productivity, and abundance of habitat edge, which is maximized by the linear shape of riparian habitats (Gregory et al. 1991). In the arid Southwest, riparian systems support at least 80% of all wildlife species (Hunt 1985, USDI Bureau of Land Management 1998). They support the highest densities of small mammals (Andersen 1994) and richest communities of butterflies (Fleishman et al. 1999, Nelson and Anderson 1999). Riparian habitats support some of the highest densities and most species-rich avian communities in the US (Knopf et al. 1988) and western Mexico (Hutto 1995), and influence the ecological dynamics of adjacent upland habitats (Strong and Bock 1990, Farley et al. 1994a, Skagen et al. 1998, Powell and Steidl 2000). In addition, many riparian bird species are riparian obligates, which is significant in light of the very small percentage (generally <1%) of land area composed of riparian habitat (Mosconi and Hutto 1982, Knopf 1985, Schmitt 1976, Hubbard 1971).

The importance of riparian systems during periods of migratory passage and as wintering habitats has begun to receive more attention, and we know these periods may be equally or more important than the breeding season in terms of population regulation (Fretwell 1972, Sherry and Holmes 1995, Hutto 1998). During the energetically demanding migration period, landbirds have to make important choices about which stopover habitats will provide enough food, cover, and water to enable a rapid and safe replenishment of fuels (Moore and Simons 1992). Mortality rates may be considerable (especially for young birds) as migrants compete for resources while avoiding potential predators in unfamiliar locations. We currently know little about the specific habitat needs of migrants. Studies have shown, however, that landbirds use riparian habitats disproportionately more frequently during migration. This is especially the case during spring migration, when the productivity of riparian habitats is higher than that of the surrounding uplands (Skagen et al. 1998, Finch and Yong 2000, Skagen et al. 2005, Kelly and Hutto 2005). Understanding migration ecology is now considered key to the conservation of migrant landbird populations (Moore et al. 1995, Hutto 2000, Heglund and Skagen 2005).

Information on the importance of riparian systems compared to other habitat types for wintering birds is also scant and is based largely on occasional species- and site-specific records (Russell and Lamm 1978, Terrill 1981, Rosenberg et al. 1991, USDI Bureau of Land Management 1996), Christmas Bird Counts, and studies that happen to include the complete annual cycle of riparian birds (Anderson and Ohmart 1977, Wells et al. 1979, Strong and Bock 1990, Farley et al. 1994a). In the only published studies focused on wintering bird distribution among a variety of vegetation types in western Mexico, the abundance of Neotropical migrants in riparian habitats and gallery forests are among the highest recorded (Hutto 1980, 1995), thus suggesting that riparian corridors are important for wintering birds. During winter, riparian habitats may be especially important in the Sonoran Desert, which lies at the northern edge of the wintering range of many western North American migratory bird species, and which represents the primary wintering area for short-distant migrant species from the central and western US. In lowland Sonora, the only other habitats for wintering birds are drier, hotter, and structurally less diverse.

Riparian zones are known to be habitats of critical conservation concern worldwide, including the southwestern US and northwestern Mexico. These habitats, which have always constituted a small component of arid landscapes, have been reduced drastically and are now fragmented and modified by desiccation, dam construction, water diversion, invasion of exotic species, overgrazing, and other factors.

In this study I sought to determine how significant riparian areas are for wintering bird communities in the state of Sonora, Mexico. Specifically, I addressed two main questions: (1) are wintering bird communities associated with riparian habitats significantly different from those associated with upland habitat types in the State of Sonora, and; (2) are the riparian habitats important in terms of their contribution to regional diversity? In order to answer these questions, I examined the community composition and species abundance patterns of wintering birds across the complete array of extant vegetation types in the state, and determined the value of each vegetation type in terms of its contribution to regional avifaunal diversity.

METHODS

STUDY AREA

Sonora is the second largest state in Mexico, covering 179,156 km². It is located at the northwestern corner of mainland Mexico between 26°18' and 32°29'N, and 108°25' and 115°03'W. The geographical features of the state make it rich and biologically diverse. Sonora is located at the latitude where the tropics meet the southern limit of the temperate region, and includes elements from both regions. It is composed of a complex mix of landscapes with elevations from sea level to 2,630 m. The lowland plains are vegetated primarily by desert and xeric shrubs. At middle elevations the northernmost extensions of tropical deciduous forest are found in the south and southeastern part of the state. In the highlands a diversity of oak woodlands and mixed coniferous forest along the eastern section border the state of Chihuahua. Riparian communities composed mainly of associations of cottonwood (*Populus* spp.) and willows (*Salix* spp.) are present discontinuously along the river courses, and mangroves (*Avicennia, Conocarpus, Laguncularia,* and *Rhizophora*) are distributed in isolated patches along the coast of the Sea of Cortés (INEGI 2000). Because of these characteristics and its location, Sonora supports a diverse community of breeding, migrating, and wintering landbirds of western North America (Kelly and Hutto 2005)

Rivers and subsurface water continue to play an important role in the economy of the state. Most rivers originate in the Sierra Madre Occidental and run to the coastal plains and into the Sea of Cortés. The most important permanent flows are from north to south and east to west, and include the Colorado, Sonoyta, Altar, Magdalena, San Miguel, Sonora, Moctezuma, Bavispe, Mátape, Sahuaripa, Yaqui, Cedros, and Mayo Rivers (Bojórquez-Tapia et al. 1985). Several large dams create important impoundments to supply water for the irrigation of extensive agricultural fields in the lowlands. Sonora is also one of Mexico's main producers of high quality beef cattle; fifteen million hectares, including pasturelands, woodlands, shrublands, and prairies with buffelgrass (*Pennisetum ciliare*) are used for raising and breeding beef cattle, having potential negative impacts, especially on the composition and structure of riparian habitats due to overgrazing (Saab et al. 1995).

SURVEY PROTOCOLS

During January and February of 2004, 2005, and 2006, avian surveys were conducted at 85 locations in 14 vegetation types following INEGI (2000) and nine riparian associations throughout Sonora, ranging from sea level to elevations over 2,000 m (Table 1). Non-repeated and randomly selected standard 10-min point counts with unlimited radius were conducted between 0700 and 1100 H. Most aquatic species and birds flying over were recorded but not used in any of the analysis. Raptors, swallows, and other aerial species were recorded only if they were perched on the vegetation or the ground within the point count area (Hutto et al. 1986, Ralph et al. 1993). Unidentified species, such as hummingbirds and *Empidonax* species, were grouped and included on the list as unknown hummingbird and *Empidonax* sp., respectively. The location and distance from the observer to each detected bird were mapped; the information gathered was entered into Excel and was managed for the analysis with SPSS 11.5.1 software package (SPSS 2002). Only the detections within a radius of 25 m from the observer were used in the analyses. Although much information was unused by restricting the data in this way, and rarer and shy or cryptic species may have been missed as a result, it was done to decrease the potential error caused by the inclusion of individuals detected in an adjacent but different habitat type and to decrease bias due to inherent differences in detectability of birds among habitats.

ANALYSES

Species were assigned to one of three residency status categories—residents, migrants, and partial migrants. Residents are those species that remain in the same area year-round. Migrants are those species that move far from their breeding areas and occupy a completely different geographical region to the south during the winter, with no overlapping populations (all long-distance migrant species). Partial migrants are those species that move seasonally but not for distances of such magnitude. As a consequence, in the southern portions of some species' distributions, populations of resident, transient, and wintering individuals could overlap during migration and winter. The species were assigned to one of these residency status categories based on published information (van Rossem 1945, Howell and Webb 1995,

Russell and Monson 1998), and personal experience (Appendix 1).

The total number of species and individuals detected, the mean number of species and individuals per count, and the percentage of resident, partial migrants, and migrant species were computed for each vegetation type and riparian association. ANOVA was performed to compare the mean number of species and individuals detected in point counts (25-m radius) by residency status, as well as the number of individuals detected for each species to determine the ones showing significant differences between non-riparian and riparian habitats. A chi-square test was performed to examine differences in the mean percentage of species recorded belonging to the residency status groups between riparian and non-riparian habitats. I also used a contingency analysis of species richness to look for differences in the expected proportions of species with preferences for non-riparian and riparian habitats, as well as those with no preferences for either habitat.

To determine if wintering bird communities associated with riparian habitats were significantly different from those associated with other habitat types, I used two classification methods. A hierarchical classification method (cluster analysis; Manly 2004) was used to compare similarities among bird communities in each habitat type, producing a dendrogram (based on presence-absence data and using complete linkage and the Ochiai measure). Secondly, a two-way indicator species analysis (TWINSPAN; McCune and Mefford 1997) was used, based on the concept that samples which constitute a group will have a corresponding set of species that characterize that group (indicator species). TWINSPAN finds the relationships between species and samples through correspondence analysis ordination. It initially classifies the samples into two groups and then refines the classification through detrended correspondence analysis (DCA), finding the indicator and associated species for the resulting groups, and based on those species, regroups iteratively within the groups into smaller clusters until a limit is met. An indicator species is the species (or the group of species) present in all of the clustered vegetation types; an associated species is present primarily in a given group although it could also be present in other vegetation types or associations. With TWINSPAN I defined the species that characterize the general vegetation groups identified by the dendrogram produced in the clustering technique. In order to perform these analyses, I used the software PC-ORD for Windows, version 3.17 (McCune and Mefford 1997).

TABLE 1. LOCATIONS AND VEGETATION TYPES SAMPLED IN SONORA, MEXICO, DURING JANUARY AND FEBRUARY (2004, 2005, AND 2006).

Location	Vegetation sampled	Elevation (m)	Latitude N	Longitude W	N Counts
Aconchi – Río Sonora, Aconchi, Río Sonora,	Riparian cottonwood-mesquite, cottonwoods, cottonwood-willow	588	29°48'14"	110°13'37"	72
Agua Caliente Springs	Riparian mesquite	606	29°50'26"	110°16'33"	1
Aribabi – Sierra Alta	Highland oaklands	1,490	30°03'25"	109°06'10"	30
Arroyo La Poza	Riparian mesquite	188	28°52'04"	110°57'43"	15
Bámori – Río Sahuaripa	Riparian cottonwood-willow, willow, willow-mesquite	516	28°51'45"	109°10'03"	76
Baviácora – Río Sonora	Riparian cottonwoods, cottonwood-willow	554	29°43'27"	110°10'29"	69
Cerro La Pintada – Tetabejo	Sarcocaulescent scrubland	188	28°34'41"	111°00'43"	20
Caborca	Sarcocrassicaulescent scrubland	324	30°47'35"	112°13'25"	30
Cajón de Onapa, Río Sahuaripa	Riparian mesquite, willow, Willow-mesquite	587	28°44'09"	109°07'59"	61
Camino a San Lázaro-San Antonio	Thornscrub	1,189	31°03'00"	110°38'32"	5
Camino a San Marcial	Grasslands	326	28°34'53"	110°15'18"	20
Cañón de Evans, road, Cananea – Bacoachi	Riparian sycamores	1,372	30°56'34"	110°07'37"	22
Cañón de Nacapule, San Carlos, Nuevo Guaymas	Oasis (*Washingtonia* and *Ficus*)	111	28°00'50"	111°02'57"	21
Coteco	Coastal sarcocaulescent scrubland	22	26°34'35"	109°18'11"	28
Cucurpe – Río San Miguel	Riparian cottonwoods	849	30°19'20"	110°42'35"	14
Desv. Playa San Nicolás	Coastal sarcocaulescent scrubland	5	28°49'43"	111°48'19"	37
Ejido Ganadero Puente El Tigre, Guaymas	Sarcocaulescent scrubland	82	28°06'22"	110°59'27"	22
El Carrizo, Rancho San Darío	Grasslands, subtropical scrub	730	30°02'59"	111°12'19"	3
El Chiculi, Hornos, Río Yaqui, Sonora	Riparian willow-mesquite-chino	57	27°46'26"	109°53'52"	20
El Cochito – km. 179, road, Agua Prieta-Moctezuma	Microphyllous scrubland	1,164	31°10'52"	109°33'53"	30
El Llano – Moctezuma	Thornscrub	638	29°43'25"	109°39'04"	9
El Resbalón – Sahuaripa	Tropical deciduous forest	654	29°07'57"	109°16'51"	33
El Sahuaral, San José de Guaymas	Coastal sarcocaulescent scrubland	5	27°59'15"	110°50'30"	22
Estero del Soldado, San Carlos, Nuevo Guaymas	Mangroves	0	27°57'23"	110°58'53"	17
Estero Paraíso – Punta Checa	Mangroves	0	29°02'21"	112°09'59"	6
Estero Santa Cruz – Kino	Mangroves	1	28°47'49"	111°52'34"	16
Estero Santa Rosa – Punta Chueca	Mangroves	0	28°58'37"	112°09'48"	16
Granados – Río Bavispe	Riparian cottonwood-willow	540	29°51'46"	109°18'01"	20
Huásabas – Río Bavispe	Riparian cottonwood-willow	554	29°55'13"	109°17'31"	10
Jécori – Río Moctezuma	Riparian cottonwoods	716	29°58'01"	109°45'39"	67
La Aduana	Tropical deciduous forest	602	27°01'53"	109°00'34"	15
La Majada, between Moctezuma-Mazocahui	Lowland oaklands	1,011	29°42'57"	109°50'45"	31
La Mesa del Campanero	Highland coniferous forest	2,139	28°22'12"	109°01'50"	19

TABLE 1. CONTINUED.

Location	Vegetation sampled	Elevation (m)	Latitude N	Longitude W	N Counts
Los Alisos	Highland oaklands, Riparian sycamores	1,358	30°33'09"	109°39'21"	35
Los Torreones	Subtropical scrub	857	29°17'23"	109°54'12"	5
Magdalena, road Magdalena-Imuris	Sarcocrassicaulescent scrubland	784	30°36'18"	110°57'37"	28
Mazatán, ca. 10 km W	Subtropical scrub	517	29°00'00"	110°13'45"	1
Mesa del Toro-Ejido Ignacio Zaragoza, Cananea	Grasslands	1,556	31°03'38"	110°03'53"	30
Sierra Pinacate (between Elegante and Tecolote)	Vegetation of sandy deserts	219	31°51'21"	113°21'28"	10
Sierra Pinacate Crater Cerro Colorado	Vegetation of sandy deserts	185	31°55'08"	113°18'05"	10
Puerto Peñasco	Vegetation of sandy deserts	16	31°21'36"	113°27'41"	20
Rancho Monte Alto-road to Puerto Libertad	Coastal sarcocaulescent scrubland	131	29°18'38"	111°51'26"	31
Rancho El 44, between Cobachi and Road to Yécora	Subtropical scrub	431	28°47'22"	110°21'28"	1
Rancho El Perú	Subtropical scrub	709	30°20'38"	111°04'39"	10
Rancho La Cuesta, km 94 road to Yécora	Subtropical scrub	391	28°35'44"	110°11'00"	1
Rancho La Noria, N	Sarcocaulescent scrubland	352	29°03'01"	110°37'56"	10
Rancho Los Cuervos, N El Carrizo)	Subtropical scrub	715	30°06'17"	111°12'37"	2
Rancho Piedras Negras (Carretera Minera Nyco)	Sarcocaulescent scrubland	352	29°16'16"	111°05'18"	18
Rancho San Darío ca. Carrizo	Subtropical scrub	724	30°04'18"	111°14'27"	1
Rancho San Fermín, ca. Cobachi	Subtropical scrub	549	28°55'14"	110°07'55"	1
Reserva de la Biosfera Pinacate	Vegetation of sandy deserts	167	31°48'16"	113°17'45"	30
Río Altar, Tubutama	Riparian cottonwoods	634	30°53'09"	111°27'39"	9
Río Cuchujaqui	Riparian baldcypress-willow	239	26°56'29"	108°53'05"	21
Río Cocóspera—Rancho Aribabi	Riparian cottonwood-willow, Cottonwood-mesquite, cottonwoods	974	30°51'15"	110°39'51"	40
Río Cuchujaqui at El Mentidero	Riparian baldcypress-willow	227	26°54'44"	108°54'46"	9
Río Cuchujaqui at La Isleta	Riparian baldcypress-willow	224	26°54'38"	108°54'51"	8
Río Matape—San José de Pimas	Riparian mesquite, willow, willow-mesquite	350	28°43'02"	110°20'50"	35
Río Mayo—Presa Mocúzari	Riparian willow-mesquite-chino, tropical deciduous forest	98	27°12'57"	109°06'47"	20
Río Mayo—Tetapeche	Riparian willow-mesquite-chino	49	27°12'23"	109°21'35"	19
Río San Miguel, Rancho San Esteban	Riparian mesquite	285	29°17'13"	110°52'02"	30
Río Santa Cruz, San Lázaro	Riparian cottonwood-mesquite, cottonwood-willow	1,284	31°09'03"	110°38'33"	19
Río Yaqui, Ónavas	Riparian mesquite	155	28°27'45"	109°32'01"	1
Río Yaqui, Sitio Nochebuena	Riparian willow-mesquite	203	28°47'45"	109°38'41"	1

TABLE 1. CONTINUED.

Location	Vegetation sampled	Elevation (m)	Latitude N	Longitude W	N Counts
Río Yaqui, San Antonio de la Huerta	Riparian willow-mesquite	187	28°37'44"	109°36'27"	1
Río Yaqui, Tónichi	Riparian willow-mesquite	166	28°35'37"	109°34'08"	2
Río Yaqui, S El Novillo	Riparian willow-mesquite	214	28°49'43"	109°37'46"	3
Río Yaqui, Soyopa	Riparian willow-mesquite, mesquite	188	28°45'02"	109°37'32"	4
San Carlos – ca. Cañón de Nacapule	Sarcocaulescent scrubland	47	27°58'58"	111°02'24"	31
San Ignacio — Terrenate	Riparian cottonwoods	784	30°42'51"	110°55'27"	19
San Javier	Tropical deciduous forest	813	28°34'58"	109°44'51"	32
San José de Pimas	Thornscrub	384	28°43'54"	110°21'49"	21
San Lázaro, S	Lowland oaklands	1,279	31°05'49"	110°39'00"	6
San Miguel, road to Punta Chueca	Sarcocaulescent scrubland	177	28°57'51"	112°03'29"	62
Santa Cruz	Grasslands, highland oaklands	1,417	31°19'56"	110°36'30"	6
Sáric – Río Altar	Riparian cottonwood-mesquite, cottonwoods, mesquite, willow, cottonwood-willow	786	31°09'25"	111°21'11"	19
Sierra La Elenita, Cananea	Highland coniferous forest	1,920	31°00'30"	110°23'06"	30
Sierra Ladrilleros-El Pinacate	Sarcocaulescent scrubland	154	31°44'28"	113°18'23"	30
Sierra Mazatán	Lowland oaklands	1,357	29°05'38"	110°12'54"	9
Sierra Mazatán, NE Presa Teópari	Riparian mesquite	663	29°13'15"	110°04'44"	22
Terapa – Río Moctezuma	Riparian cottonwood-mesquite, cottonwood-willow, mesquite, cottonwoods	565	29°40'41"	109°39'04"	88
Tónichi	Riparian willow-mesquite	186	28°35'42"	109°34'05"	31
Tubutama - Río Altar	Riparian cottonwoods, cottonwood-willow	684	30°53'17"	111°27'21"	15
Unámichi – Río Sonora	Riparian cottonwood-willow	1,048	30°39'39"	109°58'58"	20
Yécora	Highland coniferous forest	1,538	28°22'54"	108°54'39"	11
Yécora – La Palmita	Highland oaklands	1,462	28°22'19"	109°03'59"	21

RESULTS

Survey data were gathered on 1,816 standard 10-min point counts (944 in non-riparian and 872 in riparian sites, respectively), at 85 locations from sea level to 2,175 m (Table 1). A total of 32,570 individuals of 253 bird species was recorded across all vegetation types. Eighty percent of total species (203) were recorded in riparian associations, and 72% (183) in all other non-riparian vegetation types.

The number of bird species in riparian vegetation was greater than in any other vegetation type. A tally of species richness by vegetation types shows that species richness in all non-riparian vegetation types was less than 65 species per habitat type, with all but four having less than 50 species per category. In contrast, riparian habitats for the most part were richer, with all but two riparian vegetation types having 75 or more species per type, and all but three having more than 95 species per category (Table 2).

By limiting data analyses to observations within a 25-m radius, a total of 8,237 individuals of 168 species was detected (82 residents, 33 partial migrants, and 53 migrants [see Appendix 1 for the residency status and number of individuals recorded for the most common species]).

The mean numbers of species and individuals (all groups combined) detected per count in riparian habitats were significantly higher than in non-riparian habitats (Table 3). The same pattern held for mean number of species and individuals per count within the migrant and partial migrant groups, which also had significantly higher numbers in riparian habitats. In contrast, I found no significant differences in mean number of species or individuals per count between riparian and non-riparian habitats for resident species.

I found no statistically significant differences in the proportions of residents, migrants, and partial migrants in each count between riparian and non-riparian vegetation types ($\chi^2 = 4.105$, df = 2, P = 0.128; Fig. 1a). However, the general pattern suggests that the proportion of total resident species was higher in non-riparian habitats, while the proportions of total partial migrants and migrant species were higher in riparian vegetation types. When partial migrants and migrants were combined into a single migrant group and compared with residents, the difference became significant ($\chi^2 = 4.083$, df = 1, P = 0.03; Fig. 1b), with a greater proportion of resident species in non-riparian habitats and a greater percentage of migrant species in riparian habitats. The contribution

TABLE 2. VEGETATION TYPES, NUMBER OF POINTS SAMPLED, AND NUMBER OF SPECIES RECORDED IN SONORA, MEXICO, DURING JANUARY AND FEBRUARY (2004, 2005, AND 2006).

Vegetation Type	Counts/species	Elevation range (m)
Non-riparian vegetation		
Mangroves	54/53	Sea level (0)
Coastal sarcocaulescent scrubland	138/58	(0–234)
Vegetation of sandy deserts	70/17	(3–231)
Microphyllous scrubland	30/17	(1,159–1,217)
Tropical deciduous forest	79/61	(102–983)
Sarcocrassicaulescent scrubland	58/20	(307–824)
Thornscrub	45/37	(184–1,189)
Subtropical scrub	25/43	(391–878)
Sarcocaulescent scrubland	152/47	(13–551)
Grasslands	83/14	(316–1,592)
Low oaklands	54/41	(970–1,250)
High oaklands	75/61	(1,400–2,010)
Highland coniferous forest	60/37	(1,525–2,175)
Oases	21/37	(50–233)
Non-riparian vegetation (general)	944/183	(Sea level–2,175)
Riparian vegetation		
Willow–mesquite-chino	57/96	(36–102)
Mesquite desert riparian	89/108	(117–823)
Willow-mesquite	91/96	(166–823)
Willow	104/96	(348–840)
Willow-baldcypress (*Salix-Taxodium*)	31/75	(222–277)
Cottonwood-willow	230/125	(527–1,282)
Cottonwood-mesquite	23/45	(555–1,305
Cottonwood	214/125	(505-1,288)
Sycamores (*Platanus*)	33/40	(1,322–1,402)
Riparian sites (general)	872/203	(33–1,402)

TABLE 3. ANOVA RESULTS COMPARING THE MEAN NUMBER OF SPECIES AND INDIVIDUALS DETECTED IN POINT COUNTS (25-M RADIUS) BY RESIDENCY STATUS.

Residency status	General mean (N = 1,816)	Non-riparian habitats (N = 944)	Riparian habitats (N = 872)	F	P
Species					
All species	2.55	1.93	3.24	164.40	<0.01
Residents	1.32	1.36	1.29	1.15	0.28
Partial migrants	0.59	0.32	0.88	234.99	<0.01
Migrants	0.64	0.25	1.06	424.78	<0.01
Individuals					
All species	4.29	3.34	5.33	58.43	<0.01
Residents	2.06	2.15	1.94	1.92	0.17
Partial migrants	1.12	0.65	1.63	46.14	<0.01
Migrants	1.11	0.53	1.74	106.41	<0.01

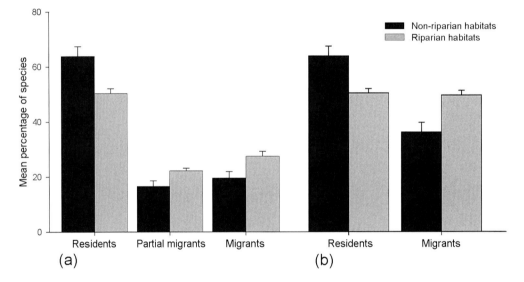

FIGURE 1. Mean percentage of bird species by residency status in riparian and non-riparian habitat groups in Sonora (mean percentage of species recorded for resident, partial migrant, and migrant species per habitat type); (a) considering the three residency status groups; (b) considering partial migrants and migrants together as a single group.

of migrant and partial migrant species and individuals to the avifauna in riparian sites is particularly important, as is the contribution of resident species and individual to non-riparian habitats (Fig. 2 a, b). Numerically speaking, migrants are an important element of the wintering avifauna of riparian environments in the state of Sonora.

However, such generalizations could be misleading because species respond ecologically and behaviorally in different ways, and they have to be assessed individually. Of the 168 species noted above, 59 (35.1%) showed significant differences in their abundances between the riparian and non-riparian habitats; 18 (10.7%) were primarily associated with non-riparian habitats, and 41 (24.4%) with riparian habitats.

Considering the community as a whole, the contingency analysis (chi-square test) shows that the residents are overrepresented in the non-riparian habitats and the frequency of the migrants is significantly higher in the riparian environments ($\chi^2 = 13.72$, df = 4, P = 0.008; Table 4). If the analysis is limited to those species with at least 20 detections (66 species) to avoid the influence of those species with low sample sizes, the differences are even more evident ($\chi^2 = 18.35$, df = 4, P = 0.001; Table 4).

The dendrogram resulting from the cluster analysis (Fig. 3) separates the habitats into three main groups. The first, near the bottom of the dendrogram, represents highland habitats, the second clusters desertscrub habitats and mangroves, and the last, at the top of the

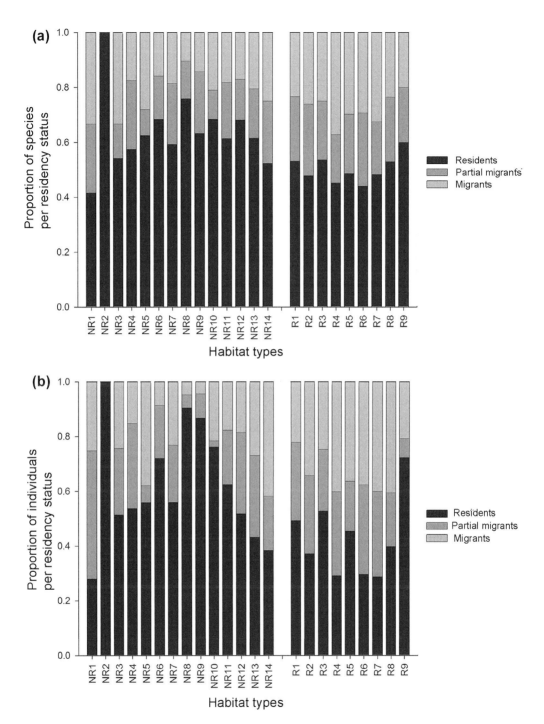

FIGURE 2. Proportional contribution of residents, partial migrants, and migrants to (a) species richness, and (b) total individuals for each riparian and non-riparian habitat (habitat types: NR = non-riparian: 1 = mangroves, 2 = microphyllous scrubland, 3 = oasis, 4= coastal sarcocaulescent scrubland, 5 = subtropical scrub, 6 = tropical deciduous forest, 7 = thornscrub, 8 = sarcocrassicaulescent scrubland, 9 = sarcocaulescent scrubland, 10 = vegetation of sandy deserts, 11 = grasslands, 12 = low elevation oaklands, 13 = high elevation oaklands, 14 = highland coniferous forest; R= riparian: 1= willow-mesquite-chino, 2 = willow-mesquite, 3 = mesquite, 4 = willow, 5 = baldcypress-willow, 6 = cottonwood, 7 = cottonwood-willow, 8 = cottonwood-mesquite, 9 = sycamores.)

TABLE 4. RESULTS OF CONTINGENCY ANALYSIS OF SPECIES RICHNESS: DIFFERENCES BETWEEN NON-RIPARIAN AND RIPARIAN HABITATS.

Status	All species (N = 168)				Species with at least 20 detections (N = 66)			
	N significantly different	Non-riparian species	Riparian species	Total	N significantly different	Non-riparian species	Riparian species	Total
Residents	53 (53.2)	15 (8.8)	14 (20.0)	82 (15.0)	18 (7.5)	11 (5.5)	9	38
Partial migrants	24 (21.4)	1 (3.5)	8 (8.1)	33 (7.1)	7 (2.6)	0 (5.3)	6	13
Migrants	32 (34.4)	2 (5.7)	19 (12.9)	53 (5.9)	1 (3.0)	2 (6.1)	12	15
Total	109	18	41	168	26	13	27	66

Note: Expected frequencies shown in parenthesis.

dendrogram, groups riparian associations (except for the sycamores [*Platanus* sp.] which are grouped within the highland habitats) with tropical deciduous forest and oases. The microphyllous scrub habitat stands by itself and independent of the other groups as a result of its poor avifauna (only six species recorded).

The contribution of these grouped habitat types to regional diversity was assessed by determining the species that were found exclusively in a particular habitat or group of habitats and would not occur if that habitat were not present in the region. Based on these criteria, riparian habitats contributed the most species unique to the regional avifauna, followed in importance by highlands, desertscrub habitats, tropical deciduous forest, oases, and mangroves (Fig. 3).

The two-way indicator species analysis (TWINSPAN) results identified those indicator and associated species that characterize each one of the vegetative clusters produced by the hierarchical analysis. It defined the existence of six groups of bird species: (1) highland vegetation species, (2) microphyllous scrubland, (3) desert scrubby vegetations and grasslands, (4) mangroves, (5) lower elevation riparian associations, and (6) tropical deciduous forest and oases (Table 5).

DISCUSSION

Riparian environments have been identified as a key habitat component of ecological systems through maintenance of dynamic ecological processes along a gradient of landscapes, which links wildlife, vegetation, and soils within terrestrial systems. They are very productive systems and represent the most valuable habitat for wildlife in general, especially in the xeric regions of the world. The results of this study support this concept.

Cottonwood riparian woodlands and their associations have been identified as the most important habitat for birds in the southwestern US (Hubbard 1971, Stamp 1978, Strong and Bock 1990; Farley et al. 1994a, b; Skagen et al. 1998), and in every case they support the highest number of species and/or densities among the studied habitats. Based on the above-cited papers that included a list of the species recorded in riparian habitats, the percentage of those riparian species in the US that were also found wintering in Sonoran cottonwood riparian associations in this study ranged from 63–86%. The differences are due primarily to resident species with distributional ranges restricted to the United States or to species whose distribution does not include the

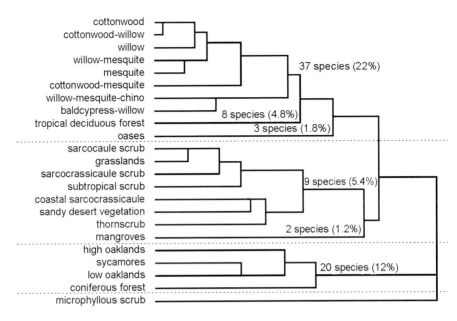

FIGURE 3. Grouping of the vegetation types resulting from a cluster analysis based on the wintering avifauna in Sonora, Mexico, based on presence-absence data. (The number of species and percentages represent the number of species unique to that habitat or cluster of habitats).

US. Although we do not know the details of connectivity among the populations involved here, the high proportion of riparian-breeding species that also use riparian associations (and mostly lowland riparian areas) in the winter in northwestern Mexico indicates the importance of these habitat types for wintering migrants. Knowing that riparian environments are important for wintering birds, an additional question might be asked: how unique are riparian bird communities during the winter in comparison with communities in other habitat types? Are they important in terms of their contribution to regional diversity?

Cluster analysis results show an interesting pattern in the composition of the avian communities—an elevational gradient separates the highland habitats from the low elevation ones, and a gradient of humidity separates dry habitat communities from ones associated with more humid riparian areas. This pattern is in accordance with the TWINSPAN ordination, which in the highlands grouped a set of 19 coniferous forest bird species, a set of 17 species in drier areas such as grasslands and scrubby vegetations, dry forest and oases shared 12 species, and the lower elevation riparian associations were typified by a group of 24 species. Mangroves had a combination of four species that defined its community.

It is important to note that the riparian vegetation in the highlands is represented by limited extensions of sycamores adjacent to oak woodlands, which explains the composition of their bird community and the affinity with this group of habitats. Tropical deciduous forest and the oases clustered near the riparian associations; they share a good number of species, maybe as a result of the extension of tropical dry forest tree species farther north along the riparian corridors, as well as the effect of the elevational gradient previously mentioned.

My approach to assessing the contribution of riparian habitats to regional diversity is similar to an approach advocated by Hylander (2006). My results indicate that riparian habitats contribute substantially to regional diversity (22% of species) in Sonora, Mexico, and are consistent in general with Sabo and Soykan's (2006) findings which state that on average, the percentage of unique riparian species is 24%, and that riparian zones increase regional richness by 38%. My results indicate that wintering bird communities in riparian habitats are richer in comparison to adjacent uplands, and of the 134 species recorded in our counts, 37 were exclusive to riparian habitats. These differences are due mostly to the increased number of migrant and partial migrant species and individuals detected in riparian habitats.

Several important factors may explain the importance of riparian habitats to winter avian diversity in Sonora. Riparian habitats provide structural complexity, which is important for

TABLE 5. RESULTS OF A TWO-WAY INDICATOR SPECIES ANALYSIS (TWINSPAN) TO IDENTIFY INDICATOR AND ASSOCIATED SPECIES CHARACTERIZING THE HABITAT CLUSTERS PRODUCED BY THE HIERARCHICAL ANALYSIS.

HIGHLAND VEGETATION CLUSTER
Indicator species:
  Acorn Woodpecker (*Melanerpes formicivorus*)
Associated species:
  Sharp-shinned Hawk (*Accipiter striatus*)
  Band-tailed Pigeon (*Patagioenas fasciata*)[a]
  White-eared Hummingbird (*Hylocharis leucotis*)
  Hairy Woodpecker (*Picoides villosus*)
  Williamson's Sapsucker (*Sphyrapicus thyroideus*)[b]
  Hutton's Vireo (*Vireo huttoni*)
  Mexican Chickadee (*Poecile sclateri*)
  Eastern Bluebird (*Sialia sialis*)
  American Robin (*Turdus migratorius*)
  Brown Creeper (*Certhia americana*)
  Olive Warbler (*Peucedramus taeniatus*)
  Crescent-chested Warbler (*Parula superciliosa*)
  Townsend's Warbler (*Dendroica townsendi*)
  Hermit Warbler (*Dendroica occidentalis*)[a]
  Grasshopper Sparrow[b] (*Ammodramus savannarum*)
  Yellow-eyed Junco (*Junco phaeonotus*)
  Pine Siskin (*Carduelis pinus*)
  Scott's Oriole (*Icterus parisorum*)

MICROPHYLLOUS SCRUBLAND
Indicator species:
  Rock Wren (*Salpinctes obsoletus*)
Associated species: none

DESERT SCRUBBY VEGETATION AND GRASSLANDS
Indicator species:
  Green-tailed Towhee (*Pipilo chlorurus*)
Associated species:
  Gambel's Quail (*Callipepla gambelii*)
  American Kestrel (*Falco sparverius*)
  Common Ground-Dove (*Columbina passerina*)
  Broad-billed Hummingbird (*Cynanthus latirostris*)[c]
  Costa's Hummingbird (*Calypte costae*)[a]
  Say's Phoebe (*Sayornis saya*)
  Brown-crested Flycatcher (*Myiarchus tyrannulus*)
  Vermilion Flycatcher (*Pyrocephalus rubinus*)
  Loggerhead Shrike (*Lanius ludovicianus*)[b c]
  Horned Lark (*Eremophila alpestris*)
  Black-capped Gnatcatcher (*Polioptila nigriceps*)[a]
  Bendire's Thrasher (*Toxostoma bendirei*)[a b c]
  Phainopepla (*Phainopepla nitens*)
  Vesper Sparrow (*Pooecetes gramineus*)
  White-crowned Sparrow (*Zonotrichia leucophrys*)
  Pyrrhuloxia (*Cardinalis sinuatus*)

MANGROVES
Indicator species:
  American Redstart (*Setophaga ruticilla*)
Associated species:
  Yellow Warbler (*Dendroica petechia*)
  Northern Waterthrush (*Seiurus noveboracensis*)
  Lincoln's Sparrow (*Melospiza lincolnii*)

LOWER ELEVATION RIPARIAN ASSOCIATIONS
Indicator species:
  Violet-crowned Hummingbird (*Amazilia violiceps*)
  Green Kingfisher (*Chloroceryle americana*)
  Sinaloa Wren (*Thryothorus sinaloa*)
Associated species:
  Elegant Quail (*Callipepla douglasii*)
  Cooper's Hawk (*Accipiter cooperii*)
  Wilson Snipe (*Gallinago delicata*)
  Plain-capped Starthroat (*Heliomaster constantii*)
  Belted Kingfisher (*Ceryle alcyon*)
  Pacific-slope Flycatcher (*Empidonax difficilis*)
  Nutting's Flycatcher (*Myiarchus nuttingi*)
  Cassin's Vireo (*Vireo cassinii*)
  Plumbeous Vireo (*Vireo plumbeus*)
  Warbling Vireo (*Vireo gilvus*)
  Happy Wren (*Thryothorus felix*)
  American Pipit (*Anthus rubescens*)
  Lucy's Warbler (*Vermivora luciae*)[a]
  MacGillivray's Warbler (*Oporornis tolmiei*)
  Black-and-white Warbler (*Mniotilta varia*)
  Painted Redstart (*Myioborus pictus*)
  Hepatic Tanager (*Piranga flava*)
  Lazuli Bunting (*Passerina amoena*)
  Varied Bunting (*Passerina versicolor*)[a c]
  Red-winged Blackbird (*Agelaius phoeniceus*)
  Lawrence's Goldfinch (*Carduelis lawrencei*)[a b]

TROPICAL DECIDUOUS FOREST AND OASES
Indicator species: none
Associated species:
  White-tipped Dove (*Leptotila verreauxi*)
  Northern Beardless-Tyrannulet (*Camptostoma imberbe*)[c]
  Nutting's Flycatcher (*Myiarchus nuttingi*)
  Ash-throated Flycatcher (*Myiarchus cinerascens*)
  Canyon Wren (*Catherpes mexicanus*)
  Five-striped Sparrow (*Aimophila quinquestriata*)
  Rock Wren (*Salpinctes obsoletus*)
  Black-and-white Warbler (*Mniotilta varia*)
  Wilson's Warbler (*Wilsonia pusilla*)
  Rufous-capped Warbler (*Basileuterus rufifrons*)
  Rufous-crowned Sparrow (*Aimophila ruficeps*)
  Streak-backed Oriole (*Icterus pustulatus*)

[a] PIF Watch List.
[b] USFWS birds of conservation concern national level.
[c] USFWS birds of conservation concern regional level [Southwestern Region] USDI Fish and Wildlife Service 2002, Rich et al. 2004).

breeding and wintering birds (MacArthur 1964, Anderson et al. 1983, Farley et al. 1994a, Sanders and Edge 1998, McComb et al. 2005). Wintering migrants were found to be more abundant in *Acacia* sp. patches with relatively high tree density and understory height in managed pasturelands in eastern Chiapas, Mexico (Greenberg et al. 1997). Compared with surrounding uplands, riparian habitats have a more complex vertical and horizontal structure, higher plant diversity, and more woody vegetation, especially in arid landscapes like Sonora.

Another possible factor is that vegetative productivity, which is higher in riparian ecosystems in general due to higher humidity and available water, and translates into a more abundant and diverse array of food items available to birds during all times of year. If this were the case, one might expect resident species to be equally or more abundant than migrants in riparian environments. However, according to my results this is not so; therefore, how can we explain the higher numbers of migrant species and individuals detected during winter in riparian environments?

The integration of migrant and resident species in the tropics and related wintering grounds can be described as a paradox; ecosystem productivity (and especially the abundance of arthropods) is low when bird abundances reach their annual high during winter. Numerous hypotheses have been proposed to explain this paradox. Greenberg (1995) proposed that a seasonal abundance of large, protein-rich insects supports the breeding productivity (feeding of young) of resident populations, while small arthropods are available year-round in sufficient biomass to support self-maintenance of adults, both resident and migrant. In Jamaica, Johnson et al. (2005) found some supporting evidence for one of Greenberg's predictions. They found more wintering migrants using habitats that provided less breeding season food resources for residents, and total abundance of birds was correlated with total arthropod biomass in winter. Johnson et al. (2005), however, suggest that other ecological factors act in synergy with food availability to affect migrant-to-resident ratios.

One of these other ecological factors could be predation. Hutto (1980) suggested that disturbed habitats supported higher abundances of wintering migrants because these habitats were underutilized by residents looking for nesting sites safe from predation, leaving them available for wintering species. This pattern has been found in habitats with edges and those that form habitat corridors (Kricher and Davis 1992, Hutto 1995, Villaseñor-Gómez and Hutto 1995, Warkentin et al. 1995). Johnson et al.

(2006) explored the ties between food resources and predation. They suggest that the availability of food resources while feeding young affects the risk of nest predation; where fewer food resources exist parents have to increase the number of feeding trips, attracting predators and reducing nest guarding time, therefore increasing the likelihood of nest predation.

To my knowledge, in western Mexico no studies have addressed these possible explanations (diet composition and seasonality, predation, and habitat disturbance), and it was beyond the scope of this study. Because of their importance to resident and migrant bird species, and because they experience impacts on and variation in the ecological factors of interest, riparian corridors in Sonora provide a good opportunity to assess these concepts and hypotheses. However, caution should be used in designing such studies. Avian assemblages on riparian tracts and adjoining uplands are not independent (Strong and Bock 1990, Knopf and Samson 1994, Saab 1999, Martin et al. 2006), and it is complicated to define the effects these habitats exert on each other. Birds can move along the riparian corridor, as well as back and forth between adjacent vegetation types. In this study, I made the practical assumption that by limiting the analyses to detections within a 25-m radius I avoided most of these effects.

During this study I did not detect any territorial behavior in insectivorous migrants, but did find that individuals of several species stayed in the same areas during the winter and showed a certain degree of site fidelity (individuals banded in November were recaptured in the same sites, and even in the same nets in February of the next year, and even after two consecutive years). Additional, research would be valuable to increase our understanding of the importance of food abundance, water, and structural complexity of riparian areas in comparison with non-riparian habitats, and the way numerous birds fleeing the cold, harsh northern winters make use of these environments, as well as deeper insights on riparian winter site fidelity and the extent to which wintering birds move about and make use of adjoining vegetation.

MANAGEMENT IMPLICATIONS

The Sonoran habitats included in this study fall with the Southwest Avifaunal Biome described in Rich et al.(2004). More particularly, they are located within two bird conservation regions (BCR): the Sonoran and Mojave Desert BCR and the Sierra Madre Occidental BCR. The southwest avifaunal biome includes more than half of the landbird Species of continental importance identified in this plan and many of the species have small population sizes, restricted ranges, high threats, and/or declining population trends. Of the primary habitats within this biome, riparian woodlands support the highest diversity of landbird species (Rich et al. 2004); according to my results, among the species associated to riparian environments, three are included in the Partners in Flight Watch List: Lucy´s Warbler (*Vermivora luciae*), Varied Bunting (*Passerina versicolor*), and Lawrence´s Goldfinch (*Carduelis lawrencei*); the Varied Bunting is also included by the USDI Fish and Wildlife Service as a species of conservation concern for the Southwestern Region (Region 2), and the Lawrence´s Goldfinch as a species of conservation concern at the national level (USDI Fish and Wildlife Service 2002). Human settlements and activities are often closely associated with and dependent on riparian ecosystems, imposing ecological pressures on riparian environments. Rich et al. (2004) also identifies agricultural and suburban development, grazing management, and habitat fragmentation as conservation issues or threats to this biome.

Due to the restricted areal extent of riparian habitats in comparison to desertscrub and highland forests habitats in Sonora and elsewhere in the Southwest, lowland riparian habitats contribute significantly to regional species richness, supporting 22% of the total avifauna in the state of Sonora. In addition to the importance of Sonoran riparian areas as habitat for wintering birds, as documented in this study, they also act as corridors that permit the northward expansion of tropical species and faunal mixture on a broader scale, and support high densities of spring migrating birds (Kelly and Hutto 2005). For these reasons, riparian areas in northwestern Mexico and southwestern US are unique and essential habitats for the wintering and migrating bird species of western North America as well as resident species, many of them of conservation concern.

ACKNOWLEDGEMENTS

This research was part of the Western North American Land Bird Project: Wintering Habitats in Sonora, a project funded by the Neotropical Migratory Bird Conservation Act (USDI Fish and Wildlife Service Agreement No. 201814J856), the Sonoran Joint Venture, the University of Montana, and Instituto de Medio Ambiente y Desarrollo Sustentable de Sonora (IMADES). I appreciate the support of Robert Mesta, Mike Scott, Dick Hutto, Rob Hazlewood, and Carol Beardmore. I was also supported by PROMEP through the Universidad Michoacana de San Nicolás de Hidalgo. Field activities were possible thanks to the hard work and great spirit of Rita Guadalupe Dávila Vindiola, Eduardo Gómez Limón, Juan José Rivera Díaz, Leonardo Villaseñor Gómez, Fátima Méndez, Philip J. Micheal, Denise Avila Jiménez, Sahira Aracely Leyva Briseño, and Rosalío León Carrasco; I am deeply indebted to them. I express my deep gratitude to Creagh Breuner, Lisa Eby, Erick Greene, Chris Guglielmo, Don Jenni, and especially Dick Hutto, for their guidance, support and important suggestions in all phases of this research. I also thank David Krueper, Janet M. Ruth, and two anonymous reviewers who provided an impressive review; their suggestions improved this manuscript enormously.

APPENDIX 1. ANOVA RESULTS COMPARING THE NUMBER OF INDIVIDUALS PER COUNT (25-M RADIUS) FOR THE MOST COMMON SPECIES WITH >15 DETECTIONS IN NON-RIPARIAN AND RIPARIAN VEGETATIONS IN SONORA (JANUARY–FEBRUARY 2004–2006).

Species	Status[a]	N[b]	Overall (N = 1,816) Mean (SE)	Non-riparian (N = 944) Mean (SE)	Riparian (N = 872) Mean (SE)	P[c]	Habitat preference[d]
Gambel's Quail (*Callipepla gambelii*)	R	79	0.04 (0.01)	0.06 (0.02)	0.02 (0.01)	3.46 (0.06)	
Black Vulture (*Coragyps atratus*)	R	70	0.04 (0.01)	0.06 (0.03)	0.01 (0.01)	3.05 (0.08)	
Turkey Vulture (*Cathartes aura*)	R	31	0.02 (0.001)	0.03 (0.01)	0.01 (0.003)	4.50 (0.03)	Nrip
Killdeer (*Charadrius vociferus*)	R	25	0.01 (0.004)	0.004 (0.002)	0.02 (0.01)	5.40 (0.02)	Rip
Spotted Sandpiper (*Actitis macularius*)	M	49	0.03 (0.004)	0.001 (0.001)	0.05 (0.01)	47.85 (<0.01)	Rip
White-winged Dove (*Zenaida asiatica*)	R	113	0.06 (0.01)	0.04 (0.01)	0.09 (0.03)	2.57 (0.11)	
Mourning Dove (*Zenaida macroura*)	R	173	0.09 (0.02)	0.11 (0.04)	0.08 (0.02)	0.39 (0.53)	
Inca Dove (*Columbina inca*)	R	34	0.02 (0.01)	0.01 (0.01)	0.02 (0.01)	0.37 (0.54)	
Common Ground-Dove (*Columbina passerina*)	R	24	0.013 (0.01)	0.001 (0.001)	0.03 (0.01)	3.65 (0.06)	
Broad-billed Hummingbird (*Cynanthus latirostris*)	R	107	0.06 (0.01)	0.07 (0.01)	0.04 (0.01)	5.40 (0.02)	Nrip
Violet-crowned Hummingbird (*Amazilia violiceps*)	R	16	0.01 (0.002)	0.001 (0.001)	0.02 (0.004)	13.69 (<0.01)	Rip
Costa's Hummingbird (*Calypte costae*)	R	2	0.03 (0.004)	0.04 (0.01)	0.02 (0.01)	3.16 (0.08)	
Unknown hummingbird	PM	17	0.01 (0.003)	0.002 (0.001)	0.02 (0.01)	9.08 (<0.01)	Rip
Green Kingfisher (*Chloroceryle americana*)	R	56	0.03 (0.004)	0.00 (0.00)	0.06 (0.01)	56.44 (<0.01)	Rip
Acorn Woodpecker (*Melanerpes formicivorus*)	R	19	0.01 (0.004)	0.02 (0.01)	0.003 (0.003)	3.48 (0.06)	
Gila Woodpecker (*Melanerpes uropygialis*)	R	215	0.12 (0.01)	0.10 (0.01)	0.13 (0.01)	1.80 (0.18)	
Red-naped Sapsucker (*Sphyrapicus nuchalis*)	M	17	0.01 (0.002)	0.004 (0.002)	0.01 (0.004)	5.63 (0.02)	Rip
Ladder-backed Woodpecker (*Picoides scalaris*)	R	64	0.03 (0.01)	0.03 (0.01)	0.04 (0.01)	2.32 (0.13)	
Northern Flicker (*Colaptes auratus*)	R	21	0.01 (0.003)	0.02 (0.004)	0.01 (0.003)	3.18 (0.08)	
Gilded Flicker (*Colaptes chrysoides*)	R	25	0.01 (0.003)	0.03 (0.01)	0.00 (0.00)	15.79 (<0.01)	Nrip
Gray Flycatcher (*Empidonax wrightii*)	M	29	0.02 (0.003)	0.01 (0.003)	0.02 (0.01)	7.12 (<0.01)	Rip
Unknown Empidonax (*Empidonax* sp.)	M	148	0.08 (0.01)	0.01 (0.004)	0.16 (0.01)	116.42 (<0.01)	Rip
Black Phoebe (*Sayornis nigricans*)	R	222	0.12 (0.01)	0.004 (0.002)	0.25 (0.02)	177.40 (<0.01)	Rip
Say's Phoebe (*Sayornis saya*)	PM	29	0.02 (0.003)	0.01 (0.003)	0.02 (0.01)	5.56 (0.02)	Rip
Vermilion Flycatcher (*Pyrocephalus rubinus*)	R	50	0.03 (0.004)	0.001 (0.001)	0.06 (0.01)	38.52 (<0.01)	Rip
Dusky-capped Flycatcher (*Myiarchus tuberulifer*)	R	18	0.01 (0.003)	0.01 (0.002)	0.01 (0.01)	3.53 (0.06)	
Ash-throated Flycatcher (*Myiarchus cinerascens*)	R	83	0.05 (0.01)	0.08 (0.01)	0.01 (0.004)	27.70 (<0.01)	Nrip
Loggerhead Shrike (*Lanius ludovicianus*)	PM	24	0.01 (0.003)	0.02 (0.004)	0.01 (0.003)	2.06 (0.15)	
Mexican Jay (*Aphelocoma ultramarina*)	R	16	0.01 (0.004)	0.01 (0.01)	0.01 (0.004)	1.08 (0.30)	
Common Raven (*Corvus corax*)	R	26	0.01 (0.004)	0.02 (0.01)	0.01 (0.003)	3.11 (0.08)	
Violet-green Swallow (*Tachycineta thalassina*)	PM	39	0.021 (0.01)	0.04 (0.02)	0.00 (0.00)	3.04 (0.08)	
Bridled Titmouse (*Baeolophus wollweberi*)	R	51	0.03 (0.01)	0.03 (0.01)	0.02 (0.01)	0.63 (0.43)	
Verdin (*Auriparus flaviceps*)	R	405	0.22 (0.01)	0.31 (0.02)	0.12 (0.01)	47.32 (<0.01)	Nrip
Bushtit (*Psaltriparus minimus*)	R	17	0.01 (0.01)	0.002 (0.002)	0.02 (0.01)	1.20 (0.27)	
Cactus Wren (*Campylorhynchus brunneicapillus*)	R	153	0.08 (0.01)	0.14 (0.02)	0.02 (0.01)	48.81 (<0.01)	Nrip
Rock Wren (*Salpinctes obsoletus*)	R	16	0.01 (0.002)	0.02 (0.004)	0.001 (0.001)	10.0 (<0.01)	Nrip
Sinaloa Wren (*Thryothorus sinaloa*)	R	19	0.01 (0.003)	0.004 (0.003)	0.02 (0.01)	5.64 (0.02)	Rip
Bewick's Wren (*Thryomanes bewickii*)	R	43	0.02 (0.004)	0.02 (0.01)	0.03 (0.01)	0.45 (0.50)	
House Wren (*Troglodytes aedon*)	PM	73	0.04 (0.01)	0.01 (0.003)	0.07 (0.01)	37.60 (<0.01)	Rip

APPENDIX 1. CONTINUED.

Species	Status[a]	N[b]	Overall (N = 1,816) Mean (SE)	Non-riparian (N = 944) Mean (SE)	Riparian (N = 872) Mean (SE)	P[c]	Habitat preference[d]
Ruby-crowned Kinglet (Regulus calendula)	M	506	0.28 (0.02)	0.06 (0.01)	0.51 (0.030)	209.68 (<0.01)	Rip
Blue-gray Gnatcatcher (Polioptila caerulea)	PM	440	0.24 (0.01)	0.13 (0.02)	0.36 (0.02)	65.25 (0.02)	Rip
Black-tailed Gnatcatcher (Polioptila melanura)	R	217	0.12 (0.0)	0.16 (0.02)	0.07 (0.01)	17.59 (<0.01)	Nrip
Black-capped Gnatcatcher (Polioptila nigriceps)	R	84	0.05 (0.01)	0.02 (0.01)	0.07 (0.01)	14.73 (<0.01)	Rip
American Robin (Turdus migratorius)	PM	22	0.01 (0.01)	0.02 (0.02)	0.00 (0.00)	1.35 (0.25)	
Northern Mockingbird (Mimus polyglottos)	PM	180	0.10 (0.03)	0.15 (0.07)	0.05 (0.01)	2.06 (0.15)	
Curve-billed Thrasher (Toxostoma curvirostre)	R	85	0.05 (0.01)	0.07 (0.01)	0.02 (0.01)	6.79 (<0.01)	Nrip
Phainopepla (Phainopepla nitens)	R	47	0.03 (0.01)	0.04 (0.01)	0.01 (0.003)	12.79 (<0.01)	Nrip
Orange-crowned Warbler (Vermivora celata)	M	145	0.08 (0.01)	0.06 (0.01)	0.11 (0.01)	9.17 (<0.01)	Rip
Yellow-rumped Warbler (Dendroica coronata)	M	436	0.24 (0.02)	0.06 (0.02)	0.43 (0.03)	116.18 (<0.01)	Rip
Black-throat. Gray Warbler (Dendroica nigrescens)	M	36	0.02 (0.004)	0.01 (0.003)	0.03 (0.01)	10.77 (<0.01)	Rip
Common Yellowthroat (Geothlypis trichas)	PM	170	0.09 (0.01)	0.031 (0.01)	0.16 (0.01)	66.33 (<0.01)	Rip
Wilson's Warbler (Wilsonia pusilla)	M	68	0.04 (0.01)	0.001 (0.001)	0.08 (0.01)	55.95 (<0.01)	Rip
Green-tailed Towhee (Pipilo chlorurus)	M	174	0.10 (0.01)	0.03 (0.01)	0.16 (0.02)	53.29 (<0.01)	Rip
Spotted Towhee (Pipilo maculatus)	PM	17	0.01 (0.003)	0.01 (0.01)	0.01 (0.002)	2.56 (0.11)	
Canyon Towhee (Pipilo fuscus)	R	56	0.03 (0.01)	0.04 (0.01)	0.01 (0.01)	9.57 (<0.01)	Nrip
Rufous-winged Sparrow (Aimophila carpalis)	R	74	0.04 (0.01)	0.05 (0.01)	0.03 (0.02)	1.59 (0.21)	
Rufous-crowned Sparrow (Aimophila ruficeps)	R	50	0.03 (0.01)	0.04 (0.01)	0.01 (0.01)	2.55 (0.11)	
Chipping Sparrow (Spizella passerina)	PM	515	0.28 (0.053)	0.14 (0.04)	0.44 (0.10)	8.32 (<0.01)	Rip
Clay-colored Sparrow (Spizella pallida)	M	39	0.02 (0.01)	0.04 (0.02)	0.00 (0.00)	3.88 (<0.05)	Nrip
Brewer's Sparrow (Spizella breweri)	M	127	0.07 (0.02)	0.09 (0.03)	0.05 (0.03)	0.67 (0.41)	
Lark Sparrow (Chondestes grammacus)	M	255	0.14 (0.03)	0.07 (0.02)	0.21 (0.07)	4.33 (0.04)	Rip
Black-throated Sparrow (Amphispiza bilineata)	R	46	0.02 (0.01)	0.04 (0.01)	0.01 (0.01)	3.41 (0.07)	
Savannah Sparrow (Passerculus sandwichensis)	PM	26	0.01 (0.01)	0.02 (0.01)	0.00 (0.00)	3.62 (0.06)	
Song Sparrow (Melospiza melodia)	PM	351	0.19 (0.01)	0.001 (0.001)	0.401 (0.03)	247.84 (<0.01)	Rip
Lincoln's Sparrow (Melospiza lincolnii)	M	47	0.03 (0.01)	0.004 (0.003)	0.05 (0.01)	16.67 (<0.01)	Rip
White-crowned Sparrow (Zonotrichia leucophrys)	M	172	0.09 (0.02)	0.04 (0.02)	0.15 (0.04)	8.40 (<0.01)	Rip
Dark-eyed Junco (Junco hyemalis)	M	60	0.03 (0.01)	0.06 (0.02)	0.001 (0.001)	7.65 (<0.01)	Nrip
Yellow-eyed Junco (Junco phaeonotus)	R	21	0.01 (0.01)	0.02 (0.01)	0.00 (0.00)	5.58 (0.02)	Nrip
Northern Cardinal (Cardinalis cardinalis)	R	134	0.07 (0.01)	0.05 (0.01)	0.10 (0.01)	9.78 (<0.01)	Rip
Pyrrhuloxia (Cardinalis sinuatus)	R	41	0.02 (0.01)	0.01 (0.004)	0.03 (0.01)	5.48 (0.02)	Rip
Red-winged Blackbird (Agelaius phoeniceus)	PM	32	0.02 (0.01)	0.00 (0.00)	0.04 (0.02)	2.57 (0.11)	
Western Meadowlark (Sturnella neglecta)	PM	21	0.01 (0.01)	0.02 (0.02)	0.001 (0.001)	0.82 (0.37)	
Great-tailed Grackle (Quiscalus mexicanus)	R	21	0.01 (0.01)	0.01 (0.001)	0.01 (0.01)	0.09 (0.76)	
Streak-backed Oriole (Icterus pustuatus)	R	34	0.02 (0.003)	0.001 (0.001)	0.04 (0.01)	28.87 (<0.01)	Rip
House Finch (Carpodacus mexicanus)	R	222	0.12 (0.01)	0.13 (0.02)	0.11 (0.02)	0.76 (0.38)	
Lesser Goldfinch (Carduelis psaltria)	R	124	0.07 (0.01)	0.02 (0.01)	0.12 (0.03)	15.48 (<0.01)	Rip

[a] Status: R = resident, PM = partial migrant, M = migrant.
[b] Number of individuals detected.
[c] ANOVA (P) analysis.
[d] Rip = preference for riparian and Nrip = preference for non-riparian habitats.

Studies in Avian Biology No. 37:69–73

POPULATION TRENDS OF YUMA CLAPPER RAILS IN THE COLORADO RIVER DELTA, MEXICO

Osvel Hinojosa-Huerta, Juan José Rivera-Díaz, Helena Iturribarría-Rojas, Alejandra Calvo-Fonseca

Abstract. The Yuma Clapper Rail (*Rallus longirostris yumanensis*) is a binationally protected marsh bird in northwestern Mexico and southwestern US. We monitored the population of Yuma Clapper Rails in the Colorado River delta, Mexico from 1999–2006. The monitoring program consists of call-response surveys at 15 transects (five point counts each) randomly located in the Ciénega de Santa Clara, northwestern Sonora. The population of Yuma Clapper Rails at the Ciénega declined 55% during the period of 1999–2002 (95% CI = 33.53–76.45; P < 0.001, β = 0.99). However, from 1999–2006 we found no change in the population of Clapper Rails (P = 0.43, β = 0.12). The Ciénega de Santa Clara maintains the largest known population of the subspecies, with an estimate of 5,974 individuals (95% CI = 4,698–7,482) for 2006. The short-term population fluctuations of Clapper Rails are likely associated with changes in the direction of water flows and the occurrence of wildfires in emergent vegetation. In the long-term, the conservation of the Yuma Clapper Rail requires binational collaboration to secure water for key wetland areas and the implementation of management strategies to maintain vegetation dynamics.

Key Words: Ciénega de Santa Clara, marshbirds, monitoring, *Rallus longirostris yumanensis*, Upper Gulf of California and Colorado River Delta Biosphere Reserve.

TENDENCIAS POBLACIONALES DEL PALMOTEADOR DE YUMA EN EL DELTA DEL RÍO COLORADO, MÉXICO.

Resumen. El Palmoteador de Yuma (*Rallus longirostris yumanensis*) es un ave de marisma protegida a nivel binacional en el suroeste de Estados Unidos y el noroeste México. Monitoreamos la población de *R. l. yumanensis* en el delta del Río Colorado, México, de 1999 al 2006. El programa consistió en conteos por llamado-respuesta en 15 transectos (con 5 puntos de conteo cada uno) localizados aleatoriamente en la Ciénega de Santa Clara, en el noroeste de Sonora. La población de la subespecie en la Ciénega de Santa Clara disminuyó 54.99% durante el periodo de 1999-2006 (I.C. 95%. 33.53–76.45; P < 0.001, β = 0.99). Sin embargo, de 1999 al 2006 no detectamos cambios en la población de *R. l. yumanensis* (P = 0.43, β = 0.12). La Ciénega de Santa Clara mantiene a la población conocida más grande de la subespecie, con un estimado de 5,974 individuos (95% I.C. 4,698–7,482) en 2006. Las fluctuaciones poblacionales de corto plazo probablemente se encuentren vinculadas con cambios en la dirección de los flujos de agua y con los patrones de incendios de la vegetación emergente. En el largo plazo, la conservación del Palmoteador de Yuma requiere de colaboración binacional para garantizar las fuentes de agua para los humedales y la implementación de estrategias de manejo para mantener el dinamismo de la vegetación.

Long-term monitoring programs can provide critical information on changes in bird populations that can guide conservation efforts and provide feedback for adaptive management plans (Ralph et al. 1993). In the Colorado River delta, recent pulse floods and agricultural drainage water have restored wetland and riparian areas (Glenn et al. 2001, Nagler et al. 2005). With effective management, these areas and their water sources can maintain critical habitat for hundreds of bird species, many of which are of special concern (Hinojosa-Huerta et al. 2004, 2007).

The Yuma Clapper Rail (*Rallus longirostris yumanensis*) is a marsh bird classified as Threatened in Mexico and Endangered in the US (Eddleman and Conway 1998, Diario Oficial de la Federación 2002). The subspecies

is distributed in the Lower Colorado Basin, from Topock Marsh, California, to the Colorado River delta in Mexico, and in mangrove marshes along the coast of Sonora (Eddleman and Conway 1998). The subspecies' population has declined due to habitat degradation and loss caused by water management practices in the Lower Colorado Basin (Eddleman and Conway 1998). In the Colorado River delta, Clapper Rails inhabit remnant wetlands (Hinojosa-Huerta et al. 2001), in particular the Ciénega de Santa Clara, which is estimated to support one of the largest populations of the subspecies with over 3,000 pairs (Hinojosa-Huerta et al. 2001).

The Ciénega de Santa Clara is located in the southeastern section of the Colorado River delta in Sonora, Mexico, within the Upper Gulf of California and Colorado River delta Biosphere

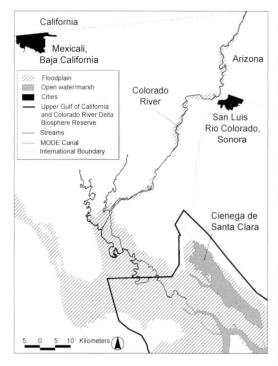

FIGURE 1. Map of the Colorado River delta, Baja California, and Sonora, Mexico.

Reserve (UGCCRDBR; Fig. 1). This 5,800 ha wetland, dominated by cattail (*Typha domingensis*), was accidentally restored in the late 1970s when brackish agricultural drainage from the Wellton and Mohawk Valleys in Arizona started to reach the area (Glenn et al. 1996). The drainage reaches the Ciénega through the Main Outlet Drain Extension (MODE) canal, as part of a temporary solution implemented by the US in the 1970s to control the salinity of Colorado River water deliveries into Mexico (Zengel et al. 1995). As such, the flow into the Ciénega is not permanently secured, emphasizing the importance of a program to monitor the ecological health of this wetland.

The criteria to establish the UGCCRDBR included protection of the Yuma Clapper Rail. Specific objectives for the management of the natural protected area include the preservation of Yuma Clapper Rail populations and its habitat, as well as maintenance of a monitoring program for the subspecies. Several efforts have been carried out to determine the status of the population in the Ciénega de Santa Clara, including initial assessments carried out in 1989 (Eddleman 1989) and 1993 (Abarca et al. 1993), and a pilot binational monitoring program in 1998 (L. Piest and J. Campoy, unpubl. data).

As a follow-up and as part of the management activities of the biosphere reserve, we designed and implemented a long-term program to monitor the population of Yuma Clapper Rails in the Ciénega de Santa Clara (Hinojosa-Huerta 2000). The general objectives of the program are to monitor ecosystem health, determine whether habitat requirements are being met for the protection of the subspecies, and guide management actions in the natural protected area. Here we present the results of the monitoring program from 1999 to 2006, including the population trends and latest population estimates of Yuma Clapper Rails at the Ciénega de Santa Clara, Sonora, México.

METHODS

We conducted surveys during the breeding seasons of 1999–2006 at 15 transects randomly located in the Ciénega de Santa Clara. These transects are a subset of the transect surveys conducted in 1999 and 2000 to determine the status of the Yuma Clapper Rail at the Ciénega (Hinojosa-Huerta et al. 2001). With the 1999 and 2000 survey data, we designed a long-term monitoring plan using the program MONITOR 6.2 (Gibbs 1995), with the objective of detecting population changes <3% per year, with a significance level of 95% and a statistical power of 90% (Hinojosa-Huerta 2000).

Our survey procedures were based on the protocol established by the USDI Fish and Wildlife Service for Yuma Clapper Rail surveys (USDI Fish and Wildlife Service 2000). The protocol consists of call-response surveys, in which taped vocalizations are broadcasted to elicit the response of the target species (Conway and Gibbs 2005). At each survey point, the surveyors recorded the number of Yuma Clapper Rails during a 2-min passive period prior to broadcasting recorded calls, and during two periods in which pre-recorded vocalizations of Yuma Clapper Rails were broadcast for 2 min, followed by 2 min of silence. Survey stations were variable distance circular plots located 200 m apart, and grouped in transects (five stations per transect). Surveys started at sunrise and continued until no later than 1030 H. Transects were either on the edge between marsh and upland or on the edge between marsh and open water. Following recommendations from standardized protocols (Conway 2002) and pilot studies in the Ciénega de Santa Clara (Hinojosa-Huerta 2000), we did not establish transects through cattail patches.

We visited each station once during early breeding season (March), and once during late breeding season (May). In addition to rails, we also recorded vegetation and water depth characteristics at each transect, as well as effects on habitat features by disturbance events such as wildfires and hydrological fluctuations.

We entered all the data in a relational database and conducted the statistical analyses using JMP IN 3.2 (Sall and Lehman 1996). Individual birds detected at several survey points were only counted at the initial detection site. To estimate population trends, we used the number of Clapper Rails detected per point, using the average for each point of the early and late breeding season counts. With this data set we ran a linear regression of detections of Clapper Rails against year, from 1999 to 2006.

We used the program DISTANCE (Thomas et al. 2002) and the May 2006 survey data to estimate Clapper Rail densities. We selected the distance models using a combination of goodness of fit test and the coefficient of variation in the parameter estimates. Estimates of abundance were based on the area of the Ciénega de Santa Clara (5,800 ha; Glenn et al. 2001), and the 95% confidence intervals of the density estimates from DISTANCE. This estimate assumes a 100% response rate from Clapper Rails to the call-response surveys. We also calculated a less conservative estimate, using a fixed 60% response rate based on L. Piest and J. Campoy (unpubl. data).

To examine changes of Yuma Clapper Rail densities at the Ciénega de Santa Clara, we generated density maps of Clapper Rails for 1999, 2002, and 2006. We used ARC/VIEW 3.1 to interpolate density polygons for the whole Ciénega, using the data from rails detected at the survey stations, a cell size of 50 m, and interpolation of data using the closest 10 survey stations to each cell. The datum for each cell is an estimate, but allows for a general observation of

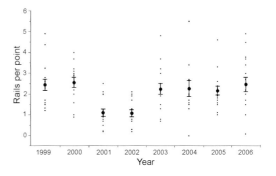

FIGURE 2. Detections of Yuma Clapper Rails by year and transect, at the Ciénega de Santa Clara, Sonora, Mexico.

the patterns of Clapper Rail distribution at the Ciénega throughout the study.

RESULTS

The average number of detections of Yuma Clapper Rails per year at the Ciénega de Santa Clara was 305.70 (SE = 31.82). The minimum number of detections was 162, which occurred during 2002, and the maximum was 370, during 2006. Overall, from 1999–2006 we found no change in detections of Yuma Clapper Rails (average change per year = 3% ± 4%, P = 0.43, β = 0.12). However, the number of Yuma Clapper Rails at the Ciénega declined 55% during the period of 1999–2002 (95% CI = 33.53–76.45; P < 0.001, β = 0.99), with detections decreasing from 364 in 1999 to 162 in 2002 (Fig. 2). The decrease in detections occurred mostly at the central lagoons, with 83% fewer detections (Fig. 3). In comparison, count numbers increased 47% in 2003–2006 (95% CI = 22–71, P < 0.001; Fig. 2). However, there was a shift

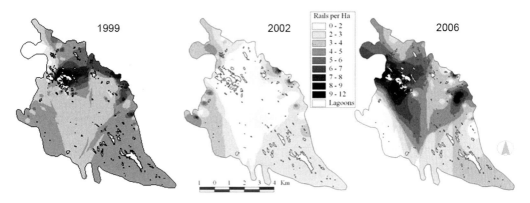

FIGURE 3. Densities of Yuma Clapper Rails per hectare at the Ciénega de Santa Clara, Sonora, Mexico, for 1999, 2002, and 2006. ARC/VIEW 3.1 was used to interpolate the density polygons from rails detected at the survey stations.

in distribution of Clapper Rails through this period, with an increase at the central lagoons and northwestern edge of the Ciénega (52% overall increase) and a decrease at the southwestern and eastern edges (34% decrease).

The estimated density of Yuma Clapper Rails at the Ciénega de Santa Clara during the May 2006 survey was 1.03 rails/ha (95% CI = 0.81–1.29, 267 detections, $\chi^2 = 0.368$, df = 1 and 82), with an estimated detection radius of 105.02 m (95% CI = 97.70–112.87). Assuming a conservative estimate of 100% response rate and a wetland area of 5,800 ha for the Ciénega, the population estimate of Yuma Clapper Rails for 2006 was 5,974 individuals (95% CI = 4,698–7,482). Assuming a fixed response rate of 60%, the population estimate was 9,956 individuals (95% CI = 7,830–12,470).

DISCUSSION

A level of uncertainty is associated with the abundance estimation of Yuma Clapper Rails in the Ciénega de Santa Clara due to the lack of a precise estimate of response rate of birds to the pre-recorded vocalizations (Conway and Gibbs 2005). However, using a conservative estimate of 100% response rate, population estimates are close to 6,000 individuals, the largest known population for the subspecies in its entire range (Eddleman and Conway 1998).

Despite fluctuations and some significant decreases during the first half of the study period, the population of Yuma Clapper Rails at the Ciénega has been stable during the last eight years and does not show a downward trend. With the information generated through the monitoring program, we conclude that the estimated number of Clapper Rails meets the conservation objectives for the subspecies in Mexico and for the UGCCRDBR (CONANP 2007).

From 1999 throughout 2006 fluctuations occurred in abundance and changes in the distribution of Clapper Rail densities at the Ciénega. These variations were likely associated with marsh habitat dynamics (Conway and Nadeau 2005). The eastern and northern parts of the Ciénega burned in 1998, just before the beginning of the monitoring program, which promoted the growth of young stands of cattail. In the following years, cattail stands became too dense and senescent, probably reducing the density of rails they could support (Conway and Nadeau 2005). This was evident during 2001 and 2002 at the central, more stable lagoons of the Ciénega, where the stand density and senescence reduced the quality of habitat for Yuma Clapper Rails.

In 2003, changes in the direction of the flow that reaches the Ciénega promoted the growth of young cattail stands at new sites, in particular in the northwestern edge. This triggered the population increase and shift in distribution observed in 2003–2005. In early 2006, another wildfire at the Ciénega burned nearly 2,000 ha, primarily in the central portion. By late spring 2006, the cattail stands grew back, and detections of Yuma Clapper Rails increased throughout the burned area (O. Hinojosa-Huerta, unpubl. data).

With the monitoring program we have been able to track the fluctuations of Yuma Clapper Rail abundance at the Ciénega and provide feedback for the management of the Biosphere Reserve. In particular, we learned that the conservation of the subspecies requires not only the maintenance of water flows, but also the maintenance of successional stages in wetlands throughout the region. This should be based upon the implementation of various management strategies, including the restoration, at a smaller scale, of the natural hydrologic regime of the Colorado River delta, with periodic pulse floods, and the implementation of prescribed fires. The actions should maintain a mosaic of large cattail patches of mixed ages interspersed with shallow lagoons, deter the invasion of the exotic saltcedar (*Tamarix ramosissima*), and prevent the senescence of the emergent vegetation (Eddleman 1989, Hinojosa-Huerta 2000, Conway and Nadeau 2005).

Despite their fairly high numbers, Yuma Clapper Rails are still threatened in Mexico, due to water management actions and the destruction of wetlands that could drastically reduce their population. The extended drought throughout the Colorado River basin has increased the pressure to improve water efficiency, resulting in less water for wetlands and wildlife (Zamora-Arroyo et al. 2006). In particular, there is increasing pressure to operate the Yuma Desalting Plant (U.S. Bureau of Reclamation 2005). This would divert the water from the MODE canal to the Yuma Desalting Plant in Arizona, and the resulting freshwater would be allocated to consumptive uses. The concentrated brine exiting the plant would be directed to the Ciénega, which would almost certainly result in the disappearance of emergent vegetation and Yuma Clapper Rails at this wetland (García-Hernández et al. 1999).

However, environmental organizations and government agencies are working together to find solutions to the water requirements in the US while maintaining the ecological values of the Ciénega de Santa Clara in Mexico (Yuma Desalting Plant/Ciénega de Santa Clara

Workgroup 2005). This approach provides a sounder framework for negotiation with clearer opportunities for reducing the risk of shortage in the basin while establishing measures to protect the Ciénega. Considering the dynamics of water management in the region and across the border, a robust monitoring program, implemented in the framework of adaptive management and providing guidelines for water use, is an essential tool to guarantee the long-term conservation of the Yuma Clapper Rail and its habitat in the United States and Mexico.

ACKNOWLEDGMENTS

This program has been funded and supported by the Sonoran Joint Venture, USDI Fish and Wildlife Service, CONANP, National Fish and Wildlife Foundation, CEDES, AEURHYC, Ejido Luis Encinas Johnson, University of Arizona, PRBO Conservation Science, and Pronatura. We thank José Campoy, Martha Gómez, Eduardo Soto, Ramsés Rodríguez and all the personnel at the Upper Gulf of California and Colorado River Delta Biosphere Reserve who have provided support for the implementation of this program. We also thank the field technicians and volunteers that have participated in the surveys, in particular Juan Butrón, José Juan Butrón, Enrique Zamora, Ricardo Olachea, Yamilett Carrillo, Robert Mesta, Pablo Valle, and Jaqueline García. We thank Courtney Conway for the helpful comments and support to improve the monitoring program for marshbirds in the Colorado River delta, as well as Lin Piest, Eduardo Palacios, and Tim Brush for their invaluable editorial feedback.

Studies in Avian Biology No. 37:74–82

DENSITIES, SPECIES RICHNESS AND HABITAT RELATIONSHIPS OF THE AVIAN COMMUNITY IN THE COLORADO RIVER, MEXICO

Osvel Hinojosa-Huerta, Helena Iturribarría-Rojas, Enrique Zamora-Hernández, Alejandra Calvo-Fonseca

Abstract. We determined the spatial and temporal patterns of avian species richness and density and explored their relationships with habitat features in the floodplain of the Colorado River in Mexico, which was subject to regeneration through pulse-floods in the last 20 yr. Our work included monthly point counts at 30 transects (240 points) from May 2002–July 2003. The average abundance per point was 29.2 individuals with an average richness of 8.6 species, and an average density of 47.7 birds per ha. The most common species were Mourning Dove (*Zenaida macroura*), Red-winged Blackbird (*Agelaius phoeniceus*), and Brown-headed Cowbird (*Molothrus ater*), but another 64 species were commonly found, including Verdin (*Auriparus flaviceps*), Song Sparrow (*Melospiza melodia*), and Abert's Towhee (*Pipilo aberti*). Surface water was the most important habitat feature related to avian richness and density regardless of vegetation type or land cover. During summer, species richness was explained by variations in water and the cover of cottonwoods (*Populus fremontii*), and the variation in bird densities was explained by variations in water and the cover of willows (*Salix gooddingii*). The dedication of instream flows and pulse floods, the maintenance of vegetation cover and structural diversity, and an increase of older riparian stands will secure the viability of existing bird populations and will increase the probability of recovery of the species that are still extirpated from the floodplain of the Colorado River in Mexico.

Key words: birds, Colorado River delta, cottonwood, floodplain, riparian, water, willow.

DENSIDADES, RIQUEZA DE ESPECIES Y RELACIONES DE HÁBITAT DE LA COMUNIDAD DE AVES EN EL RÍO COLORADO, MÉXICO

Resumen. Determinamos los patrones espaciales y temporales de la riqueza y densidad de aves y exploramos sus relaciones con las características de hábitat en la planicie de inundación del delta del Río Colorado, México, la cual se regeneró por recibir pulsos de inundación en los últimos 20 años. Nuestro trabajo incluyó conteos por puntos mensuales en 30 transectos (240 puntos) de Mayo 2002 a Julio 2003. El promedio de abundancia por punto fue de 29.2 individuos, con una riqueza promedio de 9.6 especies, y una densidad promedio de 47.7 aves por ha. Las especies más comunes fueron *Zenaida macroura*, *Agelaius phoeniceus*, y *Molothrus ater*, pero encontramos comúnmente a otras 64 especies, incluyendo a *Auriparus flaviceps*, *Melospiza melodia*, y *Pipilo aberti*. El agua superficial fue la característica del hábitat más importante en relación a la riqueza y densidad de aves, independientemente del tipo de vegetación o cobertura del suelo. Durante el verano, la riqueza de aves fue explicada por variaciones en la cobertura de agua y álamos (*Populus fremontii*), y la densidad fue explicada por variaciones en la cobertura de agua y sauces (*Salix gooddingii*). La asignación de flujos de mantenimiento e inundación, el mantenimiento de la cobertura y diversidad estructural de la vegetación, y el incremento de zonas de bosque ripario maduro permitirán asegurar la viabilidad de las poblaciones existentes de aves e incrementarán la probabilidad de recuperación de las especies que aún se encuentran extirpadas de la planicie del Río Colorado en México.

In western North America, about 95% of riparian areas have been destroyed, altered, or degraded by human activities (Ohmart 1994). However, riparian ecosystems maintain the highest diversity and abundance of birds in the region (Knopf et al. 1988, Rosenberg et al. 1991), and provide critical breeding, wintering, and migratory habitats (Knopf and Samson 1994, Skagen et al. 2005). The cumulative effects of habitat loss and degradation in riparian areas through the life cycle of birds is one of the most important factors associated with land bird population declines (DeSante and George 1994, Hutto 2000, Norris et al. 2004). Thus,

documenting the composition and status of riparian bird communities and understanding how they are associated with important biotic and abiotic components of their habitats are crucial to any conservation planning effort.

Studies of riparian ecosystem dynamics have documented the importance of base flows and pulse-flood regimes, dynamic geomorphologic processes in the floodplains, and a diverse mosaic of habitat structures to the biotic community (Richter and Richter 2000, Glenn et al. 2001, Stromberg and Chew 2002). Avian diversity and abundance show a positive response to increases in Freemont cottonwood (*Populus fremontii*) and Gooding willow (*Salix gooddingii*) cover, as well as the structural complexity of vegetation (Krueper et al. 2003, Scott et al. 2003, Anderson et al. 2004). All of these associations are important in understanding avian community response to habitat change and in considering methods for restoring habitat and functions.

However, the success of revegetation efforts in restoring riparian ecosystem function and the native avifauna has been limited. Revegetated sites have lower avian diversity, densities, and reproductive success than native sites as a result of lower habitat diversity and structure, and unnatural patterns of hydrology (Larison et al. 2001, Snell-Rood and Cristol 2003). Although natural revegetation may be stimulated by releasing water from upstream reservoirs in short pulses (Richter and Richter 2000, Sher et al. 2000, Stromberg and Chew 2002, Glenn and Nagler 2005), questions remain regarding whether degraded floodplains can be restored with a designed pulse-flood regime, and how the avian community might respond to such events.

The floodplain of the Colorado River in Mexico is a degraded environment and a classic example of US-Mexico borderlands issues, where management decisions on both sides of the border have impacts on the flora and fauna of the riparian ecosystem. Before the development of the hydraulic infrastructure in the basin, the Colorado River delta supported >200,000 ha of riparian and wetland areas (Sykes 1937). After the completion of the larger dams in the 1930s, limited base or pulse flow reached the area for nearly 50 yr, resulting in the virtual loss of cottonwood-willow forests and the invasion of exotic saltcedar (*Tamarix ramosissima*; Glenn et al. 2001). This caused the local extirpation of nine breeding bird species, including Southwestern Willow Flycatcher (*Empidonax traillii extimus*), Yellow Warbler (*Dendroica petechia*), and Bell's Vireo (*Vireo bellii*), species of conservation concern for the Colorado River delta region (Hinojosa-Huerta et al. 2004). However, a modest, but significant portion of the riparian ecosystem in Mexico has regenerated in response to large-volume water releases from US dams over the past 25 yr (Glenn et al. 2001, Zamora-Arroyo et al. 2005). The releases have simulated a natural pulse-flood regime and a base flow, thus supporting the regrowth of young and dynamic stands of cottonwood and willow, which have covered >3,000 ha despite the dominant presence of saltcedar (Nagler et al. 2005). Yet we know little about how avian communities use the riparian habitat in this region throughout the year, and how birds respond to surface water and other habitat components, all important issues in understanding how birds may respond to this regenerating habitat.

To address these questions we: (1) determined the spatial and temporal patterns of avian species richness, abundance, and community structure in a regenerating floodplain, and (2) explored the relationships of species richness, density and community structure with land cover (including surface water) and vegetation features. Finally, with this information we inferred some responses by the bird community to the current regeneration and make some recommendations regarding the restoration options for the floodplain of the Colorado River in Mexico.

METHODOLOGY

STUDY AREA

The study area was located within the floodplain of the Colorado River in Baja California and Sonora, Mexico (Fig. 1). The floodplain traverses the Mexicali Valley as the river flows toward the Gulf of California, and is confined by flood control levees on both banks. The total area is 43 000 ha, and extends for 150 km along the river. Within this region, we worked in the area from San Luis Río Colorado downstream to the confluence of the Colorado River with the Hardy River, covering 12,630 ha and extending for 65 river km. This study area included the main stem of the Colorado River, secondary streams, backwater lagoons, and portions of the major agricultural canals within the floodplain. The floodplain maintains a continuous corridor of vegetation along this stretch, dominated by saltcedar and arroweed with significant patches of cottonwood and willow (Glenn et al. 2001). Water flows in the area have been intermittent since the completion of Hoover Dam (1937), depending upon excess deliveries from the US to Mexico, and operational releases from the Mexicali Irrigation District and agricultural drainage water. These variations in flow have determined the extent and quality of riparian habitat in the floodplain, ranging from degradation due to desiccation to regeneration in response to the return of flows (Glenn et al. 1996, Nagler et al. 2005). Extended dry periods have occurred (1952–1979), in which no flows reached the area, as well as extreme flooding events of over 800 m^3 s^{-1} (1981–1983; International Boundary and Water Commission 2007). During the last 12 yr, the area has experienced significant flooding events (1993, 1998, 2002, and 2005) with a magnitude of 40–100 m^3 s^{-1}, as well as modest semi-continuous instream

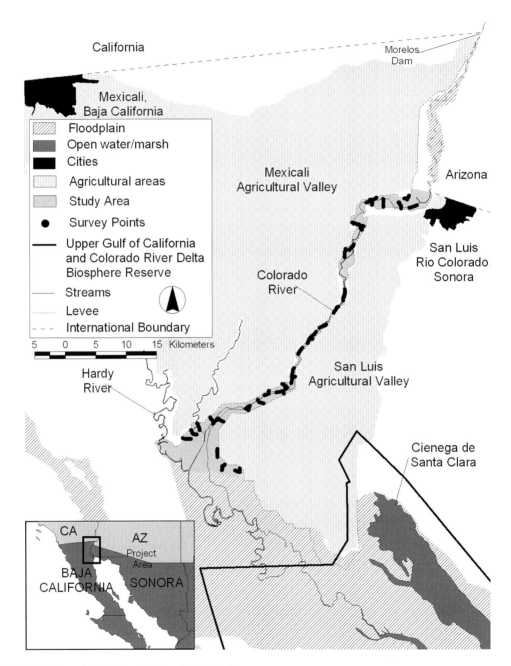

FIGURE 1. Map of the Colorado River delta, Mexico.

flows (2–8 m³ s⁻¹) during several years (1993, 1997, 1998, 1999, 2001, 2002, and 2004; Zamora-Arroyo et al. 2005).

BIRD SURVEYS

We conducted bird counts monthly from May 2002–July 2003 following a variable distance point-count methodology (Ralph et al. 1996). The levee system includes embankment structures on both sides of the river, but these levees are not continuous on both sides for the entire 65 km of the study area. Therefore the total length of levees within the study area was 146 km. We randomly selected 30 transects, at least 2 km apart, along the 146 km of levees. Each transect was composed of 8 points, 200 m apart, and extended for 1.6 km from the levee toward the main channel of the river. Transects were run by teams of two persons, mainly for security reasons, starting at sunrise and continuing until no later than 4 hours after sunrise. At each point we counted all birds heard or seen within a 5-min period, recording the distance from the observer to the bird and the time at which it was detected.

Habitat Surveys

We measured habitat features at each point along the 30 survey transects, using a survey radius of 50 m from the center of each point. At each survey point we visually estimated the percent ground coverage, and when appropriate the minimum, maximum, and average height of each of the following strata: trees (vegetation >3 m in height), shrubs (0.5–3 m), herbs (0.1–0.5 m), forbs (<0.1 m), emergent plants, bare soil, and open water. We also collected more detailed data for each stratum by estimating the percent coverage and average height of each plant species within a stratum. For open water, we recorded type (primary or secondary stream, drain, irrigation canal, or lagoon), depth, and width. The estimates of land cover were obtained with the aid of measuring tapes, global positioning system, and pacing, using relative coverage within the 50-m radius of each survey point.

Statistical Analyses

We conducted the statistical analyses using JMP IN 3.2 (Sall and Lehman 1996) and DISTANCE (Thomas et al. 2002). Detections of flyover birds were excluded from the analyses. Distance models were selected for calculating bird densities, using a combination of goodness of fit test and the coefficient of variation in the parameter estimates. Estimates of bird abundance were obtained using the study area of the point-count surveys (12,630 ha), and the 95% confidence intervals of the density estimates from DISTANCE.

For avian density, we estimated the overall density of birds per transect per visit. For species richness, we used the average number of species/point at each transect, for each visit.

We used ANOVA and Tukey-Kramer pairwise analysis to compare species richness and density among seasons. The grouping of visits by season was based on the pattern of temporal shift in the avian community, defining spring (March, April, May), summer (June, July, August), fall (September, October, November), and winter (December, January, February).

We tested for pairwise correlation of explanatory variables. If two variables showed a correlation >0.75, we excluded the variable with less value in management or ecological terms. We determined the habitat relationships with a multiple linear regression of avian density and species richness with habitat features. We conducted a forward stepwise selection of variables for each model (P < 0.25) and ran the models including only variables with P < 0.05. The values reported are means ± SE, except for estimates of density, where 95% confidence intervals are given. We used a significance level of 0.05 for all statistical tests.

RESULTS

Vegetation Cover

The Colorado River floodplain in our study sites supported a diverse array of riparian habitat types, with overall vegetative cover of 70% of which 88% was composed of shrubs and trees (Table 1). Bare soil and open water covered almost 30%. Native plants covered 34% of the floodplain of which cottonwood and willow covered 8%, while exotic plants covered 37%. Within the tree stratum, saltcedar was the dominant species (19% cover), while cottonwoods and willows covered 7% and mesquite (*Prosopis* spp.) covered <1% (Table 2). Saltcedar was also the most common shrub, followed by arrowweed (*Pluchea sericea*), seep willow (*Baccharis salicifolia*), and saltbush (*Atriplex* spp.). Cattail (*Typha domingensis*) was the dominant emergent species, but common reed (*Phragmites australis*) and bulrush (*Scirpus* spp.) were also present.

Avian Communities

We obtained a total of 109,287 bird records for 186 species. The average abundance per point was 29.2 individuals (± 1.2) with an average richness of 8.6 species (± 0.2), and an average density of 47.7 birds per ha (± 7.0). Overall,

TABLE 1. Average percent cover and height of vegetation strata in the study area within the floodplain of the Colorado River, Mexico. Confidence intervals (95% CI) are shown in parentheses. The value of water in the mean height column represents depth.

Strata	Mean cover (%)	Mean height (m)
Trees	27.55 (24.82–30.28)	4.63 (4.45–4.85)
Shrubs	35.04 (32.35–37.72)	1.72 (1.68–1.76)
Emergent	5.40 (4.32–6.49)	2.06 (1.94–2.18)
Herbs	1.93 (1.43–2.43)	0.39 (0.31–0.47)
Forbs	0.52 (0.16–0.87)	0.12 (0.09–0.154)
Water	5.65 (4.59–6.71)	0.34 (0.28–0.39)
Bare soil	23.89 (21.46–26.32)	-

TABLE 2. Average percent cover and height of plant species within the tree stratum in the floodplain of the Colorado River, Mexico. Confidence intervals (95% CI) are shown in parentheses.

Tree species	Mean cover (%)	Mean height (m)
Willow (*Salix* spp.)	5.52 (4.23–6.81)	4.89 (4.49–5.14)
Cottonwood (*Populus* spp.)	1.66 (1.16–2.17)	6.01 (5.39–6.62)
Honey mesquite (*Prosopis glandulosa*)	0.29 (-0.10–0.70)	3.81 (3.36–4.25)
Screwbean mesquite (*Prosopis pubescens*)	0.74 (0.29–1.19)	3.63 (3.37–3.89)
Saltcedar (*Tamarix ramosissima*)	19.36 (16.82–21.90)	3.50 (3.35–3.66)

the most common species were Mourning Dove (*Zenaida macroura*), Red-winged Blackbird (*Agelaius phoeniceus*), Verdin (*Auriparus flaviceps*) and Brown-headed Cowbird (*Molothrus ater*, Table 3), which together comprised 46% of all records. However, 64 species were commonly found (>10 records per visit), including Cliff Swallow (*Petrochelidion pyrrhonota*), Song Sparrow (*Melospiza melodia*), and Abert's Towhee (*Pipilo aberti*, Table 3). Thirty-eight species had <five total records, some of which were accidental or vagrant birds in the area, including Zone-tailed Hawk (*Buteo albonotatus*), White-breasted Nuthatch (*Sitta carolinensis*), Gray Vireo (*Vireo vicinior*), and Red-shouldered Hawk (*Buteo lineatus*), while others were formerly common (Ruiz-Campos and Rodríguez-Meraz 1997, Patten et al. 2001) and now have become rare, such as Lucy's Warbler (*Vermivora luciae*), Bell's Vireo, and Brown-crested Flycatcher (*Myiarchus tyrannulus*).

Average bird abundance was highest in winter ($F_{3,446} = 10.05$, P < 0.001, Tukey-Kramer pairwise comparisons among seasons P < 0.001; Fig. 2). Changes in abundance of Red-winged Blackbirds in the floodplain accounted for up to 65% of the differences in abundances among seasons, because they increased from 88,500 individuals (95% CI = 29,480–265,780, 467 observations, $\chi^2_{480} = 0.52$) in summer, to 1,473,000 individuals (95% CI = 728,285–2,979,750, 5,815 observations; $\chi^2_{89} = 0.48$) in winter, when they were the most common species detected. In addition to the common birds whose numbers remained relatively the same throughout the year, the floodplain received an influx of wintering migrants, such as Ruby-crowned Kinglet (*Regulus calendula*), Yellow-rumped Warbler (*Dendroica coronata*), and Blue-gray Gnatcatcher (*Polioptila caerulea*), which contributed to the higher abundance during this season. However, species richness is lower than in other seasons, because this is the period with less en-route migrants passing through the area (Fig. 2).

The species richness was highest in spring (March–May, $F_{3,446} = 8.89$, P < 0.001, Tukey-Kramer pairwise comparisons among seasons P < 0.02; Fig. 2). This pattern corresponds to the temporary presence of 64 species of neotropical en-route migrants that stop over in the floodplain on their way north, including Northern Rough-winged Swallow (*Stelgidopteryx serripennis*), Wilson's Warbler (*Wilsonia pusilla*), Warbling Vireo (*Vireo gilvus*), Willow Flycatcher, Pacific-slope Flycatcher (*Empidonax difficilis*), Yellow Warbler, Townsend's Warbler (*Dendroica townsendi*) and Western Tanager (*Piranga ludoviciana*). The pattern is also influenced by the arrival of 14 species of locally breeding migrants, arriving from their wintering grounds (Fig. 2).

During summer, the avifauna in the floodplain is composed of resident species and breeding seasonal visitors. Species richness and abundance is lower than during spring, as the peak of migration has passed, but there are

TABLE 3. Detections by season and relative dominance of the 10 most common species in the floodplain of the Colorado River, Mexico from May 2002–July 2003.

Species	Spring	Summer	Fall	Winter	Total	Relative dominance
Red-winged Blackbird (*Agelaius phoeniceus*)	2,501	1,178	3,932	9,167	16,778	19.00
Mourning Dove (*Zenaida macroura*)	4,162	4,056	4,072	4,244	16,534	18.72
Verdin (*Auriparus flaviceps*)	1,306	827	627	1,110	3,870	4.38
Brown-headed Cowbird (*Molothrus ater*)	1,892	1,434	71	283	3,680	4.17
Great-tailed Grackle (*Quiscalus mexicanus*)	693	342	803	1,484	3,322	3.76
Song Sparrow (*Melospiza melodia*)	979	392	361	927	2,659	3.01
Abert's Towhee (*Pipilo aberti*)	1,008	538	511	534	2,591	2.93
Cliff Swallow (*Petrochelidion pyrrhonota*)	896	703	0	694	2,293	2.60
Gambel's Quail (*Callipepla gambelii*)	813	382	184	340	1,719	1.95
Yellow-rumped Warbler (*Dendroica coronata*)	3	0	663	844	1,510	1.71

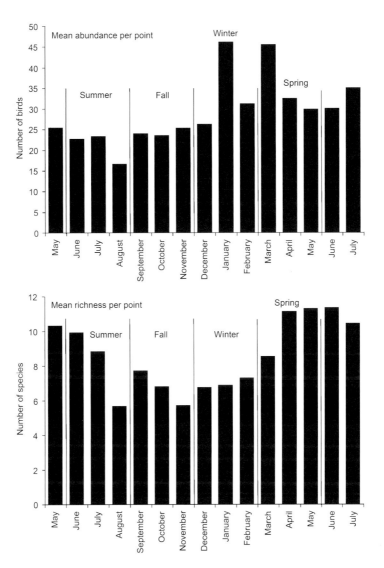

FIGURE 2. Average bird abundance and species richness per point by month in the floodplain of the Colorado River, Mexico, from May 2002–July 2003. Values for abundance are shown on the upper figure and values for richness are shown on the lower figure.

still en-route birds moving through the region, in particular *Empidonax* flycatchers (Fig, 2). The breeding bird community consisted of 61 species (four non-native), including riparian generalists, such as White-winged Dove (*Zenaida asiatica*), Blue Grosbeak (*Passerina caerulea*), Western Kingbird (*Tyrannus verticalis*), Ash-throated Flycatcher (*Myiarchus cinerascens*), and Ladder-backed Woodpecker (*Picoides scalaris*). The community also included riparian specialists, such as Yellow-billed Cuckoo (*Coccyzus americanus*), Vermillion Flycatcher (*Pyrocephalus rubinus*), and Yellow-breasted Chat (*Icteria*

virens), marsh breeders, such as Clapper Rail (*Rallus longirostris*), Least Bittern (*Ixobrychus exilis*), and Marsh Wren (*Cistothorus palustris*), and waterbirds, such as Cinnamon Teal (*Anas cyanoptera*), Snowy Egret (*Egretta thula*), and Black-necked Stilt (*Himantopus mexicanus*).

Brown-headed Cowbirds are resident in the Colorado River delta-Mexicali Valley area. However, they exhibit regional movements almost disappearing in late fall and winter (i.e., no records in November and four records in December). Their numbers increase dramatically in summer with an estimate of

105,400 individuals in the floodplain (95% CI = 84,400– 131,700, N = 757, χ^2_{370} = 0.35). The abundance of Brown-headed Cowbirds in the floodplain during the breeding season probably causes significant impacts on the productivity of riparian songbirds (Rosenberg et al. 1991).

The indices in general for the avian community in the floodplain are lower in the fall than in the other seasons, as most of the breeding residents start their southbound migration, and the influx of transient birds is not as high as during the spring, in both abundance and richness (Fig. 2).

HABITAT RELATIONSHIPS

Pooling the data from all seasons, the proportion of the landscape covered in surface water explained a significant amount of the variation in species richness (Table 4). When analyzing relationships for each season, the pattern was similar ($r^2 > 0.37$, P < 0.001). During the summer, cottonwood cover was also positively correlated with species richness (Table 4).

Considering the data pooled for all seasons, the variability in bird density was explained mostly by variations in the proportion of surface water and screwbean mesquite (*Prosopis pubescens*), both habitat features being positively correlated with avian densities (Table 4). When analyzing relationships for each season, the pattern during spring, fall, and winter was similar to that above ($r^2 > 0.22$, P < 0.03). Surface water remained important in explaining variation in bird densities during summer; but the other important habitat feature, replacing screwbean mesquite, was the percent cover of willows (Table 4).

DISCUSSION

The flows that have reached the floodplain of the Colorado River in Mexico in the last 25 yr have regenerated limited but important stands of native riparian vegetation, despite the previous dominance of saltcedar (Zamora-Arroyo et al. 2001, Nagler et al. 2005). Although causality has not been established, our results and the descriptions of the riparian community prior to flooding events (Ruiz-Campos and Rodríguez-Meraz 1997, Patten et al. 2001) suggest that the bird community has responded accordingly. Alternatively, we may be detecting more remnant bird species than expected.

Assuming that our estimates of avian indices and those from the Lower Colorado in the US (Anderson et al. 1983) are comparable and unbiased, we calculate that species richness is similar, but that densities are an order of magnitude higher in Mexico than in the US (Fig. 2). In addition, although the influence of the adjacent agricultural areas and long-lasting degradation are evident along the Colorado River in Mexico, the floodplain continues to support large populations of many species of riparian birds, many of which are protected species or are targets of continental or regional bird conservation plans (Hinojosa-Huerta et al. 2004). The floodplain also functions as an important migration link between breeding and non-breeding grounds for Neotropical migratory landbirds and some waterbirds. During spring, the floodplain provides a migration connection between the coast of the Gulf of California and the Colorado River corridor, also serving as a stopover area for birds that migrate through coastal and central California (Ecton 2003).

TABLE 4. EFFECTS AND COEFFICIENT RESULTS OF THE MULTIPLE REGRESSION MODELS OF AVIAN RICHNESS AND DENSITY AGAINST HABITAT FEATURES IN THE FLOODPLAIN OF THE COLORADO RIVER IN MEXICO, MAY 2002–JULY 2003.

Response variable/Effect	r^2	F	Coefficient	SE	Standard coefficient	t	P
Bird species richness	0.45	24.83					<0.001
Constant			20.74	1.34	0	15.49	<0.001
Water			0.84	0.17	0.67	4.98	<0.001
Bird species richness summer	0.53	17.4					<0.001
Constant			19.89	1.07	0	18.55	<0.001
Water			0.63	0.12	0.65	5.09	<0.001
Cottonwoods (*Populus* spp.)			0.32	0.13	0.32	2.49	0.02
Bird density	0.28	6.63					0.005
Constant			22.50	9.38	0	2.40	0.02
Water			2.74	1.07	0.41	2.57	0.02
Screwbean mesquite (*Prosopis* spp.)			4.21	1.45	0.46	2.90	0.01
Bird density summer	0.31	7.44					0.003
Constant			9.75	7.50	0	1.30	0.20
Water			1.84	0.73	0.39	2.54	0.02
Willows (*Salix* spp.)			1.83	0.61	0.47	3.01	0.01

Species that were considered extirpated in this region, such as Yellow-billed Cuckoo, Vermillion Flycatcher, and Clapper Rail (Ruiz-Campos and Rodriguez-Meraz 1997, Patten et al. 2001) were found to be regularly present and presumably breeding in the floodplain during our study. Although no controlled bird surveys were performed before and after the regeneration events, the historic information on vegetation dynamics in the area during the last 25 yr (Glenn et al. 1996, Glenn et al. 2001, Zamora-Arroyo et al. 2001) shows that habitat for these species disappeared from the floodplain. It is reasonable to assume that these birds returned as breeders after the regeneration of the riparian ecosystem vegetative communities.

However, not all historically present breeding species occur in the floodplain (e.g., Southwestern Willow Flycatcher, Elf Owl [*Micrathene whitneyi*], and Summer Tanager [*Piranga rubra*]). In some cases, this could be attributed to the overall status of the population, and not to the lack of appropriate habitat features in the area, as might be the case for the Southwestern Willow Flycatcher. The floodplain appears to have adequate vegetation features (young stands of willows and saltcedar with very dense mid- and understory, near shallow water areas) for breeding Southwestern Willow Flycatchers (Sogge et al. 1997), but source populations may simply be too small or too distant to colonize recently restored areas. In other cases, the lack of certain vegetation attributes might preclude the colonization of some species. For example, Summer Tanager, Lucy's Warbler, Bell's Vireo, Yellow Warbler, and Elf Owl, require older, mature trees and/or cavities that do not currently exist in the floodplain (Rosenberg et al. 1991). Although the floodplain supports significant riparian forests, the estimated median age of cottonwoods and willows is 3 yr, with a rapid turnover rate due to the prevalence of human-induced disturbance events, particularly logging, fire, and flood-prevention clear cuttings (Nagler et al. 2005). Thus, stands of older trees (>8 yr old) are missing.

Both ground and surface water have been long recognized as the foundation upon which riparian ecosystems function. Water is not only valuable as a base flow to maintain the vegetation and as pulse-flood events to maintain dynamics and enhance recruitment, it is also a land cover feature (surface water) that provides habitat for a variety of species and promotes primary productivity and insect biomass (Naiman et al. 2005). In our study, the presence of surface water was a significant predictor of both species richness and abundance, regardless of vegetation type or other land cover features.

Since surface water was a less common feature prior to the flooding events (Glenn et al. 1996, Zamora-Arroyo et al. 2001), it is reasonable to assume that the avian indices were lower then than during our study.

As expected, native trees had a positive association with the avian indices, particularly during the breeding season. Saltcedar was dominant in the upper, saltier and drier terraces, but cottonwood and willow appear to survive and reproduce successfully when adequate water is present, even where saltcedar is common (Sher et al. 2000, Stromberg and Chew 2002, Nagler et al. 2005). As with surface water, the cover of native trees was scarcer prior to the flooding events (Zamora-Arroyo et al. 2001, Nagler et al. 2005), thus it is probable that bird abundance and richness were lower then, and that the indices were enhanced at the time of our study.

The areas dominated by cottonwoods and willows still had significant cover of saltcedar, but mostly as a mid- or understory species, adding structural diversity to a site. Similar results were found in a Mojave Desert watershed, where bird diversity was not affected by the invasion of saltcedar, and the avian indices were best modeled by total vegetation volume and structural diversity (Fleishman et al. 2003).

Of major concern with respect to restoration is the screwbean mesquite, which only represents a small fraction of the vegetation cover in the floodplain, and yet is an important predictor of bird density. The proportion of mesquite in the landscape has probably been widely reduced, as it once occupied elevated terraces adjacent to the cottonwood-willow forests (Stromberg and Chew 2002). These areas are now converted into agriculture, or otherwise have become too saline for mesquite and are dominated by sparse saltcedar shrubs.

Prior to this study, no active eradication of saltcedar or restoration projects (e.g., reforestation with native riparian trees) was conducted in the floodplain of the Colorado River in Mexico. Yet, significant patches of native riparian vegetation and wetlands have naturally regenerated in response to flooding events and modest instream flows (Zamora-Arroyo et al. 2001, Nagler et al. 2005). It is reasonable to conclude that the characteristics of the bird community and the current avian indices in the floodplain are also primarily a function of the hydrologic events.

Based on the response of riparian vegetation to restored hydrologic regimes (Stromberg and Chew 2002, Glenn and Nagler 2005, Nagler et al. 2005), and considering the avian-habitat relationships we observed, we propose several key strategies to maintain and enhance habitat values for birds in the Colorado River floodplain in Mexico: (1) a base flow should be secured, to maintain existing native vegetation and maximize surface water (see Glenn et al. 2001 for details), (2) pulse-flood events should be allocated to maintain dynamism and the regeneration of native trees, (3) human-induced disturbances (fires and logging) should be avoided or minimized in the floodplain, especially if they prevent the establishment of older stands of cottonwood and willow, and (4) active manipulation may be needed to re-establish mesquite-dominated terraces.

The Colorado River basin has experienced below-average precipitation in the last 5 yr (Balling and Goodrich 2007). This has resulted in new research and analyses and has sparked discussions about shortage criteria for water deliveries in the lower basin states and into Mexico (USDI Bureau of Reclamation 2007). At the same time, water demands in the basin in the US and Mexico continue to increase (Barnett et al. 2004). Under this scenario, the probability of having unplanned flood events into the Colorado River delta has been drastically reduced (Christensen et al. 2004). Yet, several water resource management alternatives have been designed and initiated to guarantee an allocation of water to restore and maintain the Colorado River delta. These strategies include the creation of a water trust and the acquisition of water rights in Mexico to secure an instream flow (Gutiérrez-Lacayo and Hinojosa-Huerta 2007). Other strategies include guaranteeing a portion of the outflow of wastewater treatment plants for wetland restoration, as well as the dedication of agricultural drainage for this purpose (Hinojosa-Huerta et al. 2007).

Our study provides information on the status of the birds in the floodplain of the Colorado River in Mexico during a 15 mon period. We show the characteristics of an avian community and its habitat relationships in a riparian area where the vegetation was regenerated after flooding events. The patterns we observed for population levels and community structure of birds are likely to change throughout the years as characteristics in the floodplain change due to variations in water flows, restoration efforts, drought, fire, and other events. Monitoring efforts in the floodplain to document variations in numbers, species richness, and community structure of birds in relation to vegetation dynamics, water flows, and restoration efforts will provide critical information to develop better management strategies to protect and recover birds in riparian areas.

ACKNOWLEDGEMENTS

Our special gratitude is expressed to Juan Butrón, José Juan Butrón, Mauricio Butrón, Jaqueline García, Victor Ortega, Juan Rivera, Gerardo Sánchez, Pablo Valle, Michael Vamstad, Alberto Zepeda, and the numerous volunteers that helped during field activities. Our work has been possible thanks to the help of Sacha Heath, Chris McCreedy, Roy Churchwell and Steve Latta (Point Reyes Bird Observatory), Robert Mesta (Sonoran Joint Venture), Yamilett Carrillo, Meredith de la Garza and Raquel Castro (Pronatura Sonora), Consejo Nacional de Ciencia y Tecnología (CONACyT), the National Fish and Wildlife Foundation and the Wallace Foundation. Comments from Courtney Conway, Kevin Fitzsimmons, Edward Glenn, William Mannan, and William Shaw provided insight for the analysis and discussion.

POPULATION TRENDS AND ECOLOGY OF GRASSLAND BIRDS

Mountain Plover (*Charadrius montanus*) © David J. Krueper

Studies in Avian Biology No. 37:84–100

INFLUENCE OF DESERTIFICATION ON SITE OCCUPANCY BY GRASSLAND AND SHRUBLAND BIRDS DURING THE NON-BREEDING PERIOD IN THE NORTHERN CHIHUAHUAN DESERT

M. Sofia Agudelo, Martha J. Desmond, and Leigh Murray

Abstract. Desertification occurs widely in the southwestern US, but its effects on non-breeding avian communities have been poorly studied. Shrub encroachment is considered a major indicator of desertification. We studied the associations of landscape and vegetation characteristics on grassland and shrubland bird communities in 27 Chihuahuan Desert grassland patches between 2003 and 2006. Overall avian abundance, richness and diversity were low within seasons and across years. Shrubland birds were dominant during the period of study while open grassland species were in low numbers or absent from study sites. In general, variables associated with guild abundance varied among years and seasons due to differences in guild composition. Variables associated with abundance within the grassland guild were more consistent because of lower species diversity and less seasonal and annual turnover within the guild. The most consistent variable predicting grassland bird abundance at the guild level and in single-species models was the number of invasive shrubs, negatively associated with abundance. Grass cover, grass height, and degree of isolation were also important. The shrubland guild was strongly and positively associated with the density of invasive shrubs and the interaction between density of invasive shrubs and patch size, however this was not consistently reflected in the single species models. Some single-species models showed a negative association with invasive shrubs or the interaction between invasive shrubs and patch size indicating that some shrubland birds may be sensitive to levels of shrub encroachment. Single-species models for shrubland birds had variable associations with grass cover and height suggesting differences in vegetative growth among years and foraging strategies influenced site selection. This research suggests shrub encroachment into grasslands degrades grassland quality and influences species composition, making grassland patches unsuitable for open grassland species and possibly altering patch quality for some shrubland birds.

Key Words: avian guilds, Chihuahuan Desert, degree of isolation, desertification, grassland birds, invasive shrubs, landscape, patch size, shrub encroachment, shrubland birds.

LA INFLUENCIA DE LA DESERTIFICACIÓN EN LA SELECCIÓN DE SITIO POR PARTE DE AVES ADAPTADAS A PASTIZALES Y AVES ADAPTADAS A ZONAS ARBUSTIVAS DURANTE LA ÉPOCA NO REPRODUCTIVA EN EL EXTREMO NORTE DEL DESIERTO CHIHUAHUENSE

Resumen. El proceso de desertificación se ha extendido ampliamente en el suroeste de los Estados Unidos, pero sus efectos sobre las comunidades de aves en época no reproductiva han sido poco estudiados. El incremento de plantas arbustivas es considerado como un importante indicador del proceso de desertificación. La asociación del paisaje y la vegetación local con comunidades de aves adaptadas a pastizales y zonas arbustivas durante la época no reproductiva fueron estudiadas en 27 fragmentos de pastizal en el Desierto Chihuahuense entre el 2003 y el 2006, con el fin de documentar los efectos de la degradación del hábitat y la fragmentación como resultado del proceso de desertificación sobre gremios de aves en el suroeste de Los Estados Unidos. La abundancia, riqueza y diversidad total de aves fueron bajas entre estaciones y a través de los años. Las aves adaptadas a zonas arbustivas dominaron a lo largo del periodo de estudio, mientras las especies especialistas de pastizales tuvieron bajas abundancias o estuvieron ausentes en los sitios de estudio. En general, las variables asociadas con la abundancia de gremios de aves, variaron entre años y estaciones, debido a diferencias en la composición de especies dentro de cada gremio. Las variables asociadas con la abundancia del gremio de aves de pastizal fueron más consistentes debido a una diversidad menor de especies y a un cambio menor en la composición de especies dentro de este gremio, entre estaciones y años. La variable más consistente en predecir la abundancia de aves de pastizal al nivel de gremio y de especies individuales, fue el número de arbustos invasores, ejerciendo una asociación negativa con la abundancia. La cobertura y la altura de pastos, junto con el grado de aislamiento del pastizal, fueron también variables importantes. El gremio de aves adaptadas a zonas con arbustivas estuvo fuertemente asociado de manera positiva con la densidad de arbustos invasores y con la interacción entre densidad de arbustos y área del pastizal, sin embargo esta respuesta a nivel de gremio no fue consistente con lo obtenido a nivel de especies individuales. Algunos de los modelos para especies individuales mostraron una asociación negativa con la densidad de arbustos invasores o con la interacción entre densidad de arbustos y área del pastizal, indicando la posible sensibilidad de algunas especies propias de zonas arbustivas, a ciertos niveles de invasión de arbustos. Los modelos individuales para el gremio de aves adaptadas a zonas arbustivas mostraron asociaciones variables con la cobertura y altura de pastos, sugiriendo que diferencias en el crecimiento vegetativo entre años y diferentes estrategias de forrajeo influenciaron la selección del sitio. Este estudio sugiere que el grado de invasión de arbustos dentro del área del pastizal, degrada la calidad del mismo e influye en la composición de especies, convirtiendo estos fragmentos en áreas inhóspitas para aves propias de pastizal y posiblemente alterando la calidad del pastizal para algunas aves propias de zonas arbustivas.

In North America, birds associated with grasslands are exhibiting greater population declines than any other avian assemblage (Knopf 1994, Peterjohn and Sauer 1999, Coppedge et al. 2001). Similarly, 30% of shrubland birds are in decline (Sauer et al. 2006). Many bird species in these guilds are short-distance migrants that breed across the western US and southern Canada and winter in the southwestern US and northern Mexico (Howell and Webb 1995, Rising 2005). Declines have been attributed to various causes including habitat loss, degradation, and fragmentation on wintering, breeding, and migratory grounds due to agricultural activities, urban expansion, livestock grazing, habitat alteration, pesticide use, and climate change (Vickery et al 1999, Holmes and Sherry 2001, Jones and Bock 2002). The majority of research on these declining avian guilds has focused on breeding ecology and considerably less is known about non-breeding ecology, habitat use, and effects of habitat fragmentation and degradation during winter and migration (Helzer and Jelinski 1999, Coppedge et al. 2001).

In general, non-breeding birds have been found to use a wider range of habitats than breeding birds. For example, many migrant species in western Mexico broaden their habitat use in the non-breeding period to include agricultural hedgerows (Villaseñor and Hutto 1995). Seasonal changes in habitat use during stopover in Pennsylvania led Yahner (1993) to hypothesize that migrating birds may be less sensitive to fragmentation. During migration, birds do not have the opportunity to search for the most suitable stopover habitat and may be forced to use sub-optimal sites (Moore et al. 1990). Decisions involving the use of a patch, however, are scale dependent, extending from a landscape level to more local perspectives, and migrants have been found to be selective at the micro-habitat scale (Hutto 1985). Settlement at a stopover site must be driven by some ecological cues, and habitat selection during stopover should be related to the intrinsic suitability of the habitat (Moore and Simmons 1992, Kelly et al. 1999), extrinsic landscape factors (Maurer 1985, Dooley and Bowers 1998),

or a combination of the two. Selection of winter grounds should be driven by similar cues, such as resource availability (Pulliam and Dunning 1987, Ginter and Desmond 2005), but also by patch characteristics including patch size, shape, connectivity, and vegetative composition (Graham and Blake 2001, Pearson and Simons 2002).

In the southwestern US, large expanses of native perennial grasslands have been lost to shrub encroachment (Buffington and Herbel 1965, Brown 1982, Saab et al. 1995, Kerley and Whitford 2000). Where patches of intact grassland persist, these grasslands are frequently fragmented and degraded, with many experiencing various levels of isolation and shrub encroachment (Bahre and Shelton 1993, Reynolds et al. 1999). In the northern Chihuahuan Desert, the percentage of grasslands in the Jornada del Muerto Basin (New Mexico) has declined substantially. In 1858, grasslands comprised more than 80% of the area, whereas today grasses comprise only 7% of the landscape (Gibbens et al. 2005). By 1998, 59% of the area was occupied by honey mesquite (*Prosopis glandulosa*) and 25% by creosote bush (*Larrea tridentata*). The encroachment of shrubs into desert grasslands has irreversibly changed the landscape through the formation of coppice dunes where mesquite shrubs trap wind-blown sand (Gibbens et al. 1983, Gibbens and Beck 1988, Herrick et al. 1997). These landscape changes have resulted in increased runoff and soil erosion and increased invasion by non-native species (Herrick et al. 1997, Havstad et al. 2000).

The large-scale vegetation change occurring in the Chihuahuan Desert has been linked to desertification (Buffington and Herbel 1965, Schlesinger et al. 1990, Schlesinger 2002). Desertification is considered an essentially irreversible process in arid, semi-arid, and dry sub-humid areas where land degradation results from factors that include climatic variation and human activities (United Nations 1992). The reduction and alteration of vegetation cover and structure in the northern Chihuahua Desert has resulted in the formation of coppice dunes, reduced grass cover, and increased heterogeneity in soil resource distribution. This shift in resources and the degradation of the landscape has contributed to a reduction in livestock carrying capacity, a decrease in biodiversity, alteration of nutrient cycling, and increased soil erosion (Nielson 1986, Whitford 1997, 2002). The exact cause of this shift is uncertain; however, excessive livestock grazing, climatic change, and fire suppression have been implicated as possible factors (Fredrickson et al. 1998). While a large body of literature has addressed abiotic factors associated with desertification and vegetation response in the Chihuahuan Desert, little research has addressed the response of vertebrates to the desertification process. Kerley and Whitford (2000) reported an increase in rodent abundance in shrub-encroached systems in the Chihuahuan Desert. Similarly, avian species richness and abundances were higher in desertified habitats due to the combination of species with affiliations to both shrubland and grassland habitats occupying these sites (Whitford 1997). While some grassland species may persist in degraded grasslands, species breeding in open grassland did not occupy degraded sites in south-central New Mexico and these sites have likely experienced a substantial turnover in species composition over the past 150 yr (Pidgeon et al. 2001).

In this study we examined the effects of desertification, including grassland fragmentation, shrub encroachment, and the subsequent reduction and alteration of vegetation cover and structure, on abundance of various grassland and shrubland bird species during the non-breeding period in the northern Chihuahuan Desert. We hypothesized that abundance of grassland and shrubland birds would be associated with factors at both within-patch and landscape scales. At the within-patch scale we predicted that: (1) heterogeneous grasslands (grasslands with higher shrub densities) would support more diverse bird communities than homogeneous grasslands due to the presence of species from both grassland and shrubland guilds, (2) grassland birds would respond negatively and shrubland birds would respond positively to shrub density, and (3) avian abundance and community composition would differ among grassland types. At the landscape scale we predicted that: (1) grassland bird abundance would be positively related to patch size and negatively related to degree of isolation and patch shape, and (2) the shrubland avian community would not be related to landscape characteristics because of the matrix of shrub habitats within which the remaining grassland patches are embedded.

STUDY AREA AND METHODS

STUDY AREA

Research was conducted on the Jornada Experimental Range (JER) and adjacent Chihuahuan Desert Rangeland Research Center (CDRRC) during the non-breeding period for three consecutive years, between September 2003 and May 2006. Together this area comprises a block of 104,166 ha located at the northern edge of the Chihuahuan Desert, in southcentral New Mexico (32°62′N, 106°74′W). The predominant use of these sites is for research related to rangeland and livestock management and long-term studies examining desertification processes in the Chihuahuan Desert. Livestock stocking densities were low across study sites, ranging from 2.6–16.5 animal unit year/section (AUY/S) (E. Fredrickson, pers. comm.). The predominant vegetation types representative of the Jornada del Muerto Basin are grasslands of black grama (*Bouteloua eriopoda*), tobosa (*Pleuraphis mutica*), and dropseed (*Sporobolus* sp.). Dominant native invasive shrubs include creosote bush, honey mesquite, and tarbush (*Flourensia cernua*). Non-invasive native shrubs or shrub-like plants include yucca (*Yucca* sp.), longleaf jointfir (*Ephedra trifurca*), and cholla (*Opuntia* sp.) (Allred 1988, Dick-Peddie et al. 1993, Schlesinger 1994).

The climate in south-central New Mexico typically consists of hot summers and mild winters. The average maximum temperature in June is 36°C; the average minimum temperature in December is -6.8°C. Precipitation averages 23 cm annually, with 52% occurring between July and September. Summer precipitation comes in the form of intense monsoonal thunderstorms that are highly localized (Sims et al. 1978, Conley and Conley 1984). Winter precipitation is less predictable and is characterized by low-intensity precipitation covering wide areas. The elevation of the study area is approximately 1,186 m (Jornada Basin Long Term Ecological Network 2006).

PATCH SELECTION

We selected 27 grassland patches with each of nine patches being dominated by black grama, tobosa, and dropseed species, respectively. To select grassland patches as study sites, we used GIS vegetation maps of the JER and the CDRRC derived from photos and ground reconnaissance; variables included distribution, size, dominant vegetation type, and location of different grassland patches. Patch selection was based on grassland type, topography (Renfrew and Ribic 2002), patch size, patch shape, and degree of isolation (Coleman et al. 1982, With and Crist 1995). Patch size ranged from 6.18 to 684 ha.

When possible, a continuous 1,000 m permanent transect for avian surveys was established centrally within each grassland fragment and marked at 100-m intervals. Due to variation in fragment shape and size, some transects (N = 12) were composed of two or three segments, spaced by a minimum of 65 m (Whitmore 1979). Minimum distance between each 1,000 m transect was 384 m.

AVIAN SURVEYS

In the non-breeding seasons of 2003–2004, 2004–2005, and 2005–2006, study sites were surveyed three times each during the fall (1 September–15 October) and spring migration periods (15 March–30 April) and four times over the winter period (15 November–28 February), with the exception of fall 2004 when no surveys were conducted. This resulted in 2 yr of fall migration data and 3 yr of winter and spring migration data. Surveys of the same patch within a season were spaced at 3 days apart. Censuses were conducted within 4 hr after sunrise (Kirkpatrick et al. 2002). A single observer walked the transect, counting and identifying all birds within 30 m each side of the transect. Birds flying over or detected outside these 60,000 m^2 plots were not included in the analyses (Carlisle et al. 2004). Observers were careful to note the position and movement of birds to avoid double sampling. Surveys were not conducted during precipitation and winds speed exceeding 20 km/hr (Gutzwiller and Barrow 2002).

LANDSCAPE- AND WITHIN-PATCH-LEVEL VARIABLES

For each transect, we recorded a series of within-patch and landscape-level factors. ARC/INFO Software (Environmental Systems Research Institute 1990) was used to determine the area and perimeter of each grassland patch. To account for edge effects, we calculated the patch shape (perimeter-to-area ratio) and the length of disjunct edge types (Bender et al. 1998, Winter et al. 2000), differentiating between two edge types, shrubland edge (edge between the grassland patch and surrounding shrubland) and grassland edge (edge between the grassland patch and a different type of grassland patch), based on ARCVIEW maps. ARCVIEW maps of the study area were also used to calculate the percent of grass cover within 1,500 m

of the perimeter of each grassland patch as a measure of the degree of isolation.

Each winter we sampled 30 vegetation points stratified along each avian transect. Because grazing pressure was low across the study area, with an average of 9.35 (AUY/S) during the study period (E. Fredrickson, pers. comm.), vegetation sampling was conducted once annually following the growing season. We estimated percent canopy cover and percent cover of grass, forbs, and woody vegetation using a Daubenmire frame (Daubenmire 1959). Random and maximum grass heights were also recorded. Random grass height was measured at the closest standing grass and maximum grass height was defined as the tallest standing grass within 1 m of the far left corner of the frame. All shrubs within 1.5 m of each side of the transect were counted and identified, resulting in a measure of shrub density (number of shrubs per 3,000 m^2 within each patch). More specifically, we quantified the density and total number of native invasive shrubs, defined as shrub species (honey mesquite, creosote bush, and tarbush) that have increased substantially in abundance throughout the northern Chihuahuan Desert over the past 50 yr (Rango et al. 2005). The total number of invasive shrubs within a grassland patch was calculated from density of invasive shrubs per unit area multiplied by the area of the grassland patch. The invasive shrubs were the dominant shrub type (>60%) on each patch; on 21 out of the 27 plots greater than 85% of shrubs present were invasive.

STATISTICAL ANALYSIS

All landscape- and within-patch-level predictor variables were tested for normality and homogeneity of variance prior to the analysis, and nonparametric tests were used since assumptions could not be met. Differences in structural characteristics of the vegetation among the three grassland types were examined using the Kruskal-Wallis test. Bird abundance, species richness and Shannon-Weaver diversity indices (Zar 1999) were calculated at the within-patch level for each avian guild. The SPECRICH program (Hines 1996) was used to estimate species richness using the bootstrapping approach, to avoid bias by species detected only on a few occasions (Burnham and Overton 1979). Avian abundance, richness, diversity, and the abundance of grassland and shrubland birds were compared among the three grassland types using the Kruskal-Wallis test (denoted by H_1), by season and year. We also compared vegetation variables among years and grassland types using the Kruskal-Wallis test.

Predictive analyses by individual species were difficult due to low sample sizes and a bimodal distribution of species numbers. Therefore we grouped species into shrubland and grassland assemblages and also attempted to model the dominant species for each guild for data analyses (Appendix 1). Guild composition was determined based on available information on non-breeding habitat associations (Raitt and Pimm 1976, Grzybowski 1982, Igl and Ballard 1999, Niemela 2002, Desmond 2004, Desmond et al. 2005), personal observations of scientists (M. Desmond, D. Griffin, C. Mendez, R. Meyer, and D. Krueper) familiar with non-breeding grassland and shrubland birds in the Southwest, and on information on breeding habitat associations (American Ornithologists' Union 1998, Sauer et al. 2006).

We selected a subset of landscape- and within-patch-level variables from the set of all measured explanatory variables predicted to have the greatest influence on assemblage abundances. These variables were selected based on important breeding habitat described in the literature, since literature addressing the importance of these predictor variables during the non-breeding season is limited, and relevance to ecological change in the southwest. The landscape-level variables considered for inclusion in the models were: (1) patch size, (2) patch shape, (3) degree of isolation, and (4) grassland type. The within-patch level variables were: (1) density of invasive shrubs, (2) mean percent grass cover, (3) mean random grass height, and (4) interaction between density of invasive shrubs and patch size. Patch shape was correlated with patch size (Pearson $r^2 =$ 0.83, $P < 0.001$) and therefore only patch size was retained in models. Of all shrubs counted on plots, >60% were invasive shrubs. Dominant non-invasive shrubs were species not known to influence avian abundance (longleaf joint-fir, prickly pear, and yucca), therefore, we felt invasive shrubs would have the greatest impact on avian occupancy of a plot and we chose to include this variable in models as a measure of desertification. Grassland type was not included in the models because no difference in bird guild abundance, species richness or diversity, were detected among grassland types (Kruskal-Wallis, $P > 0.05$).

We performed Poisson multiple regression analyses to examine factors affecting shrubland and grassland avian abundances (count data) separately, by evaluating a set of 15 a priori balanced models, where each one of the chosen variables was represented an equal number of times (Table 1). These models represented hypotheses based on previous knowledge of habitat selection by wintering grassland and shrubland birds and the specific hypotheses of this study (Anderson and Burnham 2002). The number of parameters allowed in each model was limited by the sample size of N = 27 and did not exceed six. Only two-way interaction terms were included.

We evaluated possible over-dispersion of Poisson models using the ratio of deviance/degrees of freedom (Littell et al. 2002) and models with severe over-dispersion (greater than one) were not considered further. Subsequently, we used Akaike's information criterion corrected for small sample sizes and over-dispersed data ($QAIC_c$) for model ranking of the

TABLE 1. A PRIORI MODELS TESTED IN THE POISSON MULTIPLE REGRESSION ANALYSIS TO TEST RELATIONSHIPS BETWEEN AVIAN ABUNDANCES BY GUILD AND SELECTED PREDICTOR VARIABLES. MODEL PARAMETERS INCLUDE DENSITY OF INVASIVE SHRUBS, MEAN PERCENT GRASS COVER, PATCH SIZE, ISOLATION (DEFINED BY PERCENT GRASS COVER WITHIN 1,500 M OF THE GRASSLAND PERIMETER), MEAN RANDOM GRASS HEIGHT, AND THE INTERACTION OF DENSITY OF INVASIVE SHRUBS AND PATCH SIZE.

Model
Invasive shrubs, mean percent grass cover, mean random grass height, patch size, isolation, invasive shrubs x patch size.
Invasive shrubs.
Invasive shrubs, mean percent grass cover, mean random grass height.
Mean percent grass cover, mean random grass height.
Invasive shrubs x patch size.
Isolation, invasive shrubs x patch size.
Mean percent grass cover, mean random grass height, invasive shrubs x patch size.
Mean random grass height, patch size, invasive shrubs x patch size.
Isolation, invasive shrubs, invasive shrubs x patch size.
Isolation, mean percent grass cover, invasive shrubs x patch size.
Patch size, invasive shrubs.
Patch size, isolation.
Invasive shrubs, patch size, isolation.
Invasive shrubs, patch size, mean percent grass cover, mean random grass height.
Patch size, mean percent grass cover, mean random grass height, isolation.

a priori models (Burnham and Anderson 1998). A model containing main effects and relevant interactions was used as the global model for each season, by avian guild and common species (Anderson et al. 1994). Candidate models were evaluated using model weight (w_i) and $\Delta QAIC_c$. We determined the five most parsimonious models for each guild and dominant species by season and year and calculated the deviance, $QAIC_c$, $\Delta QAIC_c$ and Akaike weights. However, in the interest of space, we only report the top three models in our tables. The relative importance of the predictor variables across the top five models ($w + (j)$) was estimated by summing Akaike weights across the models in which each variable (j) was present. In our discussion we focus on variables with cumulative model weight of 0.5 and higher. The GENMOD procedure in SAS (SAS Institute 1999) was used to fit the Poisson regression.

RESULTS

Long-term mean precipitation for the study area (1992–2002) was 24.18 cm (Jornada Basin Long Term Ecological Network 2006). Mean precipitation in 2003 was low compared to the long-term average and relative to precipitation recorded in 2004 and 2005. Precipitation for 2004 was the highest; total annual values of 12.06 cm, 35.53 cm, and 21.81 cm were recorded for 2003, 2004, and 2005, respectively. Average winter temperatures during the study period were 7.9°C, 8.5°C, and 8.9°C for 2003–2004, 2004–2005, and 2005–2006, respectively.

Structural characteristics of the vegetation differed among the three winters, including mean percent canopy cover ($H_1 = 24.61$, P = 0.0001), mean percent grass cover ($H_1 = 6.90$, P = 0.031), mean percent forb cover ($H_1 = 18.57$, P < 0.0001) and mean maximum grass height ($H_1 = 11.93$, P = 0.0025), with all variables lowest in 2003–2004. For all years, differences were found among the three grassland types in mean percent canopy cover ($H_1 = 9.46$, P = 0.009; $H_1 = 7.70$, P = 0.02; $H_1 = 8.13$, P = 0.01, for 2004, 2005, and 2006, respectively) and mean percent grass cover ($H_1 = 7.62$, P = 0.02; $H_1 = 7.19$, P = 0.02; $H_1 = 10.40$, P = 0.005, for 2004, 2005, and 2006 respectively). Dropseed grasslands accounted for the lowest averages in mean percent canopy and grass cover. No differences were found in the number and density of invasive shrubs among years or grassland types.

AVIAN SURVEYS

In the entire 2003–2004 non-breeding period, 60 bird species were recorded on plots compared to 75 species for 2005–2006. Fifty bird species were recorded during winter and spring 2004–2005. Species richness was significantly different among seasons in all years ($H_1 = 21.05$, P < 0.0001 for 2003-2004; $H_1 = 5.73$, P = 0.01 for 2004–2005; $H_1 = 6.15$, P = 0.04 for 2005–2006), with two to three times more species observed during migration than winter (Table 2). Total avian abundance in spring was significantly different among years ($H_1 = 26.39$, P < 0.0001), with higher abundance during spring of 2006 compared to the springs of 2004 and 2005 (Table 2). Avian abundance in winter was significantly different among years ($H_1 = 20.13$, P < 0.0001), with the winter of 2005–2006 supporting significantly more birds than any other winter (Table 2). Fall abundance was significantly different between years ($H_1 = 26.39$, P = 0.001), with twice the number of birds observed in fall of 2005 than in 2003 (Table 2). Avian diversity was low across all seasons (Table 2).

Mean abundance of grassland and shrubland birds varied among the three non-breeding periods—fall migration, winter, and spring migration. Abundance of shrubland birds was significantly higher than grassland species across all seasons and years except for the fall 2003 when the difference was not significant ($H_1 = 0.40$, P = 0.57; $H_1 = 6.69$, P = 0.001 for falls 2003 and 2005, respectively; $H_1 = 6.60$, P = 0.01; $H_1 = 10.29$, P = 0.001; $H_1 = 14.43$, P = 0.0001 for winters 2003–2004, 2004–2005, and 2005–2006, respectively; $H_1 = 6.01$, P = 0.01; $H_1 = 11.96$, P = 0.0005; $H_1 = 27.59$, P < 0.0001 for springs 2004, 2005, and 2006, respectively). The fall of 2005 supported greater grassland and shrubland bird abundance and species richness compared to any other season (Table 2). The majority of dominant species (present in >40% of transects) in all years and seasons were shrubland birds. The dominant species during the fall migration period were Horned Lark (*Eremophila alpestris*) and Vesper Sparrow (*Pooecetes gramineus*) in both 2003 and 2005, as well as Loggerhead Shrike (*Lanius ludovicianus*), Brewer's Sparrow (*Spizella breweri*), Black-throated Sparrow (*Amphispiza bilineata*), Sage Sparrow (*Amphispiza belli*), and White-crowned Sparrow (*Zonotrichia leucophrys*) in 2005. The dominant species in all winters was Sage Sparrow, occurring on 46%, 68%, and 70% of transects for the winters of 2003–2004, 2004–2005, and 2005–2006, respectively. In the winter of 2004–2005, Horned Lark, Brewer's Sparrow and meadowlark species (*Sturnella* sp.) were also dominant (Appendix 1). During spring migration, Black-throated Sparrow was the dominant species each year (on 68%, 46%, and 74% of transects for 2004, 2005, and 2006, respectively). In addition,

TABLE 2. WITHIN-PATCH MEAN RELATIVE AVIAN ABUNDANCE ± SD, DIVERSITY AND RICHNESS BY YEAR AND SEASON FOR EACH OF THE 60,000 M² PLOTS.

	Fall		Winter			Spring		
	2003	2005	2003–2004	2004–2005	2005–2006	2004	2005	2006
Grassland birds	3.36 ± 4.86	4.98 ± 1.92	0.30 ± 0.66	0.72 ± 0.96	1.38 ± 0.36	0.96 ± 1.20	0.84 ± 1.32	1.32 ± 0.48
Shrubland birds	4.32 ± 3.96	9.78 ± 2.52	1.62 ± 2.16	3.42 ± 3.00	6.12 ± 1.62	2.28 ± 1.92	3.60 ± 4.80	8.46 ± 2.04
Abundance	7.74 ± 5.88	14.76 ± 3.66	1.92 ± 2.22	3.90 ± 3.00	7.50 ± 1.80	3.30 ± 2.04	4.44 ± 3.00	9.78 ± 1.98
Diversity	0.06	0.08	0.02	0.03	0.04	0.04	0.04	0.05
Richness	6.02 ± 1.50	4.94 ± 1.49	1.30 ± 0.75	0.74 ± 0.36	2.26 ± 0.76	3.34 ± 1.19	2.82 ± 1.16	4.24 ± 1.03

in 2006 Mourning Dove (*Zenaida macroura*), Western Kingbird (*Tyrannus verticalis*), Horned Lark, Brewer's Sparrow, and White-crowned Sparrow were also dominant.

LANDSCAPE- AND WITHIN-PATCH-LEVEL ASSOCIATIONS

Avian abundances (total and by guilds), richness and diversity did not differ among the three grassland types (Kruskal-Wallis, $P > 0.05$) within each season and year. Poisson regression models included within-patch and landscape scale variables for grassland and shrubland bird guilds and the most abundant or dominant species per guild (Tables 3–6).

Grassland bird-guild models

Density of invasive shrubs, degree of isolation, mean percent grass cover, and mean random grass height were the most consistent variables associated with the abundance of grassland birds across sampling periods (Table 3). These variables consistently had the highest cumulative model weights (Table 7). Density of invasive shrubs, the most consistent variable present in models, was negatively associated with grassland bird abundance across years and seasons, except in winter 2005–2006. In winter 2003–2004, spring 2004, and spring 2005 this variable was present in three–five of the top models for each season with cumulative model weights ranging from 0.59–1.00. Degree of isolation was negatively associated with the abundance of grassland birds across years and seasons (lower bird abundance on grassland patches surrounded by less grassland), except spring 2006. This variable was most important during fall 2003 and spring 2004 with cumulative model weights of 1.00 and 0.76, respectively.

Mean percent grass cover was an important variable associated with grassland bird abundance in several models across seasons and years. In the fall 2005, winter of 2003–2004, and spring 2006, this variable was present in all five models with cumulative model weights of 1.00. Across seasons this variable had a positive association with grassland bird abundance, except for the winter 2003–2004 (Table 3). Mean random grass height was strongly associated with abundance of grassland birds in the same models as the mean percent grass cover; negatively associated with abundance in the fall 2005 and winter of 2003–2004, and positively associated with abundance in the spring of 2006 (Table 3), with cumulative model weights of 1.00 for these seasons (Table 7).

TABLE 3. Top three a priori models for the grassland bird guild by season and year. explanatory variables are: density of invasive shrubs (IS), mean percent grass cover (GC), patch size (PS), isolation (I), mean random grass height (GH), and interaction of density of invasive shrubs and patch size (IS x PS). Sample size n = 27. Top five a priori models were used for analyses but only the top three are presented.

Season/year/models	Dev/df	QAIC$_c$	ΔQAIC$_c$	w_i
Fall 2003				
-I -IS x PS	11.50	-82.41	0.00	0.30
-PS -I	11.50	-82.40	0.02	0.30
-IS -PS -I	11.11	-81.58	0.83	0.20
Fall 2005				
+GC -GH +IS x PS	8.20	-212.83	0.00	0.39
+GC -GH	8.69	-212.76	0.07	0.37
-IS +GC -GH	8.88	-210.78	2.05	0.14
Winter 2003–2004				
-IS -GC -GH	2.75	10.31	0.00	0.45
-GC -GH -IS x PS	2.94	11.80	1.49	0.21
-GC -GH	3.14	11.96	1.65	0.20
Winter 2004–2005				
-IS x PS	4.84	-5.95	0.00	0.37
-IS	4.97	-5.32	0.63	0.27
+GC -GH	4.85	-4.48	1.47	0.18
Winter 2005–2006				
+IS	6.50	-24.59	0.00	0.36
+IS x PS	6.59	-24.28	0.31	0.31
-PS +IS	6.72	-22.39	2.19	0.12
Spring 2004				
-I -IS -IS x PS	3.63	-18.34	0.00	0.38
-IS -PS -I	3.65	-18.22	0.13	0.35
-IS +GC –GH	3.84	-16.98	1.36	0.19
Spring 2005				
-IS	3.22	3.42	0.00	0.54
-PS -IS	3.34	5.72	2.30	0.17
-IS +GC –GH	3.13	6.37	2.95	0.12
Spring 2006				
+GC +GH	3.62	-43.38	0.00	0.46
+PS +GC +GH +I	3.45	-41.51	1.87	0.18
-IS +GC +GH	3.71	-41.27	2.11	0.16

Grassland bird-species models

Horned Lark was consistently the most abundant and dominant grassland species on plots across seasons and years (Appendix 1). Similar to the guild models, Horned Lark abundance was most strongly associated with invasive shrubs (negatively except in winter 2005–2006), degree of isolation, mean percent grass cover (positive), and mean random grass height (mix of positive and negative associations; Table 4). Degree of isolation was strongly and negatively associated with abundance in fall 2003, spring 2004, and spring 2005.

Shrubland bird-guild models

Density of invasive shrubs and the interaction between density of invasive shrubs and patch size were the most consistent variables associated with shrubland bird abundance across seasons and years (Table 5). The density of invasive shrubs was positively associated with shrubland bird abundance in all seasons and years with the exception of spring 2004 and winter 2004–2005. This variable had a particularly strong association with shrubland birds in the fall 2003 and spring 2006, with cumulative model weights of 0.50 and 0.88, respectively (Table 7). The interaction between density of invasive shrubs and patch size was also strongly associated with shrubland bird abundance with cumulative model weights for fall 2005, winter 2005–2006, spring 2004 and spring 2005 ranging between 0.51 and 0.82 (Table 7). This variable was positively associated with shrubland bird abundance in all seasons and years except spring 2004 when the relationship was negative.

Shrubland bird-species models

Abundance and dominance of shrubland bird species was less consistent across seasons and years than grassland species. Sage Sparrow was consistently the most abundant species in

TABLE 4. Top three a priori models for Horned Lark. Explanatory variables are: density of invasive shrubs (IS), mean percent grass cover (GC), patch size (PS), isolation (I), mean random grass height (GH), and interaction of density of invasive shrubs and patch size (IS x PS). Sample size n = 27. Top five a priori models were used for analyses but only the top three are presented.

Season/year/models	Dev/df	QAIC$_c$	ΔQAIC$_c$	w_i
Fall 2003				
-IS +PS -I	4.96	-12.92	0.00	0.37
-I -IS +IS x PS	4.98	-12.85	0.07	0.36
-IS x PS	6.07	-11.02	1.90	0.15
Fall 2005				
+GC -GH	11.00	-56.82	0.00	0.42
-IS +GC -GH	11.00	-55.21	1.61	0.19
-I +GC -IS x PS	11.07	-55.08	1.75	0.18
Winter 2004–2005				
-IS	5.64	7.06	0.00	0.44
-PS -IS	5.44	7.66	0.60	0.27
+GC -GH	5.67	8.60	1.53	0.16
Winter 2005–2006				
+IS	4.11	2.64	0.00	0.32
+IS x PS	8.29	2.87	0.23	0.29
-PS -I	8.23	4.06	1.42	0.16
Spring 2004				
-I -IS -IS x PS	3.46	-9.08	0.00	0.48
-IS -PS -I	3.63	-7.56	1.53	0.23
-IS +GC -GH -PS -I +IS x PS	3.04	-7.24	1.84	0.19
Spring 2005				
-IS +GC -GH	1.13	9.04	0.00	0.55
-IS +GC -GH -PS -I +IS x PS	0.90	9.41	0.38	0.45
-IS	1.67	21.61	12.57	0.001
Spring 2006				
-IS +GC +GH	2.89	-5.87	0.00	0.35
+GC +GH	3.07	-5.64	0.24	0.31
-IS -PS +GC +GH	2.85	-4.60	1.27	0.18

all three winters (Appendix 1). Mean percent grass cover negatively, and mean random grass height positively, were associated with Sage Sparrow abundance across winters (Table 6), with cumulative model weights ranging from 0.48–1.00 (Table 7). Black-throated Sparrow was dominant and abundant over fall and spring migration. Vegetation structure was most strongly associated with abundance in fall. Mean random grass height negatively impacted abundance in both years (cumulative model weights ranging from 0.62–1.00); mean percent grass cover negatively impacted abundance in fall 2003 and positively impacted abundance in fall 2005 (Table 6). The interaction between invasive shrub density and patch size (total number of shrubs) was most influential in spring, showing a negative association with Black-throated Sparrow abundance (cumulative model weights ranging from 0.40–0.59).

DISCUSSION

As predicted, heterogeneous grasslands did support a greater diversity of birds. This was mainly due to the greater diversity of shrubland

species occupying shrub-encroached grass-lands. In addition, some grassland species, such as meadowlark species and Horned Lark have been found to exhibit flexibility, occupying both open grasslands and shrub-invaded grasslands (Whitford 1997). However, our observations that Horned Lark was, in general, negatively associated with invasive shrubs (except winter 2005–2006) conflicts with Whitford (1997) and may emphasize differences in habitat associations for breeding compared to non-breeding Horned Lark.

We predicted that landscape-scale variables such as patch size, shape, and degree of isolation would impact migratory and wintering grassland birds in a way similar to observed effects on breeding grounds (Graham and Blake 2001, Pearson and Simons 2002). However, we did not observe important grassland bird associations with patch size or shape. This could be related to differences in landscape fragmentation on breeding and non-breeding grounds or to differences in the response of breeding and non-breeding grassland birds to fragmentation. In the Chihuahuan Desert, desertification processes contribute to the fragmentation of

TABLE 5. TOP THREE A PRIORI MODELS FOR THE SHRUBLAND BIRD GUILD BY SEASON AND YEAR. EXPLANATORY VARIABLES ARE: DENSITY OF INVASIVE SHRUBS (IS), MEAN PERCENT GRASS COVER (GC), PATCH SIZE (PS), ISOLATION (I), MEAN RANDOM GRASS HEIGHT (GH), AND INTERACTION OF DENSITY OF INVASIVE SHRUBS AND PATCH SIZE (IS X PS). SAMPLE SIZE N = 27. TOP FIVE A PRIORI MODELS WERE USED FOR ANALYSES BUT ONLY THE TOP THREE ARE PRESENTED.

Season/year/models	Dev/df	$QAIC_c$	$\Delta QAIC_c$	w_i
Fall 2003				
+IS	7.53	-62.88	0.00	0.38
+IS x PS	7.76	-62.26	0.62	0.28
+PS +IS	7.82	-60.61	2.27	0.12
Fall 2005				
+IS x PS	16.25	-187.05	0.00	0.40
+IS	16.59	-186.60	0.46	0.32
+GC -GH	16.47	-185.30	1.75	0.17
Winter 2003–2004				
+IS x PS	8.12	-13.52	0.00	0.35
+IS	8.28	-13.11	0.41	0.29
+PS +I	8.36	-11.44	2.08	0.13
Winter 2004–2005				
-IS	12.53	-73.08	0.00	0.36
+IS x PS	12.79	-72.58	0.50	0.28
+GC +GH	12.34	-72.05	1.03	0.21
Winter 2005–2006				
+IS x PS	22.95	-110.66	0.00	0.44
-GC -GH	22.25	-109.85	0.80	0.29
-GC -GH +IS x PS	22.75	-107.72	2.94	0.10
Spring 2004				
-IS x PS	4.07	-53.49	0.00	0.37
-IS	4.25	-52.53	0.96	0.23
+I -IS x PS	4.10	-51.80	1.69	0.16
Spring 2005				
+IS x PS	7.85	-57.36	0.00	0.49
-I +IS x PS	7.78	-56.07	1.29	0.25
+PS -I	8.02	-55.43	1.93	0.18
Spring 2006				
+IS	11.34	-210.63	0.00	0.54
-PS +IS	11.66	-208.58	2.05	0.19
-GH -PS +IS x PS	11.34	-207.55	3.09	0.12

grasslands by a gradual interspersion of invasive shrubs into remnant grasslands, degrading grassland quality, and making it difficult to identify patch boundaries from surrounding shrublands (Mason et al. 2005). This is substantially different from traditional views of fragmentation where patch edges have distinct boundaries created by agricultural fields and forests that are easily identifiable and have been found to influence avian abundance and species composition (Winter et al. 2000, Davis 2004). The gradual fragmentation and degradation of grasslands in the Chihuahuan Desert appears to have rendered these patches unsuitable for most grassland species, and may explain why landscape-scale factors such as patch size and shape were not more important in this study.

Although not important during winter for grassland species, the degree of patch isolation was important for grassland species during two migratory periods. The lower densities for the grassland bird guild in the most isolated grassland patches (patches surrounded by less grassland) in fall 2003 were heavily influenced by the responses of Horned Lark, which was strongly negatively associated with degree of isolation in fall 2003 and spring 2004 and 2005. Although Horned Lark is a resident species in our study area, our abundance data suggest a large influx of migrants passed through the area in fall 2003, fall 2005 and spring 2004. These data suggest that isolated grassland patches across a highly fragmented landscape may be important stopover sites for Horned Lark, a generalist grassland species. However, the absence of open grassland species suggests these fragments are not suitable stopover sites for grassland specialist species. Consistent with our predictions, we did not observe shrubland bird densities to be associated with any landscape level characteristics.

For guilds and species models, we predicted several responses to within-patch-scale variables. Dominant variables associated with abundance within guilds varied among years and seasons, suggesting that variation in

TABLE 6. TOP THREE A PRIORI MODELS FOR SAGE AND BLACK-THROATED SPARROWS BY SEASON AND YEAR. EXPLANATORY VARIABLES ARE: DENSITY OF INVASIVE SHRUBS (IS), MEAN PERCENT GRASS COVER (GC), PATCH SIZE (PS), ISOLATION (I), MEAN RANDOM GRASS HEIGHT (GH), AND INTERACTION OF DENSITY OF INVASIVE SHRUBS AND PATCH SIZE (IS x PS). SAMPLE SIZE N = 27. TOP FIVE A PRIORI MODELS WERE USED FOR ANALYSES BUT ONLY THE TOP THREE ARE PRESENTED.

Season/year	Model	Dev/df	$QAIC_c$	$\Delta QAIC_c$	w_i
Black-throated Sparrow					
Fall 2003	-GC -GH	1.53	19.56	0.00	0.57
	-GC -GH +IS x PS	1.59	22.04	2.48	0.17
	+IS -GC -GH	1.59	22.07	2.51	0.16
Fall 2005	-IS	4.88	-45.43	0.00	0.38
	+GC -GH	4.69	-45.09	0.34	0.32
	+GC -GH +IS x PS	4.69	-43.58	1.85	0.16
Sage Sparrow					
Winter 2003–2004	-GC +GH	6.06	1.64	0.00	0.38
	-GC +GH +IS x PS	5.86	2.52	0.88	0.24
	-I -GC +IS x PS	5.91	2.68	1.03	0.22
Winter 2004–2005	-IS -GC +GH	7.92	-21.33	0.00	0.41
	-I -IS +IS x PS	8.56	-19.66	1.67	0.18
	-IS +PS -I	8.61	-19.53	1.80	0.17
Winter 2005–2006	-IS x PS	8.30	-29.46	0.00	0.45
	-GC +GH	8.13	-28.50	0.96	0.28
	-GC +GH -IS x PS	8.23	-26.62	2.84	0.11
Black-throated Sparrow					
Spring 2004	+I -IS x PS	2.49	12.79	0.00	0.35
	-PS +I	2.51	13.09	0.30	0.30
	-PS +GC -GH +I	2.30	14.21	1.42	0.17
Spring 2005	-IS x PS	2.24	23.54	0.16	0.31
	+IS	2.24	23.62	0.24	0.30
	-PS +IS	2.23	24.99	1.61	0.15
Spring 2006	-IS x PS	4.18	-10.61	0.00	0.38
	-IS	4.27	-9.97	0.64	0.28
	+I -IS x PS	4.21	-8.82	1.79	0.16

community composition at the guild level had a large influence on avian abundance and how the guild responded to within-patch explanatory variables.

Variables associated with abundance within the grassland guild were more consistent than the shrubland guild because of lower species diversity and less seasonal and annual turnover within this guild. The negative association of this guild with shrub encroachment is consistent with our predictions and with the literature for many grassland species (Whitmore 1981, Herkert 1994, Coppedge et al. 2001, Desmond 2004); it is most strongly reflected in the single species models for Horned Lark. This suggests that some patches were sufficiently degraded by shrub encroachment that even a grassland generalist species, such as the Horned Lark, avoided them. The mainly positive association of this guild with grass cover and negative association with grass height is reflected in the single species models for Horned Lark, consistent with Desmond et al. (2005), who reported similar results for wintering Horned Lark in Chihuahua, Mexico, and may well be driven by this species due to the lack of diversity in the grassland guild. Other studies, however, have

reported Horned Lark to be associated with heterogeneous grass cover and overgrazing during winter (Beason 1995, Kelly et al. 2006)

The shrubland bird guild was most strongly associated with density of invasive shrubs and the interaction between density of invasive shrubs and patch size, with both variables being positively associated with abundance (except spring 2004 and winter 2004–2005). However this was not consistently reflected in the single species models for Sage Sparrow and Black-throated Sparrow which did not exhibit a consistent association (positive, negative, strong, or weak) with invasive shrub density. These results are not consistent with studies on breeding Sage and Black-throated Sparrows that have found both species to be positively associated with shrub cover (Misenhelter and Rotenberry 2000, Pidgeon et al. 2006). Although the Sage Sparrow was consistently a dominant winter species in our study, the presence of other common species in winters 2003–2004 (Brewer's Sparrow) and 2005–2006 (Chipping Sparrow [*Spizella passerina*] and Lark Bunting [*Calamospiza melanocorys*]) likely influenced habitat associations at the guild level. Similar fluctuations were observed during migration

TABLE 7. RELATIVE IMPORTANCE OF PREDICTOR VARIABLES USED IN A PRIORI MODELS BY CUMULATIVE MODEL WEIGHT. VALUES ARE ORDERED BY AVIAN GUILD AND SEASON. VARIABLES ARE: DENSITY OF INVASIVE SHRUBS (IS), MEAN PERCENT GRASS COVER (GC), PATCH SIZE (PS), ISOLATION (I), MEAN RANDOM GRASS HEIGHT (GH), AND INTERACTION OF DENSITY OF INVASIVE SHRUBS AND PATCH SIZE (IS x PS).

Variable	Fall		Winter			Spring		
	2003	2005	2003–2004	2004–2005	2005–2006	2004	2005	2006
Guild level								
Grassland birds								
PS	0.51	0.10	0.14	0.00	0.23	0.43	0.22	0.22
IS	0.40	0.18	0.59	0.27	0.48	1.00	0.88	0.20
I	1.00	0.10	0.01	0.18	0.22	0.76	0.00	0.22
GC	0.01	1.00	1.00	0.23	0.00	0.27	0.29	1.00
GH	0.01	1.00	1.00	0.18	0.00	0.27	0.29	1.00
IS x PS	0.50	0.43	0.22	0.55	0.42	0.41	0.00	0.20
Individual species level								
Horned Lark								
PS	0.38	0.06	–[a]	0.40	0.26	0.44	0.447	0.34
IS	0.74	0.24	–	0.71	0.32	0.92	1.00	0.60
I	0.85	0.18	–	0.12	0.29	0.98	0.448	0.16
GC	0.12	1.00	–	0.28	0.00	0.29	0.997	1.00
GH	0.01	0.82	–	0.29	0.10	0.21	0.997	1.00
IS x PS	0.63	0.33	–	0.25	0.52	0.75	0.447	0.07
Guild level								
Shrubland birds								
PS	0.23	0.06	0.24	0.00	0.00	0.24	0.18	0.35
IS	0.50	0.32	0.40	0.45	0.09	0.33	0.08	0.88
I	0.22	0.00	0.25	0.00	0.08	0.30	0.51	0.00
GC	0.00	0.22	0.00	0.36	0.56	0.00	0.00	0.15
GH	0.00	0.28	0.00	0.36	0.48	0.00	0.00	0.27
IS x PS	0.39	0.51	0.47	0.34	0.62	0.53	0.82	0.12
Individual species level								
Black-throated Sparrow								
PS	0.10	0.01	–	–	–	0.49	0.39	0.13
IS	0.21	0.52	–	–	–	0.02	0.45	0.28
I	0.05	0.01	–	–	–	1.00	0.15	0.34
GC	1.00	0.62	–	–	–	0.35	0.00	0.05
GH	1.00	0.62	–	–	–	0.19	0.09	0.00
IS x PS	0.17	0.17	–	–	–	0.53	0.40	0.59
Sage Sparrow								
PS	–	–	0.16	0.41	0.00	–	–	–
IS	–	–	0.08	0.87	0.09	–	–	–
I	–	–	0.30	0.35	0.07	–	–	–
GC	–	–	1.00	0.52	0.55	–	–	–
GH	–	–	0.78	0.65	0.48	–	–	–
IS x PS	–	–	0.46	0.31	0.63	–	–	–

[a] not available.

resulting in inconsistent effects of invasive shrubs on guild abundance across years and seasons. This variability suggests that some shrubland species may have a stronger affinity to shrub density than others, but data encompassing the entire range of shrub densities would be necessary to test this. Finally, our measurements focused on the density of invasive shrubs and not the density of total shrubs and it is possible that birds may have been responding more to total shrub density. However, we do not think this is likely because the shrubs not included as invasive shrubs that most strongly influenced total shrub density (longleaf jointfir, prickly pear, and yucca) are not the types of shrubs typically associated with shrubland birds.

Our other measure of invasive shrubs, the interaction between invasive shrub density and patch size, presents an interesting comparison to the associations showed by invasive shrub density. This variable represents the total number of shrubs in a grassland patch. In general, the effect of this variable was consistent with that of invasive shrub density at the guild level, positively associated with the number of shrubland birds, suggesting that the abundance of shrubland birds was higher in grassland patches with a greater number and density of invasive shrubs (except spring 2004). However, results were not consistent for single species models. The observed positive association of Sage Sparrow with the total number of invasive shrubs in winter 2004–2005 but negative association with invasive shrub density indicates a possible sensitivity to shrub density, while the negative association with total number of invasive shrubs in the following winter but no association with density indicates possible avoidance of shrubs. The Black-throated Sparrow had no strong association with the total number of invasive shrubs during fall but was consistently negatively associated with this variable in spring suggesting possible seasonal shrub affiliations. A threshold level of shrub encroachment, beyond which select shrubland species will not occupy a patch, independent of its size may exist, however additional research, that includes shrub dominated plots, would be necessary to address this.

Vegetation variables (grass cover and height) were of little importance for shrubland birds at the guild level but were important in several single species models. The use of guilds may have masked important individual species associations with vegetation variables. Vegetation characteristics were important for Black-throated Sparrow during fall migration only. This species was strongly negatively associated

with mean random grass height in both falls, suggesting Black-throated Sparrow forages in a shrubland with a low stature understory. Sage Sparrow was positively associated with mean random grass height and negatively associated with mean percent grass cover in all three winters suggesting they consistently occupied shrub-dominated grasslands with an understory of tall but heterogeneous grass cover.

Contrary to our predictions, we did not detect differences in avian abundance, richness or diversity among grassland types. Although black grama, tobosa, and dropseed grasslands vary substantially in horizontal and vertical structure we only detected a consistent (not significant) lower species richness in *Sporobolus* sp. grasslands throughout the period of study. This lack of differences among grassland types may, in part, be related to the low avian abundance and richness across seasons and years. In addition, dropseed grasslands may have been dominated by fewer species that were better adapted to foraging on the small seed size produced in this grassland type. Niemela (2002) found a positive correlation between Horned Lark abundance and the production of *Sporobolus* sp. seeds in semidesert grasslands suggesting some species may exploit specific seed types.

Pulliam and Mills (1977) were able to predict the number of dominant species and bill sizes based on seed types in southwest Arizona. In this study, the Horned Lark was the third most abundant species in dropseed grasslands in 2004–2005, and together with Sage and Brewer's Sparrow , comprised >90% of all individuals detected in this grassland type. The distribution and abundance of forbs (not measured in this study) may also have an important role in the distribution and abundance of granivorous sparrows, as forb seeds have been found to be important in the diets of many sparrows (Pulliam 1980, 1986; Desmond et al., *this volume*)

Bird species abundance and dominance, and guild abundance and composition underwent substantial seasonal and among-year fluctuations throughout the period of this study, perhaps partially due to variation in food abundance, a factor not addressed in this study. The majority of species studied are granivorous during the non-breeding season (Raitt and Pimm 1976, Bock and Bock 1999) and are dependent on seed production which can vary by orders of magnitude among years, linked to the amount and pattern of monsoonal summer precipitation (Pulliam and Parker 1979, Dunning and Brown 1982, Niemela 2002). Pulliam and Mills (1977) found the winter sparrow community was more diverse in years when higher precipitation resulted in higher seed production. Similarly, we observed only one dominant resident (Sage Sparrow) when seed availability was likely low due to below normal precipitation, but three–five species when conditions for seed production improved. Pulliam and Dunning (1987) suggested that winter sparrows are facultative migrants only traveling as far south as necessary to find a seed supply capable of supporting them throughout the winter period. Therefore, avian abundance and diversity in the northern portion of wintering grounds (including southern New Mexico) should fluctuate with precipitation patterns as observed in this study. Although we experienced years of high rainfall and associated higher abundance and diversity of birds, we observed an absence of open grassland species (i.e., Grasshopper [*Ammodramus savannarum*], Baird's [*Ammodramus bairdii*], and Savannah [*Passerculus sandwichensis*] Sparrows, Chestnut-collared Longspur [*Calcarius ornatus*], and Sprague's Pipit [*Anthus spragueii*]), despite historical records of their presence in our study area (Jornada Basin Long Term Ecological Network 2006). These species were all common winter migrants occupying grasslands in the vicinity of our study area. The paucity of grassland species despite favorable conditions for seed production, suggests that other conditions rendered these patches unsuitable for occupation by most grassland species.

Migrants have been found to be less selective of habitat characteristics during the non-breeding season (Yahner 1993, Villaseñor and Hutto 1995) and patch quality may not be driving site selection for many species as they head toward wintering or breeding grounds (Moore et al. 1990). This may be particularly pertinent in the spring as through migrants move quickly northward to breeding grounds to acquire territories, but may be confounded by partial migrants that arrive early on breeding territories in our study area (i.e., Black-throated Sparrow and Horned Lark). This, along with differences in precipitation and vegetative growth among years and the foraging strategies of various species, particularly shrubland birds, likely contributed to the variable associations with within-patch characteristics in this study.

Some caution should be exercised when interpreting these results among seasons and years. First, any grouping of avian guilds masks unique life history characteristics associated with individual species (Mannan et al. 1984). For example, both *Ammodramus* sparrows and longspurs are open grassland species. However *Ammodramus* sparrows tend to be solitary and associated with medium to dense grass cover while longspurs are flocking and associated with

vegetation of much shorter stature (Desmond et al. 2005). By pooling species into a guild, some of these associations with within-patch characteristics are lost. Second, this analysis considered only semi-desert grassland fragments in the northern Chihuahuan Desert. Many of these species are widely distributed during the non-breeding period and our study area is in the northern part of the wintering grounds for many grassland and shrubland species. Population patterns observed in this study may be related to conditions in other parts of the non-breeding range of these short distance migrants. For example, Pulliam and Parker (1979) found winter Chipping Sparrow abundance was higher in the Sierra Madre Occidental of Mexico when seed production was poor in southeast Arizona. Finally, abundance alone is a poor indicator of habitat quality. Pidgeon et al. (2006) found Black-throated Sparrow abundance in Chihuahuan Desert grasslands was highest and negatively correlated with fecundity and nest success in mesquite dominated areas; these mesquite encroached habitats acted as ecological traps, suggesting factors other than avian abundance, such as measures of individual condition, should be used to assess suitability of habitat during the non-breeding season.

MANAGEMENT IMPLICATIONS

Desertification is a major conservation issue in the northern Chihuahuan Desert. Grassland patches embedded in a matrix of shrub-dominated landscapes as defined in this study no longer appear to be suitable for many migrant and wintering grassland species requiring open grassland habitat. Shrubland birds may also be sensitive to the density and distribution of invasive shrubs. Thresholds levels may exist beyond which select shrubland species will no longer occupy a patch. Research on shrubland species should address habitat associations and measures of avian condition across a gradient of shrub density and patchiness. Management efforts across the Chihuahuan Desert should identify and protect remaining expanses of desert grasslands that have not been impacted by invasive shrub encroachment. Avian community composition varies substantially among seasons and years apparently due to variation in seed production, and it is essential that suitable habitat exists throughout the non-breeding range of these short-distance migrants. Many grassland and shrubland species winter across the area that extends from southeastern Arizona, through southern New Mexico, and southern Texas, south into the Mexican Plateau to the states of

Zacatecas and San Luis Potosí; a region that has been, and continues to be, strongly impacted by desertification processes.

ACKNOWLEDGMENTS

We are grateful to the staff at the Jornada Long Term Ecological Research Network and the Chihuahuan Desert Rangeland Research Center, including B. Nolen, E. Fredrickson, D. Thatcher, J. Jao, E. García, J. Smith, and M. Thomas for their collaboration and access to the study sites and databases. D. Griffin, H. Henshaw, L. Mason, and J. McNicoll assisted with data collection. We are grateful to A. Lafón-Terrazas, one anonymous reviewer, associate editors T. Brush, D. Krueper, and J. Ruth, and editor C. Marti for their thoughtful and detailed comments that have greatly improved this manuscript. The International Arid Lands Consortium, New Mexico State University, the New Mexico Department of Game and Fish (Share with Wildlife) and the National Science Foundation funded ADVANCE Institutional Transformation Program at New Mexico State University, fund #NSF0123690 provided funding for this research. This is a New Mexico State University Agricultural Experiment Station publication, supported by state funds and the United States Hatch Act.

APPENDIX 1. BIRDS INCLUDED IN THE GRASSLAND AND SHRUBLAND GUILDS. MEAN RELATIVE ABUNDANCE FOR EACH OF THE 60,000 M^2 PLOTS ARE GIVEN FOR EACH SPECIES AND SEASON.

	Fall		Winter			Spring		
	2003	2005	2003–2004	2004–2005	2005–2006	2004	2005	2006
Grassland birds								
Scaled Quail (*Callipepla squamata*)	0.30	0.30	-[a]	-	-	0.01	0.02	0.12
Northern Harrier (*Circus cyaneus*)	0.01	0.04	-	0.02	0.03	-	-	-
Swainson's Hawk (*Buteo swainsoni*)	-	0.03	-	-	-	-	-	0.06
Ferruginous Hawk (*Buteo regalis*)	-	0.01	-	-	-	-	-	-
American Kestrel (*Falco sparverius*)	-	0.04	0.01	-	-	-	0.02	0.01
Prairie Falcon (*Falco mexicanus*)	-	0.01	-	-	-	0.01	-	-
Burrowing Owl (*Athene cunicularia*)	0.06	0.02	-	<0.01	<0.01	0.02	-	0.01
Say's Phoebe (*Sayornis saya*)	0.02	0.06	0.02	-	0.02	0.04	0.01	0.06
Horned Lark (*Eremophila alpestris*)	1.26[b]	9.00[b]	0.18	0.54[b]	0.66	0.72	0.30	0.66[b]
Vesper Sparrow (*Poecetes gramineus*)	0.66[b]	1.20[b]	-	0.05	0.18	0.18	0.12	0.06
Savannah Sparrow (*Passerculus sandwichensis*)	0.03	0.12	-	-	0.06	-	0.06	0.12
Grasshopper Sparrow (*Ammodramus savannarum*)	0.06	0.03	-	-	<0.01	-	0.01	-
Baird's Sparrow (*Ammodramus bairdii*)	0.01	-	-	-	-	0.01	0.03	0.01
Chestnut-collared Longspur (*Calcarius ornatus*)	0.96	-	-	0.12	-	-	-	-
Meadowlark species (*Sturnella* spp.)	0.60	0.54	0.12	0.12[b]	0.36	0.12	0.12	0.24
Shrubland birds								
Gambel's Quail (*Callipepla gambelii*)	0.01	0.01	-	-	-	-	0.01	0.24
Cooper's Hawk (*Accipiter cooperii*)	-	0.01	<0.01	-	<0.01	-	-	-
Red-tailed Hawk (*Buteo jamaicensis*)	-	0.03	-	<0.01	-	0.01	0.02	0.02
Merlin (*Falco columbarius*)	-	0.01	-	-	<0.01	-	-	-
White-winged Dove (*Zenaida asiatica*)	0.18	0.30	-	-	-	0.01	-	-
Mourning Dove (*Zenaida macroura*)	-	0.10	0.04	0.06	0.24	0.24	0.36	0.54[b]
Inca Dove (*Columbina inca*)	0.01	-	-	-	-	-	-	0.03
Greater Roadrunner (*Geococcyx californianus*)	-	-	-	-	0.01	-	-	0.01
Great Horned Owl (*Bubo virginianus*)	-	-	-	-	-	-	-	-
Lesser Nighthawk (*Chordeiles acutipennis*)	-	-	-	-	-	-	0.01	-
Common Nighthawk (*Chordeiles minor*)	-	-	-	-	-	0.01	0.01	0.02
Black-chinned Hummingbird (*Archilochus alexandri*)	0.04	0.03	0.04	-	-	0.02	0.02	0.02
Broad-tailed Hummingbird (*Selasphorus platycerus*)	-	-	-	-	-	0.01	0.01	0.01
Ladder-backed Woodpecker (*Picoides scalaris*)	0.02	0.06	<0.01	-	0.01	0.01	0.01	0.02
Northern Flicker (*Colaptes auratus*)	0.02	0.01	-	-	-	-	-	-
Gray Flycatcher (*Empidonax wrightii*)	-	0.01	-	-	-	-	-	-
Ash-throated Flycatcher (*Myiarchus cinerascens*)	-	-	-	-	-	0.03	0.12	0.12
Cassin's Kingbird (*Tyrannus vociferans*)	-	0.01	-	-	-	-	-	0.12
Western Kingbird (*Tyrannus verticalis*)	-	0.01	-	-	-	0.03	0.06	0.3[b]
Loggerhead Shrike (*Lanius ludovicianus*)	0.24	0.24[b]	0.05	0.04	0.06	0.06	0.07	0.24
Verdin (*Auriparus flaviceps*)	0.04	0.02	0.03	-	<0.01	0.04	-	0.01
Cactus Wren (*Campylorhynchus brunneicapillus*)	0.12	0.18	0.04	0.02	0.04	0.02	0.02	0.24

APPENDIX 1. CONTINUED.

	Fall		Winter			Spring		
	2003	2005	2003–2004	2004–2005	2005–2006	2004	2005	2006
Rock Wren (*Salpinctes obsoletus*)	0.01	0.04	-	-	-	-	-	0.06
Bewick's Wren (*Thryomanes bewickii*)	0.02	0.04	-	-	-	-	-	0.01
House Wren (*Troglodytes aedon*)	0.01	0.01	-	-	-	-	0.01	-
Ruby-crowned Kinglet (*Regulus calendula*)	0.01	0.01	-	-	-	-	-	-
Blue-gray Gnatcatcher (*Polioptila caerulea*)	0.06	0.06	-	-	-	-	-	-
Black-tailed Gnatcatcher (*Polioptila melanura*)	0.02	0.03	-	-	0.04	0.01	-	0.06
Northern Mockingbird (*Mimus polyglottos*)	0.01	-	-	-	-	0.01	0.03	0.18
Sage Thrasher (*Oreoscoptes montanus*)	0.01	0.02	-	-	-	-	-	-
Curve-billed Thrasher (*Toxostoma curvirostre*)	0.01	0.04	<0.01	-	<0.01	0.01	0.01	0.01
Crissal Thrasher (*Toxostoma crissale*)	0.06	0.02	0.06	<0.01	<0.01	0.02	-	0.04
Orange-crowned Warbler (*Vermivora celata*)	-	0.02	-	-	-	-	-	-
Yellow-rumped Warbler (*Dendroica coronata*)	0.12	0.12	-	-	0.01	-	-	-
MacGillivray's Warbler (*Oporornis tolmiei*)	-	0.01	-	-	-	-	-	-
Green-tailed Towhee (*Pipilo chlorurus*)	0.03	0.03	-	-	-	-	-	-
Spotted Towhee (*Pipilo maculatus*)	0.04	-	-	-	-	-	-	-
Canyon Towhee (*Pipilo fuscus*)	-	0.01	-	-	-	-	0.02	0.02
Rufous-crowned Sparrow (*Aimophila ruficeps*)	-	0.12	-	-	-	-	-	-
Chipping Sparrow (*Spizella passerina*)	0.36	1.02	-	0.12	1.02	0.36	0.06	0.48
Clay-colored Sparrow (*Spizella pallida*)	0.01	-	-	-	-	-	-	-
Brewer's Sparrow (*Spizella breweri*)	0.24	0.96[b]	-	1.32[b]	0.66	0.12	0.60	0.84[b]
Black-chinned Sparrow (*Spizella atrogularis*)	-	0.03	-	0.03	0.02	-	0.01	0.06
Lark Sparrow (*Chondestes grammacus*)	-	0.03	0.01	-	<0.01	-	0.02	-
Black-throated Sparrow (*Amphispiza bilineata*)	0.30	1.86[b]	0.6[b]	0.18	0.30	0.66[b]	0.36[b]	1.2[b]
Sage Sparrow (*Amphispiza belli*)	0.12	1.62[b]	-	0.66[b]	1.56[b]	-	-	0.18
Lark Bunting (*Calamospiza melanocorys*)	0.12	0.84	-	0.18	0.90	0.03	0.60	0.60
White-crowned Sparrow (*Zonotrichia leucophrys*)	0.12	0.48[b]	-	0.05	0.54	0.03	0.06	0.78
Pyrrhuloxia (*Cardinalis sinuatus*)	-	-	-	-	-	0.01	0.02	0.01
Bronzed Cowbird (*Molothrus aeneus*)	0.01	0.01	-	-	-	-	-	-
Brown-headed Cowbird (*Molothrus ater*)	-	-	-	-	-	0.01	-	0.04
Bullock's Oriole (*Icterus bullockii*)	-	-	-	-	-	-	0.02	0.12
Scott's Oriole (*Icterus parisorum*)	-	-	-	-	-	-	0.03	-
House Finch (*Carpodacus mexicanus*)	0.48	0.60	0.30	0.03	0.66	0.01	0.18	0.90
Lesser Goldfinch (*Carduelis psaltria*)	-	0.03	-	-	-	0.12	-	-
House Sparrow (*Passer domesticus*)	-	-	-	-	0.02	0.04	-	-

[a] Not present.
[b] Species present in ≥40% of transects.

Studies in Avian Biology No. 37:101–112

WINTER DIETS AND SEED SELECTION OF GRANIVOROUS BIRDS IN SOUTHWESTERN NEW MEXICO

Martha J. Desmond, Cesar Mendez-Gonzalez, and Laurie B. Abbott

Abstract. We examined the diet of granivorous sparrows in winter through stomach and crop contents and compared seed consumption with availability, on grasslands of southwestern New Mexico during January–March 2003. We collected diet samples from 18 species of sparrows at five sites. Over 65 seed species were detected in diets. Despite high seed diversity in diets, five seed species accounted for 80% of seeds consumed. The most abundant seed species detected were perennial grasses sand and spike dropseed (*Sporobolus* spp.), annual grasses feather fingergrass (*Chloris virgata*), stinkgrass (*Eragrostis cilianensis*), and annual forbs amaranth (*Amaranthus* spp.), and carpetweed (*Mollugo verticillata*). The soil seed bank at these sites was also diverse with >90 species detected. The dominant seeds in the soil seedbank samples included feather fingergrass, stinkgrass, and carpetweed. Diets of coexisting species (Chipping Sparrow [*Spizella passerina*], Brewer's Sparrow [*Spizella breweri*], Vesper Sparrow [*Pooecetes gramineus*], Savannah Sparrow [*Passerculus sandwichensis*], and White-crowned [*Zonotrichia leucophrys*]) differed within the most diverse site and among sites. Dropseed seeds were the preferred seed type of the smaller-bodied *Spizella* sparrows and the larger-bodied Vesper Sparrow. Where present, dropseed was important in the diets of all sparrow species. Depending on location, cupgrass, amaranth, and dropseed were preferred by Savannah Sparrow while Vesper Sparrow preferred cupgrass, goosefoot (*Chenopodium* spp.), dropseed, and knotweed (*Polygonum* spp.). Small-bodied sparrows specialized on small-sized seeds whereas larger-bodied sparrows exhibited preferences for seeds representing a diversity of sizes. The importance of the perennial dropseed grasses in sparrow diets emphasizes the need to examine the influence of management practices on seed production for this grassland type.

Key words: arid environments, diet, dropseed, emberizid sparrows, granivore, seed bank, seed selection, *Sporobolus*, southwestern grasslands, winter avifauna.

DIETA INVERNAL Y SELECCION DE SEMILLAS POR AVES GRANIVORAS EN EL SUROESTE DE NUEVO MEXICO

Resumen. Analizamos la dieta invernal de gorriones granivoros a traves de contenidos estomacales y de mollejas, y comparamos el consumo de semillas con su disponibilidad en pastizales del Suroeste de Nuevo Mexico durante Enero a Marzo de 2003. Colectamos muestras de la dieta de 18 especies de gorriones en cinco areas. Mas de 65 tipos de semillas fueron detectados en las dietas. A pesar de la alta diversidad de semillas encontradas, solo cinco tipos representaron el 80% de las semillas totales consumidas por las aves. Las semillas mas abundantes fueron las de pastos perenes arenosos y zacaton (*Sporobolus* spp.), pastos anuales pata de gallo (*Chloris virgata*), pasto hediondo (*Eragrostis cilianensis*), ataco anual (*Amaranthus* spp.) y alfombrilla (*Mollugo verticillata*). El banco de semillas en el suelo de los sitios tambien fue diverso, encontrando mas de 90 especies. Los tipos dominantes en las muestras de los bancos de semillas incluyeron pata de gallo, pasto hediondo y alfombrilla. Las dietas de especies simpatricas (gorrion ceja blanca [*Spizella passerina*], gorrion de Brewer [*Spizella breweri*], gorrion cola blanca [*Pooecetes gramineus*], gorrion savanero [*Passerculus sandwichensis*] y el gorrion corona blanca [*Zonotrichia leucophrys*]) difirieron dentro de los sitios mas diversos y entre las diferentes areas. Las semillas de zacaton fueron las preferidas por los gorriones de cuerpo mas pequeño del genero *Spizella* y por los gorriones de cola blanca, de cuerpo mas grande. Cuando estuvo presente, el zacaton fue importante en la dieta de todas las especies de gorriones. Dependiendo del sitio, el zacate fortuna (*Eriochloa* spp.), ataco y zacaton fueron preferidos por gorriones savaneros, mientras que el gorrion de cola blanca prefirio zacate fortuna, quinoa (*Chenopodium spp.*), zacaton y sanguinaria (*Polygonum* spp.). Los gorriones de cuerpo pequeño se especializaron en semillas de tamaño pequeño, mientras que los gorriones de cuerpo grande exhibieron preferencias por semillas de diversos tamaños. La importancia de los pastizales de zacaton perene en la dieta de los gorriones enfatiza la necesidad de examinar la influencia de las practicas de manejo sobre la produccion de semillas para este tipo de pastizales.

The production and distribution of seed resources are among the most important factors influencing the winter abundance and diversity of granivorous birds in arid and semi-arid environments (Grant 1966, Schluter and Repasky 1991, Blendinger and Ojeda 2001, Moorcroft et al. 2002). Unpredictable rainfall events result in a patchy distribution of seeds that varies substantially across years. Tracking resources at a landscape scale allows granivorous birds to select winter locations that will best meet their energy demands. Once established at a winter location, some species have been found to be mainly sedentary in nature, maintaining small home ranges (Gordon 2000, Ginter and Desmond 2005) while other species are thought to be highly mobile, tracking resources across a larger scale (Gordon 2000, Blendinger and Ojeda 2001). However, because little information is available on the diets of these birds and seed availability at foraging sites, the attributes of the seed supply that actually drive avian distribution and abundance are not well understood. This lack of information is due, in part, to difficulties in determining diet (Rosenberg and Cooper 1988).

Several studies have reported positive relationships between winter sparrow abundance and seed abundance, suggesting sparrows cue in on overall seed production (Pulliam and Parker 1979, Dunning and Brown 1982, Grzybowski 1983, Ginter and Desmond 2005). For example, Grzybowski (1983) found a positive correlation between seed production and avian abundance in winter in southwest Texas, and Ginter and Desmond (2005) found higher seed biomass during the winter on plots in south Texas where Savannah Sparrows (*Passerculus sandwichensis*) foraged (based on radio-telemetry data) compared to randomly selected plots. Dunning and Brown (1982) found winter sparrow abundance from 21 yr of Christmas bird count data to be positively correlated with monsoonal rainfall from the preceding summer, a predictor of seed production. However, Pulliam and Dunning (1987) found no relationship between sparrow abundance and seed production during 2 yr of moderate seed production and suggested the density of winter sparrows is independent of seed abundance in years where production is moderate to high.

Other studies suggest birds cue in on specific seed species (Pulliam 1986, Niemela 2002, Cueto et al. 2006), sometimes showing a preference for forb or grass seeds. Seed size, morphology, nutrient content, coat thickness, visibility, and secondary chemical compounds may all influence seed selection (Pulliam and Brand 1975, Greig-Smith and Wilson 1985, Diaz 1990, van der Meij and Bout 2000). Pulliam (1985) reports that small-bodied sparrows are more efficient at handling small seeds whereas large-bodied sparrows are equally efficient at handling large and small seeds. Niemela (2002) found a positive correlation between winter Horned Lark (*Eremophila alpestris*) abundance and the abundance of *Sporobolus* spp. seeds, and between Brewer's Sparrow (*Spizella breweri*) abundance and the abundance of buckwheat (*Eriogonum*

spp.) seeds on study sites in southern New Mexico, possibly indicating these birds were responding to the abundance of these specific seed species. Pulliam (1980) found the majority of seeds in Chipping Sparrow (*Spizella passerina*) diets to be from forbs, with the three most common seeds comprising of one grass species, Lehmann lovegrass (*Eragrostis lehmanniana*), and the forbs amaranth (*Amaranthus retroflexus*), and buckwheat (*Portulaca* spp.). Interestingly, Pulliam (1985) found that Lehmann lovegrass and buckwheat seeds were abundant in the seed bank, whereas amaranth seed was substantially less abundant. In arid parts of Argentina, granivorous birds were found to select grass over forb seeds (Marone et al. 1998, Cueto et al. 2006), and seed biomass was important, with sparrows exhibiting a preference for larger-sized grass seeds (Cueto et al. 2006). Cueto et al. (2006), however, observed that granivorous sparrows exhibited variation in seed preference, or avoidance of certain seed types, despite similarity in seed dimensions, suggesting that factors other than size alone, such as energy content (Gluck 1985), may influence seed choice.

Availability of specific seed species is influenced by rainfall pattern and season. In the arid Southwest, winter and spring rains are likely to trigger the production of forbs, whereas grass seed is produced in response to late summer monsoonal rains (Pulliam and Brand 1975). The resulting differences in seed production among years and across sites will likely result in substantial differences in sparrow diets. Pulliam (1980) found that Chipping Sparrows did not consume seeds in relation to availability following a year of high monsoonal summer rainfall and suggested sparrows maximize their rate of energy intake by selecting seeds of higher value. Pulliam (1985, 1986) hypothesized that a broad overlap in sparrow diets would exist when seeds were scarce and they would specialize or be more selective in years of moderate to high seed production. Differences in seed consumption in relation to availability for Chipping Sparrows was attributed to the toxic nature of some seed species and the high nutrient value of others (Pulliam 1980).

Few studies have examined winter emberizid sparrow diets in detail, especially comparisons of avian diet to seed availability within and among sites. We studied the diets of winter sparrows under natural conditions at five grassland sites in southern New Mexico. We examined the relative importance of different seed types including forb, annual grass, and perennial grass seeds, and we examined the influence of seed abundance and diversity on community dynamics of winter emberizid sparrows. We tested two related hypotheses: (1) coexisting sparrow species consume seed resources differently within sites and, (2) individual species consume seed resources differently among sites. To test these hypotheses we compared diets of sparrows within and among sites and examined seed selection in relation to winter avian community composition and the composition of the seed bank. Understanding seed preference and the influence of seed abundance and distribution on avian abundance and community composition is important to the conservation and management of desert grasslands and their associated avifauna.

METHODS

STUDY AREA

Study sites were located in Hidalgo County, southwestern New Mexico, within the 130,000 ha Diamond A Ranch operated by the Animas Foundation. Wintering birds tend to congregate in the vicinity of cattle watering sites (shallow ponds filled with rain water, troughs, and/or above ground tanks), therefore we chose five study sites near water sources to maximize sampling effort. We have observed that a wide variety of sparrows (Chipping, Brewer's, Vesper [*Pooeceets gramineus*], Savannah, Grasshopper [*Ammodramus savannarum*], and Baird's [*Ammodramus bairdii*]) readily use these types of sites. Field observations at our study sites confirmed that sparrows congregating in the vicinity of these sites were also foraging in the vicinity of these sites. Site locations included a variety of habitats, primarily open grassland, shrub-dominated, and disturbed habitats (Table 1).

DATA COLLECTION

Birds were captured using mist-nets during January–March 2003, from 0730 through 1700 H depending on the weather conditions. All five sites were sampled in mid-winter (January to mid-February); three sites (3–5) were

TABLE 1. STUDY SITE DESCRIPTIONS AND SPECIES PRESENT ON THE RESPECTIVE SITES.

Site	Description	Species present [a]
Site 1	Open grassland dominated by annual grasses and forbs. Water source was a depression in the ground approximately 0.25 ha and 50 m from nets.	Horned Lark (*Eremophila alpestris*) Vesper Sparrow (*Pooecetes gramineus*) Savannah Sparrow (*Passerculus sandwichensis*)
Site 2	Mixed grassland with dense cholla (*Opuntia imbricata*) patches, surrounded by oak (*Quercus* spp.) woodland. Water sources were a depression in the ground and an above ground steel tank separated by 10 m. Nets were 30 m from water sources.	Botteri's Sparrow (*Aimophila botterii*) Vesper Sparrow Black-throated Sparrow (*Amphispiza bilineata*) Grasshopper Sparrow (*Ammodramus savannarum*)
Site 3	Open mixed grassland with both perennial and annual grasses at the transition zone with a juniper-oak (*Juniperus* spp.-*Quercus* spp.) woodland. Water site was an above ground steel tank, 300 m from nets.	Mourning Dove (*Zenaida macroura*) Chipping Sparrow (*Spizella passerina*) Brewer's Sparrow (*Spizella breweri*) Vesper Sparrow Lark Bunting (*Calamospiza melanocorys*) Savannah Sparrow White-crowned Sparrow (*Zonotrichia leucophrys*) Dark-eyed Junco (*Junco hyemalis*) Chestnut-collared Longspur (*Calcarius ornatus*) House Finch (*Carpodacus mexicanus*) House Sparrow (*Passer domesticus*)
Site 4	Disturbed weedy patch surrounded by open grassland dominated by blue grama (*Bouteloua gracilis*), buffalograss (*Buchloe dactiloydes*), and dropseed (*Sporobolus* sp.). Water source was an above ground steel tank, 50 m from nets.	Vesper Sparrow Savannah Sparrow Grasshopper Sparrow
Site 5	Disturbed weedy patch surrounded by riparian vegetation and scattered bottom land grassland patches. Water sources were a concrete tank and adjacent ground level water troughs, 10 m from nets.	Vesper Sparrow Savannah Sparrow Chipping Sparrow Dark-eyed Junco Lincoln Sparrow (*Melospiza lincolnii*) Western Meadowlark (*Sturnella neglecta*)

[a] Diet analysis was only conducted on the five most common species (Brewer's, Chipping, Savannah, Vepser, and White-crowned Sparrows).

re-sampled in late-winter (late-February to mid-March). However, additional birds were captured only at site 3. Each bird was induced to regurgitate stomach and crop contents by flushing the stomach with warm water (Ford et al. 1982). Seeds from avian stomachs and crops were regurgitated onto a coffee filter which was folded and stored in a manila envelope until the seeds were counted and identified. All birds were banded with USGS bands to avoid re-sampling on the same day.

To estimate seed availability, we collected 20 random soil seed bank samples within each site during mist netting events in mid-winter. A second set of seed bank samples was collected in late-winter at the three sites that were re-sampled for birds during late-winter. Soil seed samples were taken using an aluminum can of 8.8 cm in diameter inserted to a depth of 0.5 cm, collecting a total volume of 30 cc (Pulliam 1980, 1986; Ginter and Desmond 2005). Seeds were separated from soil using a hydropneumatic root elutriator, a machine that has been specifically adapted and used to separate seeds from soil samples by using air and water pressure to separate organic and inorganic materials (Gross and Renner 1989). A thin layer of soil remains following the separation process, so samples were sieved onto a grid-pattern Petri-dish in order to conduct the final seed separation and to count all seeds. This process was repeated as many times as needed for each sample. Seeds in soil and avian diet samples were counted using a 10 x 40 power stereoscope.

To determine the weight of seed species, we consulted the values of seed mass in the literature (Pulliam and Brand 1975; Pulliam 1985, 1986; Pulliam and Dunning 1987) and also weighed seeds in the laboratory using a Mettler AE160 balance. Harper et al. (1970) reported a high degree of constancy in the mean weight of seed grains within species in a wide range of plants. We also observed this and assumed a uniform weight for all seeds of a given species. We used the weight (mg) of each seed species to estimate the seed biomass by unit area (kg/ha) for each of the five sites and to estimate the relative importance of all seed species in the avian diets at each site. We estimated the proportional abundance (% biomass) of seed species at each site and the proportion of seed consumed (% biomass) by the different bird species at each site. We also estimated the total biomass (kg/ha) of all seeds in the seed bank.

STATISTICAL ANALYSIS

To examine if soil seed bank biomass differed among sites within mid- and late-winter periods, we used analysis of variance (ANOVA) and post hoc least significant difference (LSD) tests. To determine if winter sparrows were feeding on seeds relative to availability or were being selective (showing a preference) at individual sites, we compared seed consumption (biomass) from stomach and crop regurgitation to seed availability from the soil seed bank samples (biomass) using Johnson's rank preference (Johnson 1980). Johnson's rank preference method orders food items (seed species) in a ranking system from most preferred to least preferred (or most avoided). This method also determines if significant differences exist in the preference of specific seed species consumed by individual avian species at a site. The statistical software PREFER v5.1 (Pankratz 1994) was used to perform all calculations. Two analyses were conducted for the five most common bird species in mid-winter (Chipping, Brewer's, Vesper, Savannah, and White-crowned [*Zonotrichia leucophrys*] Sparrows): first for all five species at the single site where all of them were found; then for the two most broadly distributed species across sites. In addition, this analysis was conducted on four species—Chipping, Brewer's, Vesper, and Savannah Sparrows—at a single site, comparing mid-winter with late-winter diets. We used a minimum of six diet samples for each species to conduct diet analysis. All seeds with percentages less than 5% in both the soil and avian diets were excluded from the analysis at each site.

To test the hypothesis that coexisting sparrow species consume seeds differently, we performed multivariate analyses of variance (MANOVA) to assess the differences in seed species selection, based on biomass, (SAS Institute 1990) among the same five most common sparrows within site 3. We performed individual ANOVA and post hoc LSD tests to determine where significant differences were located.

RESULTS

Precipitation was 9.78 cm below normal for 2002 and 0.13 cm above normal for early 2003. Monthly precipitation totals in late 2002 (particularly October) were above normal and may have contributed to the observed intermediate and high seed production (NOAA 2002, 2003).

The soil seed bank at the five sites was diverse, with over 90 seed species detected. Overall, dominant seeds (by biomass) included feather fingergrass (*Chloris virgata*), stinkgrass (*Eragrostis cilianensis*), and carpetweed (*Mollugo verticillata*). We collected 609 diet samples from

573 individual birds of 18 species between January and March 2003 across the five sites (Table 1). Several individuals were recaptured and resampled during the winter. We detected over 65 seed species in diets and a small number of seedlings and invertebrates. Overall, the most abundant seed species (as determined by biomass) detected in avian diets were perennial grasses including sand and spike dropseed (23% biomass), annual grasses including feather fingergrass (24%) and stinkgrass (8%), and annual forbs including amaranth (18%) and carpetweed (6%).

We examined the diets (based on biomass) of the five most common avian species within and among study sites. Chipping Sparrow (N = 60) was present at only two sites. We found 23 seed species in their stomach and crop contents, with five species (dropseed, feather fingergrass, carpetweed, threeawn [*Aristida* spp.], and amaranth) comprising 73% of their diet. Brewer's Sparrow (N = 37) was present at just one site, with 15 seed species in their stomach/crop contents, of which four seed species (dropseed, amaranth, feather fingergrass, and threeawn) comprised over 72% of their diet. Vesper Sparrow (N = 148) was present at all five sites, but only in sufficient numbers for sampling at four of the sites. Fifty-six seed species were detected in their stomach and crop contents, with five species (amaranth, cupgrass, dropseed, feather fingergrass, and panicum [*Panicum* spp.]) accounting for 59% of their diet. Savannah Sparrow was the most abundant species sampled (N = 270) and was present at four of the five sites. We detected 47 seed species in Savannah Sparrow stomach/crop contents, with five seed species (amaranth, feather fingergrass, cupgrass, stinkgrass, and dropseed) comprising over 78% of their diet. White-crowned Sparrow (N = 44) was present at only one site, with 15 seed species in their stomach/crop contents, of which two seed species (amaranth and dropseed) comprised 79% of their diet.

SOIL SEED BANK

Seed biomass from soil seed bank samples taken in mid-winter differed significantly among sites, as did seed biomass in late-winter (Table 2). Seed resources (biomass) were significantly greater at sites 1 and 3 with respect to the other sites (P < 0.05, Table 2) in mid-winter; resources were significantly greater at site 3 with respect to the other two sites (P < 0.05; Table 2) in late-winter. Site 3 had high biomass and intermediate diversity of seed resources and, based on mist netting efforts, appeared to support the highest abundance and diversity of birds. Site 1, in comparison, had a high biomass but low diversity of seeds; this site did not appear to support a large diversity or abundance of birds and did not have perennial grass seed production. We observed a decrease in seed biomass over time at the three sites where the soil seed bank was sampled again in late winter. Mean seed biomass decreased by 50% at site 3, 53% in site 4 and 44% at site 5 (Table 2).

DIETS OF COEXISTING SPARROWS

The diets of different bird species pooled across mid- and late-winter, based on percent biomass, differed significantly at site 3 (MANOVA: F = 4.62, df = 40, P < 0.01), the site with the highest diversity and abundance of birds and a high biomass and intermediate diversity of seeds. Individual ANOVAs were performed to identify the specifics of those differences in seed consumption among bird species (Table 3). We found significant differences in consumption of dropseed grass seeds among sparrows, with Brewer's Sparrows consuming significantly higher proportions than Savannah and White-crowned Sparrows. Chipping Sparrows consumed more threeawn seeds than Savannah, Vesper, and White-crowned Sparrows. Savannah Sparrows consumed significantly higher proportions of cupgrass than all

TABLE 2. COMPARISONS OF SOIL SEED BANK—MEAN (SD) BIOMASS (KG/HA), SPECIES RICHNESS, AND SHANNON-WEINER DIVERSITY INDEX (H'; ZAR 1999)—AT FIVE SITES DURING MID-WINTER (JANUARY–MID-FEBRUARY 2003) AND AT THREE SITES DURING LATE-WINTER (LATE FEBRUARY–MID-MARCH 2003). SPECIES RICHNESS AND DIVERSITY WERE CALCULATED WITH DATA POOLED ACROSS MID- AND LATE-WINTER PERIODS.

Site	Mid-winter [a]	Late-winter [b]	Richness	H'
Site 1	141.5 (104.2)[c]		24	1.4
Site 2	60.2 (40.7)[d]		33	2.5
Site 3	114.5 (82.4)[c]	56.8 (50.2)[c]	39	2.1
Site 4	67.9 (48.2)[d]	32.2 (20.7)[d]	40	1.9
Site 5	41.2 (27.5)[d]	23.1 (23.2)[d]	44	2.4

[a] $F = 7.68_{4,95}$, P < 0.01.
[b] $F = 5.25_{2,57}$, P < 0.01.
Note: Means with the same superscript within a column did not differ significantly (P > 0.05).

TABLE 3. COMPARISON OF THE DIETS (PERCENT BIOMASS BY SEED SPECIES), AMONG FIVE COEXISTING SPECIES (WHITE-CROWNED [WCSP], VESPER [VESP], SAVANNAH [SAVS], CHIPPING [CHSP], AND BREWER'S [BRSP] SPARROWS AT SITE 3 POOLED ACROSS MID- AND LATE-WINTER.

Seed species	Plant type[a]	Seed size[b]	WCSP	VESP	SAVS	CHSP	BRSP	$F_{4,265}$	P-value
Dropseed (Sporobolus spp.)	PG	0.1	15.89[d]	28.27[cd]	18.03[d]	20.72[cd]	45.18[c]	2.56	0.04
Threeawn (Aristida spp.)	PG-AG	0.5	0.0[d]	2.00[d]	1.24[d]	11.53[c]	8.29[cd]	4.19	0.01
Cupgrass (Eriochloa spp.)	AG	1.0	0.0[d]	0.72[d]	18.96[c]	0.41[d]	0.10[d]	10.99	0.01
Feather fingergrass (Chloris virgata)	AG	0.35	0.37[d]	12.74[c]	15.33[c]	19.27[c]	9.49[cd]	2.75	0.03
Stinkgrass (Eragrostis cilianesis)	AG	0.1	3.51[c]	1.76[c]	3.45[c]	3.73[c]	5.77[a]	1.25	0.29
Amaranth (Amaranthus spp.)	FO	0.4	63.32[c]	24.47[c]	30.93[d]	10.30[e]	9.92[e]	16.73	0.01
Carpetweed (Mollugo verticillata)	FO	0.08	1.14[d]	3.90[d]	3.74[d]	15.72[c]	5.92[cd]	4.42	0.01
Other			15.77	26.14	8.32	18.32	15.33		

[a] PG = perennial grass, AG = annual grass, FO = forb.
[b] Size = Average seed weight (mg).
Note: Means with the same superscript within row did not differ significantly (P > 0.05).

other sparrow species. Savannah, Vesper, and Chipping Sparrows consumed more feather fingergrass seeds than White-crowned Sparrows. Consumption of stinkgrass did not differ among the five sparrow species. Consumption of amaranth differed significantly among sparrows with White-crowned Sparrows consuming significantly higher proportions than all other sparrow species; Savannah Sparrows consumed more amaranth seeds than Vesper, Chipping, and Brewer's Sparrows. Chipping Sparrows consumed significantly higher proportions of carpetweed seeds than Savannah, Vesper, and White-crowned sparrows.

COMPARING SOIL SEED BANK WITH SPARROW DIETS IN MID-WINTER

Comparisons of sparrow diets with soil seed banks in mid-winter were conducted in two ways: first by comparing sparrow diets with seed banks at a single site that supported the largest diversity of birds in mid-winter (Table 4) and secondly by comparing sparrow diets with seed banks across multiple sites, using a smaller sample of bird species that were found at multiple sites (Table 5). We present data on the most common and the most preferred seeds consumed; although not always the most preferred, the most common seeds comprised a substantial proportion of sparrow diets. Based on both percent biomass and ranked preference in sparrow diets, sparrows did not consume seeds in proportion to relative abundance (based on biomass) in the seed bank, but rather exhibited different degrees of seed preference (Tables 4 and 5). Preferred seeds were consumed at a substantially greater rate compared to availability, as measured by Johnson's rank preference.

At site 3, the only site where White-crowned Sparrow were found, amaranth and dropseed were both the preferred seeds and the most common seeds in the White-crowned Sparrow diet (Table 4). Chipping Sparrow exhibited a preference for dropseed, while carpetweed, feather fingergrass, and dropseed were the most common seeds in their diet. Brewer's Sparrow exhibited a preference for dropseed and stinkgrass, while dropseed was the most common seed in their diet (Table 4).

Savannah and Vesper Sparrows were the two most widely distributed species (each found at four of five sites) and exhibited varying patterns in diet composition across sites in mid-winter (Table 5). Cupgrass was the preferred seed of Savannah Sparrow at sites 1, 3, and 5 (Table 5). Cupgrass was not detected in the soil seed bank or Savannah Sparrow diets at

TABLE 4. COMPARISON OF THE DIETS (% BIOMASS AND PREFERRED RANK) OF MULTIPLE SPECIES WITH AVAILABLE SOIL SEED BANK (% BIOMASS) AT A SINGLE SITE (SITE 3) DURING MID-WINTER (JANUARY–MID-FEBRUARY 2003) USING JOHNSON'S RANK PREFERENCE (RANK). A BLANK SPACE MEANS THAT THE SEED SPECIES WAS NOT PRESENT AT THE SITE OR PROPORTIONS WERE <5% IN BOTH THE SOIL AND SPARROW DIETS.

Seed	White-crowned Sparrow[a] (*Zonotrichia leucophrys*)			Chipping Sparrow[b] (*Spizella passerina*)			Brewer's Sparrow[c] (*Spizella breweri*)			Savannah Sparrow[d] (*Passerculus sandwichensis*)			Vesper Sparrow[e] (*Pooecetes gramineus*)		
	Diet	Soil	Rank	Diet	Soil	Rank	Diet	Soil	Rank	Diet	Soil	Rank	Diet	Soil	Rank
Dropseed (*Sporobolus* spp.)	22.0	2.5	2.0[f]	18.8	2.5	1.0[f]	45.3	2.5	1.0[f]	17.2	2.5	4[g]	34.4	2.5	1.0[f]
Threeawn (*Aristida* spp.)	0.0	7.6	5.0[h]	12.8	7.6	4[gh]	4.6	7.6	5.0[h]	1.4	7.6	7.0[i]	1.2	7.6	4.0[i]
Cupgrass (*Eriochloa* spp.)										20.0	0.6	1.0[f]			
Feather fingergrass (*Chloris virgata*)	0.3	13.9	6.0[h]	19.5	13.9	5.0[hi]	10.4	13.9	6.0[h]	13.8	13.9	6.0[i]	11.3	13.9	5.0[i]
Stinkgrass (*Eragrostis cilianensis*)	5.0	2.5	3.0[f]				8.8	2.5	2.0[f]	7.6	2.5	2.0[g]			
Amaranth (*Amaranthus* spp.)	53.2	5.5	1.0[f]	1.3	5.5	2.0[g]	5.1	5.5	3.0[g]	26.5	5.5	3.0[h]	15.2	5.5	2.0[g]
Purslane (*Portulaca* spp.)	6.7	5.7	4.0[g]	12.1	5.7	3.0[gh]	9.2	5.7	4.0[g]	5.1	5.7	5.0[i]	9.3	5.7	3.0[h]
Carpetweed (*Mollugo verticillata*)	2.2	34.7	7.0[i]	26.2	34.7	6.0[i]	8.7	34.7	7.0[i]	6.0	34.7	8.0[k]	6.8	34.7	6.0[i]

[a] $F_{0, 38} = 298.98$, W = 1.80, P = 0.05.
[b] $F_{5, 10} = 11.09$, W = 2.19, P = 0.05.
[c] $F_{6, 20} = 94.40$, W = 1.88, P = 0.05.
[d] $F_{7, 60} = 270.89$, W = 1.77, P = 0.05.
[e] $F_{6, 26} = 344.70$, W = 1.84, P = 0.05.
Note: Seed species preferences that are ranked with the same superscript within a column (by bird species) did not differ significantly.

TABLE 5. Comparison of the diets (% biomass and preferred rank) of two broadly distributed species with soil seed bank (% biomass) at multiple sites during mid-winter (January–mid February 2003) using Johnson's rank preference (rank). Seed species ranked with the same superscript letter within a column (by bird species) did not differ significantly. A blank space means that the seed species was not present at the site or proportions were <5% in both the soil and sparrow diet.

Savannah Sparrow

Seed	Site 1[a]			Site 3[b]			Site 4[c]			Site 5[d]		
	Diet	Soil	Rank	Diet	Soil	Rank	Diet	Soil	Rank	Diet	Soil	Rank
Dropseed (Sporobolus spp.)	12.3	2.5	1.0[i]	17.2	2.5	4.0[j]	2.7	6.4	3.0[i]			
Threeawn (Aristida spp.)				1.4	7.6	7.0[m]						
Cupgrass (Eriochloa spp.)				20.0	0.6	1.0[i]				14.3	1.1	2.0[i]
Feather fingergrass (Chloris virgata)	54.6	66.1	3.0[i]	13.8	13.9	6.0[l]	40.3	36.5	4.0[k]			
Stinkgrass (Eragrostis cilianensis)				7.6	2.5	2.0[i]	20.5	31.0	2.0[i]	5.1	6.5	3.0[j]
Amaranth (Amaranthus spp.)				26.5	5.5	3.0[k]	16.7	1.2	1.0[i]	41.1	6.1	1.0[i]
Purslane (Portulaca spp.)				5.1	5.7	5.0[l]						
Carpetweed (Mollugo verticillata)	11.6	4.3	2.0[i]	6.0	34.7	8.0[n]						
Vervain (Verbena spp.)	0.0	10.2	4.0[k]							0.0	17.9	
Clover (Trifolium spp.)										0.0	26.0	
Neckweed (Veronica peregrine)										0.0	16.9	
Unidentified seed												

Vesper Sparrow

Seed	Site 1[e]			Site 2[f]			Site 3[g]			Site 5[h]		
	Diet	Soil	Rank	Diet	Soil	Rank	Diet	Soil	Rank	Diet	Soil	Rank
Dropseed	32.6	2.5	1.0[i]	18.8	6.7	2.0[i]	2.5	1.0	1.0[i]			
Threeawn				6.2	11.0	5.0[kl]	1.2	7.6	4.0[l]			
Cupgrass				1.1	25.3	7.0[m]						
Feather fingergrass	27.5	66.1	3.0[i]		34.4		11.3	13.9	5.0[l]			
Stinkgrass				4.4	5.2	3.0[j]				7.9	6.5	3.0[j]
Amaranth				1.9	10.9	4.0[k]	15.2	5.5	2.0[i]	26.1	6.1	2.0[i]
Purslane							9.3	5.7	3.0[k]			
Carpetweed	16.2	4.3	2.0[i]				6.8	34.7	6.0[m]			
Vervain	0.0	10.2	4.0[i]							0.0	17.9	
Clover										0.0	26.0	
Neckweed										0.0	16.9	
Goosefoot (Chenipodium spp)				12.9	0.6	1.0[i]						
Panicum (Panicum spp.)				26.9	15.9	6.0[l]						
Knotweed (Polygonum spp.)										13.9	1.1	1.0[i]
Unidentified seed												

[a] $F = 55.53_{3,6}$, $W = 2.32$, $P = 0.05$.
[b] $F = 270.89_{7,60}$, $W = 1.77$, $P = 0.05$.
[c] $F = 76.32_{3,116}$, $W = 1.75$, $P = 0.05$.
[d] $F = 1232.99_{3,49}$, $W = 1.78$, $P = 0.05$.
[e] $F = 57.83_{3,7}$, $W = 2.21$, $P = 0.05$.
[f] $F = 344.70_{6,2v}$, $W = 1.84$, $P = 0.05$.
[g] $F = 176.90_{5,3v}$, $W = 1.81$, $P = 0.05$.
[h] $F = 70.47_{5,31}$, $W = 1.83$, $P = 0.05$.

Note: Seed species ranked with the same superscript within a column (by bird species) did not differ significantly.

site 4; amaranth was the preferred seed type of Savannah Sparrow at this site. Amaranth was equally preferred by Savannah Sparrow at site 5 (Table 5). In comparison with seed preference, amaranth, feather fingergrass, and stinkgrass were variously the most common seeds in Savannah Sparrow diets (on a biomass basis) at different sites; only at site 5 did the most common seed coincide with a preferred seed type. Cupgrass was both the preferred and the most common seed species in the diets of Vesper Sparrow at site 1. Goosefoot (*Chenopodium* spp.) was preferred by Vesper Sparrow at site 2, while the most common seed in its diet was panicum. Dropseed was both the preferred and most common seed species in the diet at site 3. Knotweed and amaranth were preferred at site 5 where amaranth was the most common seed in Vesper Sparrow diets (Table 5). Seeds that were never consumed but were abundant in the soil included vervain (*Verbena* spp.), clover (*Trifolium* spp.), and neckweed (*Veronica peregrina*) (Table 5).

SEED PREFERENCE AMONG SPARROWS FOR MID- VERSUS LATE-WINTER

Diets of four sparrow species (Chipping, Brewer's, Vesper and Savannah Sparrows) were compared in mid- and late-winter at site 3. Dropseed remained the preferred seed of three species (Chipping, Brewer's and Vesper Sparrows) in both mid- and late-winter; however, their preferences for other seed species changed between mid- and late-winter (Table 6). Amaranth was important for Chipping, Brewer's, and Vesper Sparrows in the mid-winter period but by late-winter was ranked lower (Table 6). Purslane remained relatively important for these same three species in both mid- and late-winter. Interestingly, threeawn ranked relatively low for the three species in mid-winter but was the second-most preferred seed species for Chipping and Brewer's Sparrows in late-winter; it was not found in the diet of Vesper Sparrow in late-winter (Table 6). Stinkgrass contributed less than 5% of Vesper and Chipping Sparrow diets in mid-winter but was relatively important in diets in late-winter.

Savannah Sparrow preferences changed substantially between mid- and late-winter. It was the only species to include the large-sized cupgrass seeds in its diet and it ranked as the preferred seed in mid-winter, followed by stinkgrass and amaranth. In late-winter, Savannah Sparrow preference switched to the small-sized dropseed, followed by purslane and feather fingergrass.

TABLE 6. COMPARISON OF DIET PREFERENCES IN MID- AND LATE-WINTER FOR FOUR SPARROWS AT SITE 3 USING JOHNSON'S PREFERENCE RANK. STATISTICS FOR MID-WINTER ARE FOUND IN TABLE 4.

Seed	Chipping Sparrow[a] (*Spizella passerina*)		Brewer's Sparrow[b] (*Spizella breweri*)		Savannah Sparrow[c] (*Passerculus sandwichensis*)		Vesper Sparrow[d] (*Pooecetes gramineus*)	
	Mid-winter Rank	Late-winter Rank	Mid-winter Rank	Late-winter Rank	Mid-winter Rank	Late-winter Rank	Mid-winter Rank	Late-winter Rank
Dropseed (*Sporobolus* spp.)	1.0[ae]	1.0[e]	1.0[e]	1.0[e]	4.0[h]	1.0[e]	1.0[e]	1.0[e]
Threeawn (*Aristada* spp)	4.0[fg]	2.0[f]	5.0[g]	2.0[f]	7.0[i]		4.0[h]	
Cupgrass (*Eriochoa* spp.)					1.0[e]			
Feather fingergrass (*Chloris virgata*)	5.0[gh]	5.0[h]	6.0[g]	5.0[h]	6.0[i]	3.0[fg]	5.0[h]	5.0[g]
Stinkgrass (*Eragrostis cilianensis*)		4.0[h]	2.0[e]	4.0[h]	2.0[k]	5.0[g]		3.0[fg]
Amaranth (*Amaranthus* spp.)	2.0[f]	7.0[i]	3.0[f]	6.0[i]	3.0[k]	4.0[fg]	2.0[f]	4.0[g]
Purslane (*Portulaca* spp.)	3.0[g]	3.0[g]	4.0[f]	3.0[g]	5.0[k]	2.0[f]	3.0[g]	2.0[f]
Carpetweed (*Mollugo verticillata*)	6.0[h]	6.0[i]	7.0[h]	7.0[i]	8.0[k]	6.0[h]	6.0[i]	6.0[h]

[a] $F = 77.17_{6,35}$, $W = 1.81$, $P = 0.05$
[b] $F = 78.75_{6,6}$, $W = 2.24$, $P = 0.05$
[c] $F = 37.93_{6,7}$, $W = 2.18$, $P = 0.05$
[d] $F = 32.70_{5,10}$, $W = 2.04$, $P = 0.05$

Note: Seed species ranked with the same superscript within a column (by bird species) did not differ significantly.

DISCUSSION

Seed production varied substantially across our five study sites (41.2–141.5 kg/ha) and was similar to or higher than reported seed production in southeast Arizona, which was found to be low (7.4–44.2 kg/ha) during years of below normal precipitation (Pulliam and Dunning 1987), and to vary widely (0.2–88.9 kg/ha) in relation to summer precipitation (Pulliam 1986). The higher production at some of our sites was likely related to the slightly disturbed nature of some sites (vicinity of cattle watering areas). Similar to Pulliam (1986), we observed a substantial decline in seed availability from mid- to late-winter, suggesting that winter sparrows and possibly other granivores consumed large quantities of seed.

In general, diets of sparrows and the soil seed bank samples at our sites were diverse. In many cases, the preferred seeds (dropseed, cupgrass, amaranth, goosefoot, knotweed, and carpetweed) were not the most abundant in sparrow diets or the soil seed bank. In a few cases the dominant seeds in the soil seed bank samples were also the most common but not preferred in sparrow diets (stinkgrass at site 1 for Savannah Sparrow and perhaps Vesper Sparrow, carpetweed at site 3 for Chipping Sparrow, and featherfinger grass at site 4 for Savannah Sparrow). Threeawn only appeared important in late winter after substantial declines in available seed biomass.

With the exception of the perennial dropseed, panicum, and threeawn species, sparrow diets consisted of annual grass and forb seeds (panicum and threeawn species can be perennial or annual depending on the species). This may reflect the slightly disturbed nature of our study sites. However, these results are similar to Pulliam's findings (1980, 1986) that annual grass and forb seeds were dominant in Chipping Sparrow diets in southeast Arizona, even though several perennial grass species were also present. Forb seeds tend to be unarmored (lacking the awns of many grass species), making it easy for sparrows to consume these seeds without husking. Forbs also tend to produce many seeds that fall in clumps in the immediate vicinity of the plant (Brown et al. 1979). High densities of forbs may result in a clumped distribution and high abundance of seeds that allow sparrows to quickly consume large quantities to meet their energy requirements. Annual grasses also produce large quantities of seed as do perennial grasses in the genus *Sporobolus* (dropseed grasses). Dropseed was apparently not available on Pulliam's (1980, 1986) study site. However, the similarly small-sized Lehmann lovegrass, an exotic perennial that also produces numerous seeds, was the dominant perennial grass seed and important in Chipping Sparrow diets in Pulliam's study.

Some seed species present in the soil seed bank were never detected in avian diets, suggesting that sparrows avoided, or at the very least did not prefer, certain seed species. For example, vervain (*Verbena* spp.) was relatively abundant in the soil seed bank at site 1 and neckweed (*Veronica peregrina*) and clover were abundant in the soil seed bank at site 5, yet these species were never detected in avian diets. Pulliam (1980) also observed this for Chipping Sparrow in southeast Arizona. Avoidance of abundant seed suggests that other factors such as toxicity (Sherbrooke 1974, Pulliam 1980, Henderson 1990), nutrient content (Glück 1985, Greig-Smith and Wilson 1985, Diaz 1989), accessibility, seed coating, and digestibility (Greig-Smith and Crocker 1986) may influence seed preferences.

In southeast Arizona, interspecific competition among sparrow species has been found to affect resource selection (Pulliam 1975, Pulliam and Mills 1977, Pulliam 1986). There is evidence in our results to suggest that sparrows partitioned seed resources at the site where we caught the greatest number of species. This site had the combination of a high abundance and an intermediate diversity of seeds. We observed substantial differences in seeds present in the diets of sparrows captured at this site and seeds were not consumed in relation to availability. White-crowned and Brewer's Sparrows had a narrower diet than other species. White-crowned Sparrow exploited amaranth seeds (63% of their diet), a medium sized forb seed that was relatively large, and swallowed whole (no husking required). Brewer's Sparrows specialized on dropseed (45% of diet), a small, unarmored grass seed. The apparent narrower diet, however, may be due, in part, to the smaller sample sizes for these two species compared to the other three dominant sparrows.

Pulliam (1986) argued that sparrow species should have less dietary overlap when seed production is high. In years of high seed production, such as the year of our study, he suggested little or no overlap will occur among co-existing species because sparrows will specialize on seeds they consume the most efficiently. Based on seed biomass and handling time, Pulliam (1985) predicted smaller sparrows should specialize on smaller seeds and larger sparrows on larger seed sizes. However, he suggested that large bodied sparrows should be equally efficient at handling small and large-sized seeds whereas small bodied sparrows would be most efficient at handling small-sized seeds. We observed the two small-bodied sparrows (Chipping and Brewer's Sparrows) to exhibit a preference for the small-sized seeds supporting Pulliam's assertion that small-bodied sparrows specialize on small-sized seeds when seed production is intermediate to high. However, our observations related to the diets of the larger-bodied sparrows did not follow Pulliam's theory; seed preferences varied among the three larger-bodied sparrows from large- to small-sized seeds. Benkman and Pulliam (1988) suggested resource partitioning is less pronounced in emberizid sparrows because they consume a smaller range of seed sizes and these seeds have fewer structural defenses. The observed variability in seed size preferences by the larger-bodied sparrows in our study suggests that seed size and availability are not the only factors driving seed selection by larger-bodied sparrows. The observed variability in the diets of Savannah and Vesper sparrows across sites supports the assertion that larger-bodied sparrows can efficiently consume a greater variety of seed sizes. This was especially evident for the larger Vesper Sparrow that had a different preferred seed at each of the four sites where it was present, with preferred seed sizes ranging from 0.1 to 1.8 mg.

Changes in seed preferences are likely related to changes in the relative abundance of seeds throughout the winter and due to changes in avian community composition. We observed a shift in seed preferences by sparrows from mid- to late-winter at site 3 where seed biomass declined by 50% over the same time period and the relative abundance of seed species changed. Dropseed remained the preferred seed species for sparrows in mid- and late-winter with the exception of Savannah Sparrow. This seed species had a slight increase in relative abundance in late-winter compared to mid-winter, and this seed species increased in Chipping and Brewer Sparrows diets in late winter. The larger, armored threeawn seeds also became substantially more important in the diets of both sparrows despite a substantial decline in relative abundance (7.6% vs 0.7%) between mid- and late-winter, respectively. The small stinkgrass seed was not consumed by Chipping Sparrow in mid-winter but was part of their diet in late winter likely because this seed species had a higher relative abundance in late-winter. Diets changed substantially for Savannah Sparrow between the two winter periods whereas Vesper Sparrow diets changed somewhat but dropseed remained the preferred seed species during both periods. The large-sized cupgrass was preferred by Savannah Sparrows in mid-winter; however,

cupgrass had almost disappeared from the soil seed bank samples by late-winter. In response, it also disappeared from Savannah Sparrow diets and was replaced by the smaller sized dropseed. Pulliam (1980, 1986) also observed a shift in diet for Chipping Sparrow from mid- to late-winter with a diet shift toward larger, armored seeds. We did not observe a clear dietary shift in any of the dominant species. Chipping and Brewer's Sparrows, however, did consume substantially more of the large-sized, armored threeawn seeds in late winter but their diet included a diversity of seed sizes and types during both winter periods.

Winter sparrows consumed a large diversity of seed throughout the winter period. Perennial and annual grasses and forb seeds were all important components of sparrow diets. The dominance of a few key seed species in the diets of all winter sparrow species has strong implications for the management of granivorous birds and associated habitats in the southwestern United States and northern Mexico. Dropseed seeds were important in the diets of all five sparrow species. Based on our study, results indicate that seeds from dropseed are an important component of winter sparrow diets. This is an abundant perennial grass species in the Chihuahuan Desert and management of grasslands with a large dropseed component may influence seed production and distribution. Proper grassland management during the growing season is critical to ensure sufficient seed production for granivorous sparrows. Additional data are needed on the effects of the timing and intensity of livestock grazing and other management practices on seed production in grasslands containing dropseed species.

ACKNOWLEDGEMENTS

This research was funded by the USDA National Research Initiative, Managed Ecosystems Program fund #2005-35101-15366 to M. Desmond, the National Science Foundation funded ADVANCE Institutional Transformation Program at New Mexico State University, fund #NSF0123690, the New Mexico Agricultural Experiment Station, T & E Inc., the Mexican National Council of Science and Technology (CONACyT), and the National Park Service United States-Mexico Affairs Office. We thank the personnel from Animas Foundation at the Diamond A Ranch (Gray Ranch) for their support especially to B. Brown, K. Peterson, J. Medina, D. Hadley, S. Hadley, S. Smith, and A. Laudert. R. Kochevar, and M. Gill from the New Mexico Department of Agriculture State Seed Laboratory assisted with seed identification. W. Gould assisted with statistical advice. A. Cabrera generously provided us with the Spanish translation of the abstract. We thank T. Brush, J. Dunning, D. Krueper, C. Marti, J. Ruth, and one anonymous reviewer for helpful comments on the manuscript. This is a New Mexico Agricultural Experiment Station publication, New Mexico State University, Las Cruces, New Mexico supported by state funds and the United States Hatch Act.

Studies in Avian Biology No. 37:113–124

DISTRIBUTION AND ABUNDANCE OF BREEDING ARIZONA GRASSHOPPER SPARROW (*AMMODRAMUS SAVANNARUM AMMOLEGUS*) IN THE SOUTHWESTERN UNITED STATES: PAST, PRESENT, AND FUTURE

Janet M. Ruth

Abstract. The Arizona Grasshopper Sparrow (*Ammodramus savannarum ammolegus*) breeds in desert grasslands of southeastern Arizona and southwestern New Mexico in the US, and in adjacent parts of northern Sonora and Chihuahua, Mexico. Roads that were surveyed in 1982 and 1987 in Arizona and New Mexico were relocated and roadside survey protocols were repeated in 2004 and 2005 to identify changes in distribution or abundance of the subspecies during the subsequent 17 yr. The Sonoita and San Rafael valleys in Arizona and the Animas Valley in New Mexico remain as primary population centers, supporting the highest mean numbers of singing males per stop, as well as the largest populations of Arizona Grasshopper Sparrows in the US. Mean number of singing males per stop was highest in the San Rafael Valley. Mean number of singing males per survey stop showed an increasing pattern from 1982–1987 and a subsequent decline to the present (2004–2005). Present bird densities are intermediate in value between 1982 and 1987 values. Small populations remain in the Altar, San Pedro, Sulphur Springs, and San Bernardino valleys in Arizona. The valleys evaluated in this and historical surveys represent the areas in which almost all Arizona Grasshopper Sparrows breed in the US; if any additional areas exist, they support peripheral, small, or remnant populations. Although historic, current, and future land use, and current and future threats differ among valleys, the primary factors posing threats to the future of Arizona Grasshopper Sparrow populations appear to be loss and/or degradation of habitat due to exurban development, overgrazing, and the effects of long-term drought.

Key Words: abundance, *Ammodramus savannarum ammolegus*, Arizona, distribution, Grasshopper Sparrow, New Mexico, semi-desert grasslands, Southwest, status.

DISTRIBUCIÓN Y ABUNDANCIA DE *AMMODRAMUS SAVANNARUM AMMOLEGUS* ANIDANDO EN EL SUROESTE DE LOS ESTADOS UNIDOS: PASADO, PRESENTE Y FUTURO

Resumen. Ammodramus savannarum ammolegus anida en los pastizales desérticos del sureste de Arizona y suroeste de Nuevo México en los Estados Unidos, y en las áreas contiguas del norte de Sonora y Chihuahua en México. Los sitios en los que se realizaron censos durante 1982 y 1987 al margen de caminos en Arizona y Nuevo México fueron ubicados y se repitieron los protocolos en 2004 y 2005 para identificar cambios en distribución o abundancia de estos gorriones después de 17 años. Los valles de Sonoita y San Rafael en Arizona y el Valle de las Animas en Nuevo México se siguen siendo los centros poblacionales principales, manteniendo los promedios más altos de machos territoriales por parada, al igual que las poblaciones más grandes de *A. savannarum ammolegus* en los Estados Unidos. El número promedio más alto de machos territoriales por parada se encontró en el Valle de San Rafael. El promedio de machos por parada mostró un incremento de 1982 a 1987, y una disminución posterior hacia el presente (2004/2005). Las densidades de aves en la actualidad muestran valores intermedios con relación a las densidades de 1982 y 1987. Poblaciones pequeñas continúan existiendo en los valles de Altar, San Pedro, Sulphur Springs y San Bernardino, en Arizona. Los valles evaluados en este trabajo además de las prospecciones históricas representan las áreas en las que casi todos los individuos de *A. savannarum ammolegus* anidan en los Estados Unidos; en caso de que existan áreas adicionales, esas áreas mantienen poblaciones periféricas, pequeñas o remanentes. Aunque la historia del uso de suelo y las amenazas actuales y futuras difieren entre los valles, los factores primarios que imponen amenazas a futuro para las poblaciones de *A. savannarum ammolegus* son aparentemente la pérdida y/o degradación de hábitat debido al desarrollo suburbano, pastoreo intensivo y los efectos de sequía a largo plazo.

Endemic grassland birds have shown steeper, more consistent, and more widespread declines than any other guild of North American bird species (Knopf 1994). Documenting population status and trends, and understanding distribution, life histories, and ecology are essential in conservation planning for such avian species of concern. Southwestern semi-desert grasslands support an important suite of breeding grassland birds of conservation concern (Rich et al. 2004), and much remains to be learned about their status and ecology (Herkert and Knopf 1998).

The Arizona Grasshopper Sparrow (*Ammodramus savannarum ammolegus*) is a subspecies (Oberholser 1942) of the widely distributed Grasshopper Sparrow and has a disjunct breeding population in the desert grasslands of southeastern Arizona, southwestern New Mexico, and adjacent parts of northern Sonora and Chihuahua, Mexico (Vickery 1996, Williams 2007). Although poorly documented, its winter range is believed to extend from southern Arizona south to Sinaloa and Morelos, Mexico, and Guatemala (Land 1970, Vickery 1996). Detailed physical descriptions and discussions of Arizona Grasshopper Sparrow taxonomy can be found in Strong (1988) and Vickery (1996).

Strong (1988) and Corman and Wise-Gervais (2005) adequately document the Arizona Grasshopper Sparrow in Arizona. However, documentation of its presence in New Mexico requires some clarification. Arizona Grasshopper Sparrows were first detected in New Mexico in June 1977, in the Animas Valley (Meents 1979). The first surveys targeting this subspecies were conducted in June 1987 (Williams 1991). Forty-five individuals were counted on a 19-stop Breeding Bird Survey (BBS)-style survey route on 10 June 1987, and seven specimens were collected by Williams on 17 July 1987, which were verified as *A. s. ammolegus* (Williams 1991, 2007). In July and August 1987, Strong (1988) also found Arizona Grasshopper Sparrows in the Animas Valley.

The Grasshopper Sparrow is of conservation concern. Peterjohn and Sauer (1999) found that the species showed a significant range-wide population decline between 1966 and 1996. The Arizona Grasshopper Sparrow subspecies is listed as high priority for desert grassland habitats in the Partners in Flight Bird Conservation Plans for both Arizona (Latta et al. 1999) and New Mexico (New Mexico Partners in Flight 2007). USDI Fish and Wildlife Service (2002) includes Arizona Grasshopper Sparrow on the list for the Sierra Madre Occidental Bird Conservation Region (BCR #34), which includes the desert grasslands of southeastern Arizona and southwestern New Mexico. The subspecies is also classified as Endangered in the State of New Mexico.

The USDI Fish and Wildlife Service (USFWS) contracted two reports on the status of this subspecies in the last 25 yr through the Arizona Natural Heritage Program and the Arizona Game and Fish Department (Mills 1982, Strong 1988), but this information has not been updated in the subsequent 17 yr. Concerns regarding

Arizona Grasshopper Sparrow have focused on apparent fluctuations or possible cyclical variations in a relatively small breeding population (Strong 1988, Williams 1997), evidence of a long-term decline in the New Mexico population (Williams 2007), and similar anecdotal information for Arizona. Limited information about its breeding ecology, the effects of habitat loss due to suburban development, and the effects of habitat modification due to overgrazing and alteration of natural fire regime are also concerns. Recent conservation interest has led to recognition of the need for additional information about population status and trends of Arizona Grasshopper Sparrow, as well as home range and territory size, presence of population sources or sinks, and causes of population declines (Latta et al. 1999, New Mexico Partners in Flight 2007).

The objectives of this study were to: (1) document the current distribution and abundance of Arizona Grasshopper Sparrow using historical survey methods in a more clearly described and repeatable format to make any future surveys replicable; and (2) compare current distribution and abundance of Arizona Grasshopper Sparrows with historical data (Mills 1982, Strong 1988).

METHODS

SITES

The grasslands of southeastern Arizona and southwestern New Mexico have been variously described as plains or plains-mesa grasslands and semi-desert or desert grasslands along an elevational gradient (Dick-Peddie 1993, Brown 1994). They support a variety of native annual and perennial bunchgrasses including three-awns (*Aristida* spp.), gramas (*Bouteloua* spp.), curly mesquite (*Hilaria belangeri*), cane beard-grass (*Andropogon barbinodis*), wolftail (*Lycurus phleoides*), and plains lovegrass (*Eragrostis intermedia*), as well as the exotic Lehman (*E. lehmanniana*) and Boer (*E. curvula* var. *conferta*) lovegrasses.

Identification of historical survey locations involved relocating road segments in the US that were surveyed in previous studies (Mills 1982, Strong 1988). Major foci were the Sonoita and San Rafael valleys in Arizona and the Animas Valley in New Mexico, with less intense efforts in Arizona's Altar, San Pedro, Sulphur Springs, and San Bernardino Valleys. The following areas were surveyed (Fig. 1):

    Sonoita Valley (Santa Cruz and Pima counties)—from Box Canyon in the north, Mustang Mountains in the east, Canelo Hills in the south, and just beyond

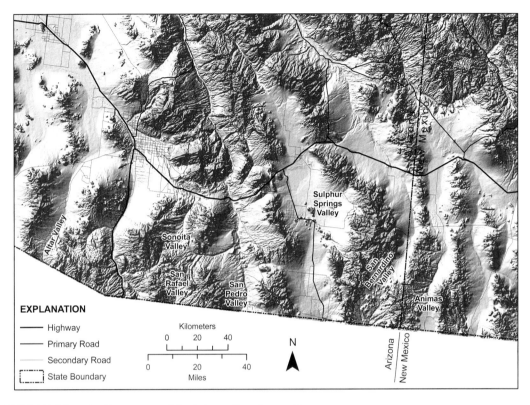

FIGURE 1. Map of valleys surveyed for Arizona Grasshopper Sparrows.

Sonoita in the west (lat/long ranges from 31°35′03″ to 31°44′16″N; and from 110°29′23″ to 110°40′32″W).

San Rafael Valley (Santa Cruz County)—the central San Rafael Valley and Campini Mesa (from 31°20′05″ to 31°29′06″N; and from 110°29′13″ to 110°39′04″W).

Animas Valley (Hidalgo County)—the Diamond A (formerly Gray) Ranch in the southern part of the valley (from 31°24′10″ to 31°33′14″N; and from 108°52′31″ to 108°55′10″W).

Altar Valley (Pima County)—within and near the Buenos Aires National Wildlife Refuge (NWR) (from 31°29′51″ to 31°38′46″N; and from 111°27′57″ to 111°32′44″W).

San Pedro Valley (Cochise County)—the southern part of the valley in the area around the Coronado National Memorial and Palominas (from 31°20′56″ to 31°26′20″N; and from 110°07′17″ to 110°13′41″W); in 2005, an additional historical survey was repeated in the Allen Flats area northeast of Benson and south of the Winchester Mountains (from 32°13′45″ to 32°17′06″N; and from 110°04′29″ to 110°09′10″W).

Sulphur Springs Valley (Cochise County)—just west and northwest of the Chiricahua Mountains from McNeal to Willcox (from 31°35′26″ to 32°11′43″N; and from 109°25′39″ to 109°45′20″W); in 2005, an additional historical survey was repeated in the Fort Grant area southwest of the Pinaleño Mountains (from 32°33′27″ to 32°35′20″N; and from 109°58′12″ to 110°05′34″W).

San Bernardino Valley (Cochise County)—from Rucker Canyon Road in the southwest to the Geronimo Surrender Monument in the northeast (from 31°36′30″ to 31°41′26″N; and from 109°06′53″ to 109°15′05″W).

ROADSIDE SURVEYS

Methods and survey locations were designed to cover the known historical range of Arizona Grasshopper Sparrow (Mills 1982, Strong 1988). Methods were replicated, as accurately as possible, to enable comparisons between historical and current data. Based on their written descriptions, the road segments were relocated and resurveyed. Strong described their methodology as "driving roads within [the] historical range [of the Arizona Grasshopper Sparrow]." They "stopped in areas of suitable habitat, or at predetermined intervals in large patches of continuous habitat…stops were made in areas of marginal habitat, but areas of obviously unsuitable habitat were not censused" (Strong 1988:8). Detailed information about stop locations was not available in their reports. However, based on informal surveys conducted in 2002 and 2003, I determined that using a standard 0.5-mile (0.8 km) interval between stops usually resulted in the same number of stops listed by Strong for a particular road segment. On occasion, it was not possible to accurately resurvey a particular road segment, either for safety reasons or because a segment was no longer publicly accessible or identifiable. This resulted in different numbers of road segments, stops on a segment, and/or mileage (Table 1). All roadside survey stops were recorded with a global positioning system unit and described with visual and mileage cues to facilitate relocation in the future. Historical road segments were surveyed and observations were included in these results even if no Grasshopper Sparrows were recorded in 2004 and/or 2005.

Additional surveys of areas not covered in earlier surveys, hereafter termed non-historical surveys, were conducted in the Sonoita, San Rafael, Altar, Sulphur Springs, and Animas valleys to supplement historical routes. These data are included in the initial summaries of birds recorded in 2004–2005, but are not included in the comparisons between historical and current survey results for the valleys supporting the vast majority of the population. Data from non-historical surveys are only mentioned when the information offers additional insights. These additional segments were selected based on personal observation of potentially promising Grasshopper Sparrow habitat within the general breeding distribution of the subspecies.

Most of Mills' and Strong's surveys were conducted from 0445 to 0900 H, and occasionally in late afternoon. On sunny, warm mornings, Grasshopper Sparrow singing activity began to decrease between 0700 and 0800 H; however, on cool, cloudy mornings singing activity continued well beyond 0800 H (J. Ruth, pers. obs.). In 1987, surveys in the Sonoita and San Rafael Valleys were conducted three times during the breeding season (July and August), varying the time to ensure one early survey in order to address any potential temporal variation in singing intensities (Strong 1988). The relatively late timing of breeding surveys, both historical and current, is due to the fact

TABLE 1. SUMMARY INFORMATION ABOUT ROAD SEGMENTS SURVEYED BY VALLEY.

Valley	Mileage[a]			Number of road segments			Total number of stops		
	Mills	Strong	Ruth	Mills	Strong	Ruth	Mills	Strong	Ruth
Sonoita (AZ)	79	79	69/81	25	23	20/24	168	145	139/171
San Rafael (AZ)	50	50	44/48	13	15	14/17	105	99	88/98
Animas (NM)	NA	22	24/33	NA	5	5/7	NA	45	49/56
Altar (AZ)	14	3	14/25	1	2	3/9	11	9	20/51
San Pedro and Allen Flats (AZ)	15	2	11/11	4	1	3/4	30	6	24/24
Sulphur Springs and Fort Grant (AZ)	49	7	23/25	8	1	4/5	34	11	29/34
San Bernardino (AZ)	20	17	16/16	3	2	3/3	19	17	25/25
Santa Cruz (AZ)	16	2	6/6	7	2	2/2	24	6	6/6

[a] Mileage rounded to nearest whole number. Mills' data were gathered in 1982 (Mills 1982) and Strong's data were gathered in 1987 (Strong 1988). Mills and Strong data include some survey segments that could not be repeated in 2004–2005. Ruth data are from 2005 and x/y indicates values for repeated historic surveys (x) and a cumulative value including new surveys conducted (y).

that Arizona Grasshopper Sparrows usually breed in mid- to late-summer in response to the monsoon season, beginning to sing in July and carrying food for young from late July through August (Corman and Wise-Gervais 2005).

Current surveys were conducted between 14 July and 14 August 2004, and between 16 July and 18 August 2005. Most surveys were conducted twice during the breeding season, from 0445 to 1100 H MST in AZ (0545–1100 H MDT in NM). Every effort was made to ensure that one survey on every segment was conducted from 0445 to 0700 H. In areas where historical surveys and my previous informal surveys indicated that Grasshopper Sparrow populations were small or nonexistent, surveys were only conducted once in order to maximize effort in core areas. Methodological differences from Mills and Strong were due primarily to staff and time limitations.

Neither Mills (1982) nor Strong (1988) clearly described the amount of time spent at each survey stop, although there was a reference in Strong (1988) to some test surveys that used 3-min intervals (it is possible that this was their standard time frame). Therefore, I used the standard 3 min per stop as described in the BBS methodology. I have no reason to believe detectability of singing males was different either among valleys or years (J. Ruth, pers. obs.). Neither Mills nor Strong mentioned any distance limitation on the recorded observations at their survey stops. For consistency I also recorded all singing males seen or heard from the stop point and did not estimate or record distance. On many occasions singing males were heard, but never seen. Estimating distance to unseen singing males would have been difficult, and would have taken additional time. Limited time and resources to complete these surveys across the region precluded me from adding to the protocol.

Both Mills and Strong used taped playback of Grasshopper Sparrow songs to supplement their surveys. Neither described their protocol other than to say that taped playback was used to stimulate a response if no singing males were heard. Their data did not distinguish between the number of birds recorded without and with taped playback. Therefore, in order to be consistent, I also used taped playback. However, I only played a taped song after the standard 3 min had elapsed at each stop and recorded additional individuals separately in my records. A tape recording that included the primary and sustained songs and the trill was played for 1–2 min, in approximately the four cardinal directions. It was my observation (as well as Mills' and Strong's) that if there were

male Grasshopper Sparrows in the area, they responded quickly and aggressively to the recording. Because females sometimes respond by coming in and giving a trill call, I made every effort to separate out these additional individuals in my recorded observations in order to include only one individual of a pair. For purposes of comparability with the data from the historical surveys, these two numbers were combined. The maximum number of singing males recorded (total number during the 3 min + any additional singing males observed with taped playback) was used to calculate mean number of singing males per stop and singing male abundance.

ANALYSES AND STATISTICAL METHODS

I analyzed and compared bird survey results using mean number of singing males per stop. This provides a more standardized measure than abundance (total number of singing males); it is not as dependent on repeating the exact number of historical road surveys or survey stops. This is important because, in some cases, a few surveys conducted by Mills and/or Strong were not repeated in 2004 and/or 2005, or it was not possible to survey the same number of stops (Table 1). Surveys that recorded no birds were included in calculations of mean number of singing males per stop in order to be consistent and comparable with historical survey reports. In general, calculating the mean without the zero segments would have resulted in slightly higher values. Information about the total number of singing males recorded for a particular valley and year are presented in the text, where appropriate, and in Table 2.

Among-year differences in the mean number of singing males per stop for each valley, using road segments as replicates, were evaluated using one-way analysis of variance (ANOVA). Regional among-year and among-valley differences in numbers of singing males per stop, using road segments as replicates, were evaluated using two-way ANOVA. For the two-way ANOVA, data from the three valleys supporting the main populations of Arizona Grasshopper Sparrows were used, and only those segments with data available for all four years were included. In all cases, Tukey's multiple comparison procedure, with alpha = 0.05, was used to compare means among years.

RESULTS

An assumption of this study is that it documents the breeding distribution and abundance of Arizona Grasshopper Sparrows. The

TABLE 2. COMPARISON OF MEAN (SE) NUMBER OF SINGING MALE ARIZONA GRASSHOPPER SPARROWS PER STOP FOR EACH VALLEY, USING A ONE-WAY ANOVA TO EXAMINE ANNUAL DIFFERENCES. LETTERS REPRESENTING THE TUKEY GROUPING (A, B) ARE PLACED BEHIND EACH YEAR. TOTAL NUMBERS OF SINGING MALES RECORDED IN EACH VALLEY BY YEAR ARE PROVIDED FOR REFERENCE.

Valley	Year	N^a	Mean number of singing males per stop (SE)	Results of ANOVA	Total number of singing males
San Rafael	1982 B	13	1.22 (0.26)	$F_{3,57} = 6.90$; $P < 0.01$	130
	1987 A	15	2.51 (0.29)		265
	2004 A	16	2.49 (0.23)		205
	2005 A	17	2.79 (0.24)		269
Sonoita	1982 A	25	1.07 (0.16)	$F_{3,92} = 1.72$; $P = 0.17$	204
	1987 A	23	1.67 (0.27)		300
	2004 A	24	1.60 (0.22)		271
	2005 A	24	1.48 (0.18)		263
Animas	1982	NA			
	1987 A	5	1.84 (0.57)	$F_{2,16} = 0.38$; $P = 0.69$	87
	2004 A	7	1.44 (0.42)		68
	2005 A	7	1.27 (0.39)		76
Altar	1982 A	1	0.18 (—)	$F_{3,14} = 0.88$; $P = 0.48$	2
	1987 A	2	1.15 (0.65)		11
	2004 A	6	0.59 (0.12)		15
	2005 A	9	0.59 (0.20)		18
San Pedro	1982 A	4	0.25 (0.15)	$F_{3,8} = 2.00$; $P = 0.19$	9
	1987 A	1	1.33 (—)		8
	2004 A	3	0.67 (0.33)		11
	2005 A	4	0.50 (0.19)		11
Sulphur Springs	1982 A	8	0.04 (0.04)	$F_{3,14} = 1.63$; $P = 0.23$	1
	1987 A	1	0.00 (—)		0
	2004 A	4	0.15 (0.09)		4
	2005 A	5	0.26 (0.12)		10
San Bernardino	1982 A	3	0.04 (0.04)	$F_{3,8} = 0.45$; $P = 0.72$	1
	1987 A	2	0.19 (0.19)		3
	2004 A	4	0.06 (0.06)		2
	2005 A	3	0.11 (0.11)		3

[a] N = number of road segments.

objectives of the study did not include confirming the breeding status of this subspecies, which is documented elsewhere (Vickery 1996; Corman and Wise-Gervais 2005). However, during the surveys I did record numerous individuals and pairs of Arizona Grasshopper Sparrows carrying food in the Sonoita, San Rafael, and Animas Valleys, a behavior regularly recognized by Breeding Bird Atlas projects (Corman and Wise-Gervais 2005) as confirming breeding. All of these observations occurred during the time period of August 4–16 in either 2004 or 2005.

Although, as discussed elsewhere, use of measures of total numbers of singing males recorded in a valley to look for difference among valleys or years is generally inappropriate, use of these measures as an index of which valleys support the largest populations of Arizona Grasshopper Sparrows is acceptable. This is because the surveys were designed to sample the entire area in each valley that supported birds, given the limits imposed by available roads. Therefore, those valleys in which large numbers of singing males were recorded represent valleys with large populations, and

those with substantially lower numbers have small populations. In 2004–2005 the San Rafael, Sonoita, and Animas Valleys supported the largest populations of Arizona Grasshopper Sparrows in the US, and the other valleys supported much smaller populations (Table 2).

ANNUAL VARIATION BY VALLEY

Comparisons of mean number of singing males per stop among years are first presented separately for each valley due to the likelihood that different factors (e.g., land use, management practices, precipitation, soil characteristics) act differently on birds and habitats in different valleys and therefore temporal patterns may vary among valleys. For ease of reference, the dates used for Mills' and Strong's surveys are 1982 and 1987, respectively, the years in which they collected data.

Sonoita Valley

I found no evidence of significant differences in mean number of singing males per stop among years in the Sonoita Valley (Table 2). However, the pattern was one of lowest numbers in 1982, highest in 1987, and was intermediate in 2004 and 2005. I found no evidence of overall expansion or contraction of distribution in the valley—of the 20 historical road segments that were resurveyed, birds continued to be recorded on 18 segments, birds were recorded on one that had not had Grasshopper Sparrows historically, and no birds were recorded on one that had birds historically. The four new (non-historical) road segments were located within the portion of the valley that had been historically surveyed, three of them within the Bureau of Land Management (BLM) Las Cienegas National Conservation Area.

San Rafael Valley (including Campini Mesa)

I found significant differences in mean number of singing males per stop among years in the San Rafael Valley (Table 2). Values in 1982 were significantly lower than the values in 1987, 2004, and 2005. There was no evidence of significant differences among the latter 3 yr, although the pattern was for the highest numbers in 2005 and intermediate numbers in 1987 and 2004. I found no evidence of overall expansion or contraction of distributions in the valley—of the 14 historical road segments that were resurveyed, birds continued to be recorded on all 14. The four new (non-historical) road segments were located in the southern portion of the valley that had been historically surveyed, in the new San Rafael Short Grass Prairie Preserve State Park (Arizona).

Animas Valley

Mills (1982) did not conduct surveys in the Animas Valley, so data are only available for 1987, 2004, and 2005. I found no evidence of significant differences in mean number of singing males per stop among years in the Animas Valley (Table 2). However, the pattern was one of highest numbers in 1987, and declining numbers in 2004 and 2005. I found some evidence of a minor southward contraction of distributions in the valley—on the northernmost of the five historical road segments, six individuals were recorded in 1987, but only one was recorded in 2004 and none in 2005. This area appeared to no longer contain optimal habitat, since it was dominated by shrubs with little grass cover (J. Ruth, pers. obs.). The two new (non-historical) road segments were located at the southern end of the portion of the valley that had been historically surveyed.

Interpreting results for the remaining valleys requires more caution. The sample sizes of road segments surveyed were small, total numbers of individuals recorded were low, and in these sparsely populated valleys, different locations and numbers of road segments were surveyed in different years (both historical and current). The values for mean number of singing males per stop are substantially lower for all of these valleys than for the previous three valleys (Table 2).

Altar Valley

I found no evidence of significant differences in mean number of singing males per stop among years in the Altar Valley (Table 2). However, the pattern was one of the lowest numbers in 1982, highest in 2005, and numbers were intermediate in 1987 and 2004. I found some evidence that the size and distribution of the small population in the Altar Valley has shifted during the time period between these surveys and historical surveys. Of the three historical road segments that were resurveyed, birds continued to be recorded on two of them. However, the majority of the singing males recorded in 2004 and 2005 were observed on new (non-historical) road segments centered on the road called Pronghorn Loop on the USFWS Buenos Aires NWR.

San Pedro Valley

I found no evidence of significant differences in mean number of singing males per stop among years in the San Pedro Valley (including Allen Flats; Table 2). The pattern was one of the lowest numbers in 1982, highest in 1987, and numbers were intermediate in 2004 and 2005. An additional observation from 2005 is notable. Five of the 11 singing males recorded for the San Pedro Valley were observed on a new (non-historical) road segment and were singing from territories in two large center-pivot irrigated alfalfa fields along Palominas Road (runs north from Palominas, AZ between Highway 92 and Hereford Road; 31°24′07″N, 110°07′24″W).

Sulphur Springs Valley

I found no evidence of significant differences in mean number of singing males per stop among years in the Sulphur Springs Valley (including the Fort Grant area) (Table 2). The pattern was one of the lowest numbers in 1987 (zero), highest in 2005, and numbers were intermediate in 1982 and 2004. Three of the ten individuals in 2005 were recorded on a new (non-historical) road segment (Turkey Creek Road—running east from the intersection of the 90°bend in Highway 181 and Kuykendall Cutoff Road).

San Bernardino Valley

I found no evidence of significant differences in mean number of singing males per stop among years in the San Bernardino Valley (Table 2). The pattern was one of the lowest numbers in 1982, highest in 1987, and numbers were intermediate in 2004 and 2005.

REGIONAL VARIATION BY VALLEY AND YEAR

When looking for regional patterns using the data from the three valleys that support the majority of the Arizona Grasshopper Sparrow population in the US (San Rafael, Sonoita, and Animas valleys), I found evidence of significant differences in mean number of singing males per stop among both valleys and years (Table 3). Using pooled data across years, the San Rafael Valley shows significantly higher values than either the Sonoita or Animas valley, but the Tukey test results do not allow discrimination between the Sonoita and Animas valleys. However, the general pattern is one of lowest numbers for Animas Valley and intermediate numbers for Sonoita Valley. Using pooled data across valleys, 1982 shows significantly lower numbers than 1987, but the Tukey test results do not allow discrimination among the other years. However, the general pattern was one of the lowest numbers in 1982, highest for 1987, and intermediate numbers for 2004 and 2005. I found no evidence of interactions between valley and year affecting mean number of singing males per stop (Table 3).

DISCUSSION

DISTRIBUTION AND STATUS OF ARIZONA GRASSHOPPER SPARROW

To the best of my knowledge, the valleys sampled in this and historical surveys represent the areas in which almost all Arizona Grasshopper Sparrows breed in the US. In Arizona, this is consistent with the results of the Arizona Breeding Bird Atlas (Corman and Wise-Gervais 2005). If any additional areas exist, they support peripheral, remnant populations with small densities and numbers. For example, a rapidly declining, small population has been monitored in the Playas Valley, New Mexico, just to the east of the Animas Valley population (Williams 1997), and some historically surveyed road segments in the Santa Cruz Valley were informally surveyed, but the habitat was suboptimal and no birds were recorded in 2005 (J. Ruth, pers. obs.). In addition, Arizona Grasshopper Sparrows bred in northern Sonora, Mexico, in 1982 (Mills 1982) and 1986 (Strong 1988) and Flesch (2008) reports a relatively high density of Grasshopper Sparrows (0.84 ± 0.09 territories/ha) at Rancho Los Fresnos in the Upper San Pedro watershed along the border in northern Sonora. Based on observations in the Animas Valley just north of the border, they are probably found in the grasslands that stretch into northwestern Chihuahua as well.

Concentrations of Arizona Grasshopper Sparrows, both mean number of singing males per stop and total number recorded, in the Sonoita, San Rafael, and Animas Valleys of the US in 2004–2005 are consistent with their distribution 20–25 yr ago (Mills 1982, Strong 1988). Of all areas surveyed, these three valleys have also retained the largest stretches of continuous, open, high-quality desert grassland with little shrub component. Although breeding

TABLE 3. COMPARISON OF REGIONAL MEAN (SE) NUMBER OF SINGING MALE ARIZONA GRASSHOPPER SPARROWS PER STOP IN THE THREE VALLEYS SUPPORTING THE MAJORITY OF THE POPULATION, USING A TWO-WAY ANOVA TO EXAMINE DIFFERENCES BY YEAR AND BY VALLEY. LETTERS REPRESENTING THE TUKEY GROUPING (A,B) ARE PLACED BEHIND EACH VALLEY OR YEAR.

Variable class	Variable	N[a]	Mean number of singing males per stop (SE)	Results of ANOVA
Valley	San Rafael A	40	2.29 (0.21)	$F_{2,124} = 9.74; P < 0.01$
	Sonoita B	80	1.55 (0.12)	
	Animas B	15	1.24 (0.28)	
Year	1982 B	30	1.19 (0.15)	$F_{3,124} = 6.37; P < 0.01$
	1987 A	35	2.09 (0.22)	
	2004 AB	35	1.81 (0.20)	
	2005 AB	35	1.77 (0.21)	
Valley × Year				$F_{5,124} = 1.57; P = 0.17$

[a] N = number of road segments.

Notes: Values for mean number of singing males per stop are pooled across years or across the three valleys for this analysis. Valley × Year represents an interaction term between the two variable classes.

Grasshopper Sparrows tolerate a small shrub component in their grassland habitat, for the most part they avoid grassland with extensive shrub cover (Vickery 1996; J. Ruth, pers. obs.).

Despite differences in numbers of birds among the valleys, it would be difficult to state with certainty which of the three valleys supported the largest populations based on these data. Total numbers of singing males recorded represents an inappropriate measure, being potentially confounded by several variables—differences in the amount of land in appropriate grassland habitat within the valleys, differences in the mean number of singing males per stop, as well as total mileage, number of road segments, and number of stops surveyed. Perhaps the best example of this would be a comparison of data on the Sonoita and San Rafael Valleys. According to Southwest ReGAP data (USGS National Gap Analysis Program 2004), the Sonoita Valley supports 44% more grassland (339,800 km^2, primarily in the Apacherian-Chihuahuan piedmont semi-desert grassland and steppe land-cover classification) than the San Rafael (190,000 km^2 of the same classification). In addition, in 2005 about 70% more miles and 75% more stops were surveyed in the Sonoita Valley than the San Rafael Valley (Table 1). In spite of this, in 2005 the total number of singing males recorded in the San Rafael was basically the same as the Sonoita Valley (Table 2). This phenomenon may be at least partially explained by the fact that mean number of singing males per stop were significantly higher in the San Rafael Valley than in the Sonoita Valley (Table 3). It is not appropriate to take the values of mean number of singing males per stop as calculated in this study and extrapolate to a population estimate.

Although most of the analyses did not show statistically significant differences among years, the overall pattern in Arizona Grasshopper Sparrow population, as measured in this study, is one with the lowest numbers in 1982, highest numbers in 1987, and subsequent declines from 1987 to 2004–2005. In most cases numbers recorded in 2004–2005 were lower than 1987 but higher than 1982, with the exception of the San Rafael Valley.

Some cautionary notes should be offered regarding the value of these survey data to determine long-term trends. First, much of the information we have suggests that, like many southwestern grassland species, Arizona Grasshopper Sparrow populations show substantial annual and/or short-term fluctuations. Using only four survey data points from widely separate years can obscure short-term fluctuations and provide misleading information

about long-term trends. We can not determine where these four points fall along what may be a fluctuating line. As an example, Strong (1988) reported the results of some additional surveys conducted in 1986. For the Sonoita and San Rafael Valleys, substantial declines occurred in mean number of singing males per stop and total number of singing males recorded between 1982 (Mills 1982) and 1986 and then a large increase occurred from 1986–1987 (Strong 1988). These results and my observations from informal surveys prior to 2004 (J. Ruth, unpubl. data) indicate that substantial annual variation can occur in Arizona Grasshopper Sparrow numbers. In a system with substantial short-term fluctuations, there is no real substitute for continuous, long-term datasets for determining long-term population trends. Having recognized these caveats, we can state that our results provide evidence that current Arizona Grasshopper Sparrow populations in the two valleys in Arizona supporting the largest populations have not increased beyond the values recorded in 1987 nor have they declined below the values recorded in 1982.

Secondly, a major assumption in this study and its predecessors is that measures of mean number of singing males per stop and abundance are reliable measures of good habitat. The literature indicates that this is not always the case (Van Horne 1983, Vickery et al. 1992). Birds may be found in habitats or areas because of loss of or exclusion from optimal habitats, habitat degradation, competition, or site fidelity (something that Vickery et al. [1992] found for some Grasshopper Sparrow populations). Just as no good substitute for long-term population monitoring exists for determining population trends, demographic studies are important for determining whether birds are successfully reproducing and surviving in particular habitat types or sites. However, in a recent literature review, Bock and Jones (2004) found that per capita reproductive success usually is positively correlated with density.

Thirdly, in making comparisons across years and across different surveys, it is always important to ensure consistent methodologies. The use of replicable methodologies such as limited-radius point counts or distance sampling in both the historical and current surveys would have provided more consistent approaches and would have allowed for easier replication in the future. It would have had the additional advantage of allowing for actual density estimates. Another consistency factor relates to observer differences. It is possible that significant differences existed in the abilities of Ruth, Strong, and Mills to detect

Grasshopper Sparrow song—notoriously high-pitched and difficult for some observers to detect. In 1987 Mills and Strong did conduct a joint test of observer differences, and found no obvious differences in the total number of singing males observed along a road segment, although stop-by-stop comparisons showed more variation (Strong 1988). Surveys in 2004–2005 were all conducted by a single observer (J. Ruth). Although not a formal test of the sort reported by Strong, I informally tested my ability to detect Grasshopper Sparrow songs on one occasion in the field with an experienced colleague. We each recorded similar numbers of singing individuals during timed intervals.

Finally, one of the limitations of the current surveys is the lack of habitat data collected, primarily a result of limited time and resources. The collection of data about the habitat type and condition, and the land use characteristics at the survey points (e.g., rural vs. exurban, ungrazed vs. moderately grazed vs. heavily grazed, cropland) would have allowed for comparisons of bird data with habitat condition or type and would have provided valuable baseline information for future replications.

FACTORS POTENTIALLY AFFECTING GRASSHOPPER SPARROW HABITAT

The scope of this study did not permit a detailed evaluation of the factors influencing desert grassland ecosystem dynamics, a subject about which there are many differing opinions. However, many good references do exist that provide details about the history and ecology of this region (Dick-Peddie 1993, McClaran and Van Devender 1995, Finch 2004). Several, often inter-related factors influence desert grassland ecosystem dynamics, and therefore Arizona Grasshopper Sparrow populations. Major factors include grazing practices, suburban and agricultural development, drought, changes in historical fire regimes, and encroachment by shrubs and exotic plants.

The issue of grazing impacts in the arid Southwest is a contentious one (Finch 2004). However, there seems little doubt that historical overgrazing in this part of the country (Bahre 1995, Finch 2004) have had long-term, substantial impacts on the structure, composition, and distribution of desert grasslands today, and that such intense grazing has had negative effects on grassland bird species (Saab et al. 1995, Finch 2004). Nevertheless, the effects of grazing vary widely depending on grazing intensity, stocking rates, season and length of grazing, environmental conditions, and land use history (Merola-Zwartjes 2004).

Although we have no data on sparrow numbers prior to domestic cattle grazing, the results of this study provide no reason to conclude that well-managed grazing is incompatible with Arizona Grasshopper Sparrow habitat, because some of the highest numbers were recorded on grazed lands in the San Rafael and Sonoita Valleys. Without sites that have never been grazed by domestic cattle, it is not possible to know how numbers in historically ungrazed habitats might compare. However, evidence shows that Arizona Grasshopper Sparrows do respond to grazing pressures in arid grasslands. Studies have shown that they were significantly more abundant on ungrazed sites than on grazed sites (Bock and Webb 1984, Bock et al. 1984, Bock and Bock 1988) and suggest that Grasshopper Sparrows respond negatively to grazing due to its effects on grass structure (J. Ruth et al., unpubl. data).

In much of southeastern Arizona, low-density suburban or exurban development is a substantial threat (Bahre 1995, Merola-Zwartjes 2004). This was predicted by both Mills (1982) and Strong (1988). The complete loss of grassland habitat is the most obvious result of suburban, or agricultural, development, but less is known about the effects of habitat degradation in remaining, fragmented grasslands. Bock et al. (2008) found Grasshopper Sparrow abundance in the Sonoita Valley to be lower in undeveloped grassland plots than in exurban grassland plots, and abundance was negatively correlated with the number of homes within 250 m. These results indicate that although many bird species were positively associated with exurban development, Grasshopper Sparrow was not one of them.

The impacts of drought on desert grasslands is something over which humans have little direct control. However, drought interacts extensively with, and may exacerbate the impacts of, grazing, fire, shrub encroachment, plant structure, and community composition in affecting grasslands and the bird species that live there.

THE HISTORY AND FUTURE OF ARIZONA GRASSHOPPER SPARROW HABITAT

Each of the valleys surveyed have different land-use histories and are influenced by different combinations of the above-mentioned factors, which have implications for Arizona Grasshopper Sparrow populations.

The Sonoita Valley supports an extensive area of good grassland habitat. Ranching has been the primary land use and will continue to be important in the future. However, the primary threat, especially around Sonoita and Elgin, may be exurban development. Agricultural development in the form of an expanding local wine industry poses a secondary threat (Strong 1988). Land ownership offers some habitat protection. The Audubon Appleton-Whittell Research Ranch comprises private and federal land dedicated to research and preservation and has not been grazed since 1968. Much of BLM land is part of the Las Cienegas National Conservation Area (NCA) and is bordered by additional state or USDA Forest Service land; it is managed for multiple-use and leased for grazing but protected from development. The central portion of the valley is primarily privately owned, and is the main focus of exurban and agricultural development pressure. As a primary population center of Arizona Grasshopper Sparrows, development, grazing practices, and other management decisions in the Sonoita Valley will have significant impacts on the future of this subspecies.

The San Rafael Valley supports an extensive area of good grassland habitat. The main land use is ranching and it is primarily in private ownership, with the exception of some Coronado National Forest and Arizona State Park land. Ranching and grazing practices will continue to be a primary factor influencing grassland habitat in the foreseeable future. Although the threat of exurban development seems less immediate here, there is land currently on the market, posing the threat of future development. If development activities in the San Rafael Valley increase in the future, they could have significant impacts on a primary population center of Arizona Grasshopper Sparrows.

The Animas Valley also supports an extensive area of grassland habitat. However, the current condition of the grasslands reflects the impacts of a combination of recent grazing practices and severe drought (Williams 2007; J. Ruth, pers. obs.) The primary land use in the southern part of the Animas Valley is ranching and will likely continue to be in the future. Land is primarily in private ownership and faces no immediate threat from development. Arizona Grasshopper Sparrow habitat is located primarily on the Diamond A (formerly Gray) Ranch, administered by The Animas Foundation as a working ranch. A continuous, long-term data set from Arizona Grasshopper Sparrow surveys exists for the Animas Valley (and adjacent Playas Valley) (Williams 2007). Because these surveys were conducted earlier in the breeding season, it is not possible to compare results directly with the results of this study. However, the patterns are consistent and the

results disturbing. Williams (2007) documents a significant population decline in the Animas and Playas Valleys over 15 yr (1992–2006). In 2005 and 2006, a slight upswing was observed in the Animas Valley—a time when cattle were removed from the Diamond A due to the ongoing drought. Although the Playas Valley initially supported a population similar to the Animas Valley (Williams 1991), it now appears nearing extirpation (Williams 2007). As a result of these findings, the New Mexico Department of Game and Fish changed its listing of Arizona Grasshopper Sparrow from Threatened to Endangered in 2006. Grazing management decisions in the Animas and Playas Valleys, in combination with future precipitation levels, will likely have significant impacts on populations there.

The Altar Valley is at the western edge of the Arizona Grasshopper Sparrow's range (Brown 1994, Flesch 1997). In the 1800s it was primarily open grassland but is now quite degraded; mesquite encroachment is a substantial problem (Bahre 1995, Flesch 1997). Remaining open grasslands administered by the Buenos Aires NWR, have not been grazed since establishment in 1985 and do not face threats from development. The presence of more Arizona Grasshopper Sparrows in the Altar Valley than historical surveys indicated is consistent with other recent findings (Flesch 1997, Corman and Wise-Gervais 2005). This is encouraging evidence that this small population is at least somewhat larger and more broadly distributed than historical surveys suggested. The suitability of grasslands in the Altar Valley for this small population is dependent on the ongoing efforts of the refuge to restore the desert grassland ecosystem through shrub and exotic grass reduction and prescribed fire.

In their current condition, the remaining valley grasslands within the historical range of the Arizona Grasshopper Sparrow do not provide either prime or substantial habitat. Grassland habitat in the San Pedro Valley, including Allen Flats, has been almost entirely lost or degraded due to suburban and agricultural development. The few patches of remaining fragmented grassland support the relict of a larger population with little hope for future improvements. Arizona Grasshopper Sparrow use of irrigated alfalfa fields raises a concern; it seems likely that the timing of harvest poses threats to nesting birds (i.e., destruction of nests and fledglings), therefore creating a potential sink for this remnant population.

The Sulphur Springs Valley, including the Fort Grant area, has been severely impacted by agricultural development and is primarily private and state land. Abandonment of historical cropland (Bahre 1995) has left a fragmented landscape of degraded desert grassland, abandoned agricultural fields, and desert scrub habitat. Much of the remaining grassland is tobosa (*Hilaria mutica*) grassland, which did not appear to provide habitat for the few remaining Arizona Grasshopper Sparrows in 2004–2005 (J. Ruth, pers. obs.). The Sulphur Springs Valley population is a relict population maintaining a precarious existence in the few suitable grassland patches remaining.

The San Bernardino Valley has a long history of cattle grazing, and ownership is a patchwork of state and private lands. Strong (1988) reported that the valley held suitable habitat although he recorded only a few individuals. During 2004–2005, it was my assessment that very little open grassland remained in the valley, and what remained was sparse, heavily grazed, and degraded from conversion to desert scrub. The habitat appeared extremely marginal, as evidenced by survey results. However, Corman and Wise-Gervais (2005) report observations of Arizona Grasshopper Sparrows in parts of the San Bernardino Valley that were not accessible (private land with no public roads) during this study. In addition, anecdotal observations in 2007 (J. Ruth, pers. obs.) suggest that some areas may provide more promising Grasshopper Sparrow habitat in years with better rains.

FUTURE — INFORMATION AND RESEARCH NEEDS

My results suggest that we are observing either a gradual decline in Arizona Grasshopper Sparrow numbers, at least in the short-term, and/or the subspecies is at the low end of a fluctuating population cycle. The following research priorities would provide the scientific information that land managers need to manage grasslands for Arizona Grasshopper Sparrows and other associated species.

1. *Continuous, regular surveys to monitor the status of Arizona Grasshopper Sparrow populations.* It might be most efficient to target limited resources toward regular monitoring of populations in the primary population centers — Sonoita, San Rafael, and Animas Valleys — with occasional surveys in areas supporting smaller populations.

2. *Life-history research.* Research is needed to understand the habitat preferences, breeding ecology, life history, and demographics of Arizona Grasshopper Sparrows in order to identify factors that influence reproductive success and survivorship throughout the subspecies' range, and to determine if differences exist between this subspecies and others. It would be particularly useful to conduct studies in all three valleys supporting major populations to determine variation within the subspecies.

3. *Research on causes of population declines.* Without more intensive, directed research on the effects of various management regimes and land use changes on bird numbers and demographics, we cannot determine the causes of the population trends. Implementing conservation measures is hopeless without such information. This will require collaborative efforts between land managers and researchers to design and monitor management activities, hopefully in an iterative, adaptive management framework where the results of the monitoring and research will influence future management decisions.

ACKNOWLEDGMENTS

Surveys conducted in 2004 were funded by Arizona Game and Fish Department; those conducted in 2005 were funded by Arizona State Parks. Permission to conduct surveys on their land was granted by the BLM (Las Cienegas NCA), the USFWS (Buenos Aires NWR), Arizona State Parks (San Rafael Short Grass Prairie Preserve), the Animas Foundation (Diamond A Ranch), the Audubon Appleton-Whittell Research Ranch (Research Ranch), and Ross Humphreys (owner of the conservation easement adjacent to the San Rafael Short Grass Prairie Preserve). Housing was provided by the Research Ranch, the San Rafael Short Grass Prairie Preserve, and the Buenos Aires NWR. Assistance in evaluating Southwest ReGAP data was provided by L. Gass, and T. Stanley provided statistical advice. Valuable reviews of previous versions of this manuscript were provided by C. Bock and P. Vickery, and J. F. Villaseñor-Gómez assisted with a Spanish translation of the abstract.

NEW TECHNOLOGY APPLICATIONS AND
BIRD CONSERVATION PLANNING

Great-tailed Grackle (*Quiscalus mexicanus*) © David J. Krueper

Studies in Avian Biology No. 37:126–137

SEASONAL PASSERINE MIGRATORY MOVEMENTS OVER THE ARID SOUTHWEST

Rodney K. Felix Jr., Robert H. Diehl, and Janet M. Ruth

Abstract. Biannually, millions of Neotropical and Nearctic migratory birds traverse the arid southwestern US-Mexico borderlands, yet our knowledge of avian migration patterns and behaviors in this region is extremely limited. To describe the spatial and temporal patterns of migration, we examined echoes from weather surveillance radar sites across the American Southwest from southern Texas to southwestern Arizona during spring 2005 and 2006 and fall 2005. After taking steps to identify radar echoes dominated by birds, we determined migrants' speeds, directions, and altitudes. Our results show that in spring, migrants generally flew lower and faster than in fall, although much of this overall pattern may be driven by higher fall altitudes and higher ground speeds at some of the easternmost sites in the borderlands. Seasonal differences in migrants' altitudes can be partially explained by seasonal differences in the altitudes of favorable winds. Seasonal differences in migrant ground speeds might arise for many reasons including variation in winds aloft or the presence of naïve hatch-year birds in fall. In addition, migrating bats may also be present throughout the region in varying degrees in radar data. Flight directions across the region were generally north in spring and south in fall, but also were consistent with the premise that songbird migration in North America is comprised of distinct regional migratory systems.

Key Words: altitude, Arizona, borderlands, Doppler, landbirds, migration, New Mexico, radar, Texas, velocity.

MOVIMIENTOS MIGRATORIOS ESTACIONALES DE AVES PASSERIFORMES SOBRE EL SUROESTE ÁRIDO

*Resumen.*Millones de aves migratorias neotropicales y neárticas atraviesan dos veces por año el área fronteriza del suroeste árido de los Estados Unidos y México, y aún así nuestro conocimiento sobre los patrones y el comportamiento migratorio es extremadamente limitado. Para describir los patrones espaciales y temporales de la migración, examinamos los ecos de radares de vigilancia climatológica a lo largo del suroeste Norteamericano, desde el sur de Texas al suroeste de Arizona durante las primaveras de 2005 y 2006, y el otoño de 2005. Después de identificar los ecos del radar dominados por aves migratorias, determinamos sus velocidad, dirección y altitud. Nuestros resultados muestran que en primavera, los migrantes vuelan más bajo y más rápido que en otoño, aunque este patrón general puede deberse a altitudes mayores en el otoño y a mayores velocidades con respecto al terreno en algunos de los sitios más al este en el área fronteriza. Las diferencias estacionales en la altitud de los migrantes pueden explicarse parcialmente por diferencias estacionales en la altitud de los vientos dominantes. Las diferencias estacionales en la velocidad de las aves migratorias con respecto al terreno pueden ser debidas a diversas razones incluyendo la variación en los vientos ascendentes o la presencia de aves del primer año sin experiencia en el otoño. Además, murciélagos migratorios pudieron estar presentes en toda la región en mayor o menor medida en los datos del radar". La dirección general de vuelo en la región fue hacia el norte en primavera y al sur en otoño, pero también fue consistente con la premisa de que la migración de aves canoras en Norteamérica incluye distintos sistemas migratorios regionales.

The bird conservation community increasingly recognizes the need to understand more about migration ecology and the value of stopover sites and resources to en route migratory birds (Moore et al. 1995, Hutto 1998, Moore 2001, Heglund and Skagen 2005). Migration is arguably the most hazardous period of a migratory bird's annual life cycle (Sillett and Holmes 2002). Birds must overcome multiple natural challenges including high energy demands, competition, predation, severe weather, and finding suitable foraging and resting habitat in unfamiliar terrain. Discussions of migration ecology regularly consider anthropogenic effects on the physical, biological and environmental components of migrating birds' terrestrial and aquatic stopover habitats, including en route habitat loss or degradation, and effects of global climate change on habitat and migration phenology (Moore et al. 1995, Root et al. 2003, MacMynowski et al. 2007). However, it is less common to consider the physical atmosphere as migration habitat. Flying migratory wildlife requires what could be called migration aerohabitat. Migratory birds, bats, and insects are uniquely susceptible to atmospheric disturbances and human use of the air space. Tall anthropogenic structures such as communication towers and wind turbines (Manville 2001, Cooper et al. 2004), and meteorological and climatic phenomenon (e.g., storms, adverse wind speeds and directions) represent threats to migratory birds in their aerohabitat. Conversely, migrating birds themselves present risks to humans via bird-aircraft collisions. Much remains unknown about patterns in bird flight altitude, speed, direction of travel, abundance, and density, as well as the seasonal and annual variation in these migration characteristics, all occurring across broad regional scales. Understanding broad migratory patterns en route and aloft is important to any avian conservation plan that addresses natural and anthropogenic factors affecting migrants across all phases of their life cycles (Ruth et al. 2005). In addition, documenting historical regional-scale migration patterns and behaviors provides baseline data needed to predict or model future changes in these patterns in response to factors such as climate change.

Moore et al. (1995) and Kelly and Hutto (2005) point out that what we know about passerine migration in North America is largely based on research conducted east of the Mississippi River. However, many factors potentially affect western migrants that are unique to the western landscape or at the very least are manifested in a different way and affect our ability to understand western migration dynamics. Western migrants face physical obstacles such as the Rocky Mountains and vast arid ecosystems that dominate the landscapes they must cross. These relatively unpopulated expanses also present logistical challenges to the field-based research and monitoring efforts that characterize most bird migration research. Methodologies that allow for remote collection of migration data across large landscapes, such as the use of weather surveillance radars, overcome some of these logistical obstacles, improve our understanding of migratory biology at broad spatial scales, and help guide future research.

The Sonoran and Chihuahuan Deserts, the Sierra Madre Occidental, and the Tamaulipan brushlands of the US-Mexico borderlands region typify the sort of potentially inhospitable landscapes that western birds must traverse during migration. Our knowledge of migration patterns and ecology in the borderlands region is extremely limited, and much of what we know comes from site-specific banding station data focused on documenting the critical importance of riparian stopover habitats to migrants (Kelly et al. 1999, Finch and Yong 2000, Skagen et al. 2005, Paxton et al. 2007). We know much less about migrant use of other habitat types or larger-scale migrant distributions and behavior

aloft in this region. Continuing research will take advantage of additional weather surveillance radar products not analyzed for this paper and begin to describe densities of migratory birds aloft and make associations with stopover habitat.

We report here on the first results of a larger study examining migratory behavior and patterns across the 1,500 km of the US-Mexico borderlands region. Using data collected by weather surveillance radars, we identified biological targets likely to be migratory birds. We determined the altitude, speed, and direction of birds during migration and explored how these general flight behaviors varied seasonally and among sites in the borderlands region.

METHODS

We retrieved data from seven WSR-88D (weather surveillance radar, 1988 design year, Doppler capable) sites across the American Southwest (Fig. 1; Table 1). These so-called Level II data include reflectivity, a measure of radar echo intensity determined by the density and size of targets, and radial velocity, a measure of target velocity relative to the radar (Crum et al. 1993). Both reflectivity and radial velocity measurements are made in discrete volumes of atmosphere or pulse volumes whose dimensions are determined by how space is partitioned along radii from the radar (1 km intervals for reflectivity and 0.25 km for velocity) and the width of the pulsed radar beam (~1°). A sweep comprises a complete rotation of the radar (360°) at a specific elevation angle of the radar's beam. Depending on a radar's mode of operation, elevations range from 0.5° to 19.5°. This study is confined to data from 3.5° elevation sweeps

FIGURE 1. Locations of seven WSR-88D radars used in this study.

TABLE 1. GEOGRAPHIC COORDINATES OF RADARS ACROSS THE SOUTHWEST THAT WERE USED IN THIS STUDY (LISTED WEST TO EAST).

WSR-88D call sign	City	North latitude (°)	West longitude (°)
KFSX	Flagstaff, AZ	34.57	-111.20
KEMX	Tucson, AZ	31.89	-110.63
KABX	Albuquerque, NM	35.15	-106.82
KEPZ	El Paso, TX	31.87	-106.70
KMAF	Midland, TX	31.94	-102.19
KDFX	Del Rio, TX	29.27	-100.28
KBRO	Brownsville, TX	25.92	-97.42

taken approximately three hours past the end of local civil twilight (when the sun is 6° below the horizon) from 20 March to 20 May 2005 and 2006, and from 10 August to 20 October 2005. Sampling data from this time period allowed us to avoid bias associated with variation in target speed and direction during the onset of nocturnal migration. Hereafter, we refer to any sweep from a specific date at a specific radar site as simply a representative sweep, unless otherwise specified.

We identified radar echoes caused by migrants in a two-step process. First, by visual inspection, we rejected reflectivity sweeps that contained non-biological echoes—usually caused by precipitation or ground clutter. Second, we distinguished migrants from other biological echoes by their airspeeds, which we determined by vector subtracting wind velocity from ground velocity (Gauthreaux and Belser 1998).

ESTIMATING WIND VELOCITY

The number of radars used in this study was limited by the availability of radiosonde data for target identity; radiosonde launch stations coincide with seven WSR-88D stations in the borderlands region. Radiosondes are balloon-launched meteorological instrument packages programmed to collect data at certain atmospheric pressures (Office of the Federal Coordinator for Meteorology 1997). These atmospheric pressures correspond to altitudes (meters) above sea level (ASL). We retrieved archived data on vertical profiles of wind speed and direction gathered using these radiosondes. Balloons are typically launched twice daily, at 0000 Coordinated Universal Time (UTC; 1700 H MST the previous calendar day) and 1200 H UTC (0500 H MST). The 0000 UTC launch time is nearest peak nocturnal migration, the focus of this study, across most of the borderlands region. Therefore, wind and target ground velocity data (see below) used in target identity are separated by either four or five hours, depending on time zone. Other sources of winds aloft information either did not improve

spatial and temporal coverage or were not sufficiently accurate.

ESTIMATING TARGET GROUND VELOCITY

We determined target ground velocities using Level II radial velocity data from ~3.5° sweeps during the peak of nocturnal migration (local civil twilight plus 3 hr). These higher elevation sweeps have several advantages over lower elevation sweeps when estimating target ground velocities. Loss of data through beam obstruction caused by relief in terrain is nearly absent, and there is less ambiguity in altitude-specific measures of speed and direction (particularly of higher altitude targets). Also, there is less spatial separation between radar and radiosonde data, because the beam intersects the migratory layer relatively close to the radar site. Finally, data from higher elevation angles are less affected by refraction, because the beam propagates through rather than along horizontal moisture and temperature gradients.

We constructed vertical profiles of target speed and direction for ~3.5° radial velocity sweeps using methods outlined by Browning and Wexler (1968) and implemented in SAS (SAS Institute 2003). We present a variation on methods well established in the meteorological literature, so they are reviewed only briefly here. The approach determines speed and direction from velocity-azimuth displays (VADs) calculated from radial velocity data centered on a focal range and including velocities within a ±1 km range window. In the typical VAD, radial velocities for all available azimuths within a sweep are modeled as a function of the horizontal and vertical Cartesian coefficients comprising target velocity in three-dimensional space (Browning and Wexler 1968, eq. 1). These coefficients are estimated using non-linear least-squares minimization, and speed and direction are in turn calculated from the coefficients. The window is then advanced one range bin (250 m) away from the radar and the VAD recalculated. This process is repeated out to the maximum range of available velocity data, which varies depending primarily on the height of targets. Because the radar's ~3.5° elevation beam travels up and away from the earth (which simultaneously curves out from beneath the beam), an increase in range corresponds to a predictable increase in altitude (Diehl and Larkin 2005, eq. 1). Therefore the succession of VADs calculated at incrementally increasing range enables the construction of vertical profiles of target speed and direction (in m ASL). For each least-squares minimization on data from a focal range, we compute an adjusted r^2 as a measure of how well predicted radial velocities explain variation in observed velocity data. These, in addition to visual correspondence between observed and predicted radial velocities (Fig. 2a, b), offered statistical and heuristic feedback respectively on the reliability of ground speed and direction estimations used in calculating target airspeeds.

IDENTIFYING TARGETS

For each date, target ground velocities were combined with wind velocity data according to altitude ASL. We calculated targets' headings and air speeds across altitudes during the hours around peak nocturnal migration by subtracting available wind velocities from targets' ground velocities. We determined that targets were migrants if airspeed was ≥6 m/s (Schaefer 1976, Larkin 1991, Gauthreaux and Belser 1998). From the resulting profile of migrant-dominated velocities (Table 2), we determined which

altitude stratum corresponded with the mode, or highest reflectivity (i.e., the stratum with the highest migrant density (Gauthreaux and Belser 1998)) on that given day. From these modal strata, migrants' flight altitudes, speeds (relative to both the ground and air), and directions of travel were retained for further statistical analysis. Where we specify directions of travel in this paper, we are indicating the migrants' (or winds') directions of travel over ground. We subsequently subtracted radar tower elevations (meters ASL) from the modal strata altitudes to determine migrants' above ground level (meters AGL) altitudes for use in statistical analyses. Some migrants were probably present at altitudes that were not considered in analyses. However, by using the modal observation we selected altitudes where migrants were most dominant. Modal migrant altitudes are subsequently referred to simply as migrant altitudes.

Considering Bruderer's (1997) accounts of airspeeds of fast and slow intermittent flapping bird species (all ≥11 m/s), it is more likely we have mistaken some insects for birds rather than mistaken any birds for insects. We considered migrating bats to be indistinguishable from birds and that they could be present locally in large numbers in some of our data. As an example, in reflectivity data we observed patterns typical of biological targets entering the radar beam from point locations (Russell and Gauthreaux 1998). These patterns were observed shortly before and after local civil twilight and were closely associated

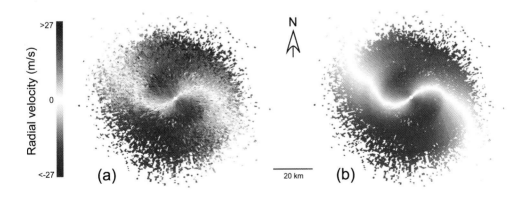

FIGURE 2. Vertical wind direction shear in observed (left) and predicted (right) data. (a) Observed radial velocity data from a 3.5° beam elevation sweep at Del Rio, Texas 27 March 2006, 0424 UTC where blue indicates movement toward the radar; red is movement away. The S-shaped Doppler null (in white; a region where movement is tangential to the radar) shows typical direction shear; in this case targets' directions of travel shift from being toward the NW to toward the NNE with increased distance from the radar (and so also with increased altitude). (b) Predicted radial velocities from VADs of observed data used to estimate speed and direction. Close correspondence between observed and predicted radial velocities demonstrate how accurately VADs estimate speed and direction from radial velocity data.

TABLE 2. VERTICAL PROFILE OF WIND VELOCITIES AND TARGET GROUND AND AIR VELOCITIES, AN EXAMPLE FROM DFX ON 27 MARCH 2006 AT 0424 UTC.

Altitude ASL (m) [a]	Wind direction (°)	Wind speed (m/s)	Target ground direction (°)	Target ground speed (m/s)	Target heading (°)	Target air speed (m/s)
610	325	11.3	320.9	12.8	293.6	1.7
771	330	11.3	326	14.2	310.4	3
914	335	11.8	330.9	15.5	318.1	3.8
1,219	335	12.9	345.6	17.3	12.4	5.3
1,488	335	12.9	6	16.4	56.7	8.6 [b]
1,737	335	11.3	16.3	17.3	56.7	11.5 [b]
1,829	335	10.8	17.8	17.5	55.2	12.1 [b]
2,068	22	6.2	20.6	17.7	19.8	11.6 [b]
2,134	35	5.1	22	18.1	17	13.2 [b]
2,438	60	6.2	29.1	18.1	15.2	13.1 [b]
2,743	55	7.2	37.4	17.8	26.1	11.1 [b]
3,105	50	10.8	46.8	16.8	41.2	6.0 *

[a] Altitudes shown are those provided in the radiosonde report from Del Rio, Texas on 27 March 2006 at 0000 UTC.
[b] Movements characterized by air speeds ≥6 m/s are considered to be dominated by birds.

geographically with several known colonies of Mexican free-tailed bats (*Tadarida brasiliensis*) in the easternmost range of our study area (B. French, pers. comm.). However, these patterns dissipated, and resembled ambient reflectivity before the times when sweep data were collected for target identification. Like Able (1977), we assume that migrating bats are rare relative to birds in most geographical locations; however, the relative abundances of migrating bats and birds remain poorly understood and likely vary geographically and seasonally.

STATISTICAL APPROACH

We examined the effects of geographic location (i.e., radar site) and season on migrant altitude, ground speed, and ground direction across seven radar sites and three seasons. Nonparametric statistics were used throughout because data often failed to meet assumptions of normality and homoscedasticity, in some cases even after data transformation. Pooling data across sites, we used Kruskal-Wallis analysis of variance by ranks to test for overall differences between the seasons for altitudes (AGL) and ground speeds. We used simple correlation analyses on the seasonal median values for each site to describe to what extent seasonal flight altitudes were similar on a site-by-site basis. We used the same Kruskal-Wallis approach to test for differences in altitude and ground speed between sites within seasons, and within sites between seasons. Where overall differences in altitudes or ground speeds were significant among seasons across sites, among sites within seasons, or within sites among seasons, nonparametric Tukey-type multiple comparisons

of ranks tests (Q statistic) were used to identify among which seasons or sites they occurred (Zar 1999). Alpha levels were adjusted for comparisonwise error rates.

Median directions of travel relative to the ground (with 25% and 75% quantiles) were determined using circular statistics (Zar 1999). Pooling data across sites, we used Mardia-Watson-Wheeler tests (W statistic) to look for differences in ground direction within seasons. Where significant differences were found, we used Tukey-type multiple comparison tests of circular ranks (Q statistic) to identify differences among specific sites.

RESULTS

From 434 representative sweeps evaluated for each spring season (20 March–20 May, across seven WSR-88D sites), those dominated by migrants were retained for further analysis— 235 in 2005 (56%) and 180 in 2006 (43%). Of the 504 sweeps evaluated in fall 2005 (10 August–20 October), we retained 214 (45%) for analysis. The number of migrant-dominated evenings at an individual radar site during a season varied from 17 at Brownsville (BRO), Texas in spring 2006 to 40, also at Brownsville, in spring 2005. Most rejected sweeps were excluded from analysis due to the presence of precipitation. They were also rejected when ground clutter or other anomalous echoes were present, when Level II data were corrupt, when radiosonde reports were missing, or when dominated by insect-like targets (i.e., target airspeeds fell below 6 m/s; Table 3).

Shear—variation in the speed or direction of the wind with altitude (Fig. 3 in Diehl and

TABLE 3. NUMBER OF SWEEPS PER SEASON CONSIDERED AND RETAINED FOR ANALYSIS AND CRITERIA FOR THEIR REJECTION.

	Spring 2005	Fall 2005	Spring 2006
Total sweeps	434	504	434
Sweeps rejected for:			
Precipitation dominant	134	230	175
Unavailable/corrupt radar data	20	31	12
Unavailable radiosonde data	10	3	12
High variability in target velocity	22	9	12
Low target airspeeds	13	17	43
Sweeps retained for analysis (N)	235	214	180

Larkin [2005]; Fig. 9 in Larkin [2005]) — occurred at all sites in all seasons. Shear was particularly common, and its specific structure conspicuously stable, at Midland (MAF) and Del Rio (DFX), Texas. At Del Rio, 34 of 39 migrant-dominated sweeps in fall 2005 exhibited some degree of shear, and the specific structure of shear in spring (Fig. 2a) at this site varied relatively little (see below). Although wind velocities that vary with altitude may be advantageous at times for multiple, separate, and simultaneous layers of migrants traveling in different directions, reflectivity data at Midland and Del Rio failed to support the presence of such a pattern in this case. Further visual review confirmed that reflectivity data at these sites were dominated by single, continuous, layers of migrants.

FLIGHT ALTITUDE

Flight altitudes differed among seasons when pooled across all sites ($\chi^2 = 40.92$, P < 0.0001, df = 2); migrants flew significantly lower in both springs than in fall (Table 4a). Within each season, migrants used significantly different altitudes among sites (spring 2005: $\chi^2 = 80.45$, P < 0.0001, df = 6; fall 2005: $\chi^2 = 73.82$, P < 0.0001, df = 6; spring 2006: $\chi^2 = 25.22$, P = 0.0003, df = 6), but showed no apparent geographical pattern (Table 4a). Median flight altitudes for each season and where among-site significant differences occurred within each season are presented in Table 4a.

Additionally, radar-site median migrant altitudes in spring 2005 and spring 2006 were significantly positively correlated (r = 0.76, P < 0.05), suggesting that birds on a site-by-site basis migrated at consistent altitudes in spring. In contrast, radar-site median migrant altitudes in fall 2005 were not correlated with altitudes in either spring (r = 0.17, P = 0.72, spring 2005 v. fall 2005; r = 0.35, P = 0.44, spring 2006 v. fall 2005) indicating that site-specific differences exist in flight altitudes between spring and fall. We determined (by within-site among-season analysis of variance by ranks) that site-specific

seasonal differences in altitude occurred at Flagstaff (FSX), Arizona ($\chi^2 = 15.40$, P = 0.0005, df = 2), Midland ($\chi^2 = 43.12$, P < 0.0001, df = 2), Del Rio ($\chi^2 = 30.14$, P < 0.0001, df = 2), and Brownsville ($\chi^2 = 9.26$, P < 0.01, df = 2); which seasons at these sites are significantly different are presented in Table 5. We found no among-season differences in altitude at Tucson (EMX), Arizona, Albuquerque (ABX), New Mexico, and El Paso (EPZ), Texas (each site P ≥ 0.29). At Midland and Del Rio in particular, fall altitudes were much higher than those of both springs. The large differences at these two sites explain most of the significant difference in altitudes between seasons across all sites (Fig. 3; Table 4a).

GROUND SPEED

Migrants' ground speeds were significantly different among seasons when pooled across all sites ($\chi^2 = 67.48$, P < 0.0001, df = 2; Fig. 4); migrants flew significantly faster in spring than in fall (Table 4b). However, most of this difference can be attributed to variation at three of the seven sites, Midland, Del Rio, and Brownsville (Tables 4b, 5). Midland ($\chi^2 = 11.34$, P = 0.003, df = 2), Del Rio ($\chi^2 = 38.13$, P < 0.0001, df = 2), and Brownsville ($\chi^2 = 18.02$, P < 0.0001, df = 2) were the only sites with significant differences in ground speed within sites among seasons; which seasons are significantly different at these sites are presented in Table 5.

We found no significant differences in ground speeds within season among sites during spring 2005 ($\chi^2 = 9.24$, P = 0.16, df = 6) or fall 2005 ($\chi^2 = 12.07$, P = 0.06, df = 6), although general patterns could be observed. In spring 2005 median daily ground speed was highest at the easternmost sites (Brownsville, Del Rio, and Midland), and lowest at the westernmost sites (Flagstaff and Tucson) (Table 4b). Fall 2005 median ground speed was highest at the central sites in New Mexico and west Texas (Albuquerque, El Paso, and Midland), and lowest at Del Rio (Table 4b).

TABLE 4. SUMMARY OF STATISTICS FOR DAILY MIGRANT (A) FLIGHT ALTITUDE, (B) GROUND SPEED, AND (C) GROUND DIRECTION OF TRAVEL AT EACH WSR-88D SITE FOR EACH SEASON.

	FSX	EMX	ABX	EPZ	MAF	DFX	BRO	All Sites
(a) Flight altitude (m AGL)								
Spring 2005								
N	32	35	30	31	31	36	40	235
Median	817.6	1,708.5	971.8	896.9	600.6	1,194.5	1,846.9	1,206.7
25% quantile	473.3	1409.7	363.1	574.7	554.7	915.5	1,515.2	641.2
75% quantile	1,352.7	1,962.2	1,415.3	1,206.7	969.5	1,661.0	2,471.5	1,846.9
MC[a]	C	AB	C	C	C	ABC	A	
Fall 2005								
N	25	25	25	27	36	39	37	214
Median	1,352.7	1,535.2	995.0	1,456.7	2,213.9	2,665.9	2,133.8	1,785.5
25% quantile	856.1	819.9	671.8	574.7	1,669.0	2,021.9	1,578.1	953.9
75% quantile	1,384.0	1,803.5	1,384.0	1,898.6	2,410.9	3,123.6	2,698.4	2,335.4
MC	D	BCD	D	CD	ABC	A	AB	
Spring 2006								
N	24	32	24	26	23	34	17	180
Median	1,384.0	1,621.9	942.3	1,167.8	985.0	1,515.2	1,515.2	1384.0
25% quantile	875.3	1,132.9	336.6	574.7	615.9	1,066.5	1,233.4	881.5
75% quantile	1,872.9	2,022.0	1,474.3	1,934.5	1,295.9	17,99.8	2,006.3	1841.4
MC	AB	A	AB	AB	AB	B	AB	
(b) Flight ground speed (m/s)								
Spring 2005								
Median	11.64	11.64	12.52	12.44	13.09	13.40	14.17	12.44
25% quantile	9.63	9.01	9.87	8.63	9.77	10.19	10.45	9.74
75% quantile	15.74	13.04	15.43	15.44	18.76	16.44	17.71	15.86
MC	not significantly different across sites within season							
Fall 2005								
Median	9.33	8.55	11.25	9.66	9.96	7.95	9.21	9.27
25% quantile	7.90	7.14	8.39	7.45	7.60	5.76	6.77	7.38
75% quantile	11.44	10.83	14.85	11.90	12.33	10.48	11.87	11.86
MC	not significantly different across sites within season							
Spring 2006								
Median	11.10	11.24	12.30	9.59	14.88	15.94	13.06	12.19
25% quantile	7.97	9.55	9.32	7.01	10.13	11.92	10.06	9.27
75% quantile	12.73	13.67	15.58	12.42	17.50	17.95	14.49	15.39
MC	BC	BC	ABC	C	AB	A	ABC	
(c) Flight direction (°)								
Spring 2005								
Median	359.03°	335.42°	42.90°	73.30°	23.68°	7.52°	22.97°	
25% quantile	329.04°	322.70°	2.00°	331.91°	358.30°	355.95°	13.13°	
75% quantile	37.88°	350.78°	86.08°	90.06°	51.87°	28.44°	32.53°	
MC	AB	A	B	B	B	B	B	
Fall 2005								
Median	157.02°	173.36°	161.92°	160.95°	187.31°	196.54°	175.27°	
25% quantile	113.08°	154.12°	140.14°	126.04°	160.08°	169.14°	169.22°	
75% quantile	182.30°	182.36°	179.28	228.22°	211.18°	212.70°	189.30°	
MC	AB	AB	B	AB	AB	A	B	

TABLE 4. SUMMARY OF STATISTICS FOR DAILY MIGRANT (A) FLIGHT ALTITUDE, (B) GROUND SPEED, AND (C) GROUND DIRECTION OF TRAVEL AT EACH WSR-88D SITE FOR EACH SEASON.

	FSX	EMX	ABX	EPZ	MAF	DFX	BRO	All Sites
(c) Flight direction (°)								
Spring 2006								
Median	322.52°	335.83°	6.49°	18.16°	3.42°	9.02°	22.49°	
25% quantile	308.88°	329.35°	352.87°	339.26°	345.54°	3.07°	11.20°	
75% quantile	349.04°	1.59°	86.53°	67.87°	16.00°	19.65°	34.76°	
MC	A	AB	C	C	BC	C	C	

[a] MC shows where multiple comparisons of ranks identify statistical differences (different letters) within-season across sites in flight altitude, ground speed, and ground direction.

Migrants' median daily ground speed across all seven sites in spring 2006 was slightly lower than the previous spring (Table 4b). Comparisons of ranked mean daily ground speeds in spring 2006 showed significant differences among sites ($\chi^2 = 34.07$, P < 0.0001, df = 6), yet multiple comparison of ranks for that season showed much overlap in ground speeds (Table 4b).

FLIGHT DIRECTION

Median directions of travel at all sites in spring 2005 were seasonally appropriate (i.e., in a generally northward direction), however there were significant differences among sites (W = 109.63, P < 0.001, critical W at $\chi^2_{0.05, 12} = 21.03$). Travel was slightly east of North at all sites except Flagstaff and Tucson (Fig. 5; Table 4c). Migrants moving through the central part of the region, Albuquerque and El Paso, showed the highest variation in direction (range of circular dispersion between 25% and 75% quantiles); smallest variations in direction occurred at easternmost sites Del Rio and Brownsville (Fig. 5; Table 4c).

Median directions of travel in fall 2005 were significantly different among sites (W = 52.54, P < 0.001, critical W at $\chi^2_{0.05, 12} = 21.03$), yet they remained seasonally appropriate (i.e., in a generally southward direction) and varied about due south with migrants through westernmost sites tending to move somewhat to the east of south. Migrants at Flagstaff showed the largest departure from due south, deviating almost 23° east of south. Circular dispersions in the direction of travel of migrants varied across the borderlands region but without any geographic pattern. The smallest ranges in circular dispersion occurred at Tucson and Brownsville, and the largest at Flagstaff and El Paso (Fig. 5; Table 4c).

Migrants' directions of travel were again seasonally appropriate in spring 2006, and again directions among sites were significantly different (W = 58.72, P < 0.001, critical W at $\chi^2_{0.05, 12} = 21.03$). Travel was slightly east of north, with the exception of Flagstaff and Tucson, where travel was west of north (Fig. 5; Table 4c). First and third quartiles of ground direction overlapped at all sites with those of spring in the previous year, with the largest difference in median direction at El Paso (Fig. 5; Table 4c). Fifty-five degrees separated the median directions of travel at El Paso between spring 2005 and spring 2006.

DISCUSSION

In summary, our results show that in spring, migrants generally flew lower and faster than in

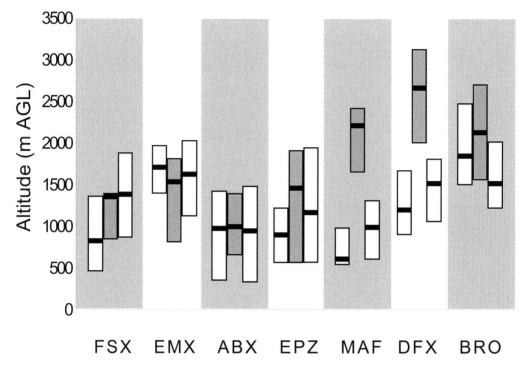

FIGURE 3. Median daily altitudes AGL (± 25% quantiles) of migrant-like targets at each radar site during spring 2005 (left white bar), fall 2005 (middle grey bar), and spring 2006 (right white bar).

TABLE 5. WITHIN-SITE AMONG-SEASON COMPARISONS OF FLIGHT ALTITUDES AND GROUND SPEEDS USING NON-PARAMETRIC MULTIPLE COMPARISONS OF RANKS TESTS (Q).

Radar site	FSX	EMX	ABX	EPZ	MAF	DFX	BRO
Flight ground speed							
Spring 2005	-	-	-	-	A	A	A
Fall 2005	-	-	-	-	B	B	B
Spring 2006	-	-	-	-	A	A	AB
Flight altitude							
Spring 2005	B	-	-	-	B	B	AB
Fall 2005	AB	-	-	-	A	A	A
Spring 2006	A	-	-	-	B	B	B

Note: Different letters indicate significant differences within sites among seasons. Significant differences are those comparisons with Q values >$Q_{(0.017), 3}$ = 2.827, an estimated critical value adjusted for comparisonwise error rates (Table B.15 in Zar 1999), indicates $Q_{(0.02), 3}$ = 2.713 and $Q_{(0.01), 3}$ = 2.936). Dashes indicate non-significance.

fall, although much of this overall pattern may be driven by patterns at a few of the radar sites.

Much of the seasonal variation in migrant flight altitude across the region may be explained by the seasonal differences at Midland and Del Rio. Spring migrants at these two locations might have experienced more favorable and less variable winds than did fall migrants, perhaps owing to relatively consistent directional wind shear in spring. In such conditions where winds are stable from day to day, birds typically concentrate at certain altitudes, selecting winds favorable for migration or avoiding winds unfavorable for

migration (Richardson 1978). Winds aloft data at these sites might suggest the former condition (selection of favorable winds) may be at work in spring and the latter (avoidance of unfavorable winds) at work in fall. However, caution should be exercised in evaluating such hypotheses with winds aloft data; the combined spatial and temporal separation of winds aloft data (provided by radiosondes) from the representative sweeps we analyzed was as much as 50 km and 5 hr (Midland). Such separation in place and time makes it difficult to define what winds aloft are favorable or unfavorable using our methods.

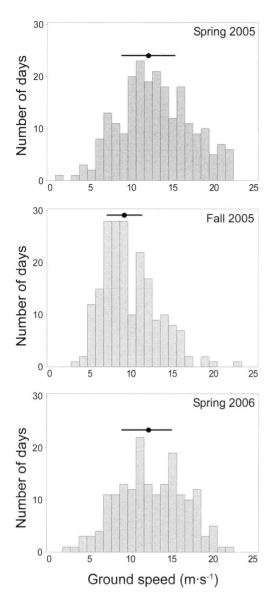

FIGURE 4. Histogram of ground speed estimates during spring 2005, fall 2005, and spring 2006 where each observation represents one ground speed estimate per day. Error bars represent season median ground speeds ± one quartile.

Proceeding with caution, however, we can say, based on comparison of winds (as measured by radiosondes) with migrant directions of travel from our results, that spring winds were more favorable for migration (moving in the same direction as the migrants) than fall winds. During both springs at Midland and Del Rio, more favorable southerly winds occurred at lower altitudes, which is where migrants tended

to concentrate, whereas wind directions above 2 km AGL were from the west. Winds were generally unfavorable for fall migration at all altitudes at Midland and Del Rio, but higher altitude migrants at these two sites at least had some chance of encountering more favorable winds due to the winds' greater variability in direction. The northerly winds presumably favorable to fall migrants were scarce but had a greater likelihood of occurring at higher altitudes, which is where migrants tended to concentrate. To more accurately interpret any winds effects at these or any site would require comparisons of prevailing winds at every altitude and migrants' possible responses therein on a day-by-day basis, and then only after closer spatial and temporal association between radar and winds aloft data is achieved. Such a full analysis was beyond the scope of this study, but would be useful in further understanding the patterns observed here.

Radar data suggest that the majority of spring migrants are found at altitudes ranging from 650 to 1850 m (AGL) and fall migrants at altitudes ranging from 950 to 2,350 m (AGL). However, these results should not be interpreted to mean that migrants did not fly at lower altitudes. WSR-88D radars in general are ill-suited for studies of low flying targets, particularly when using higher beam elevation data such as that from the 3.5° sweeps used in this study. This geometry, together with the constraints imposed by radiosonde data (which has a relatively low vertical resolution), yielded minimum altitude observations of around 250 m AGL. Therefore, while this work shows that considerable migration occurs above 500 m AGL, we were not able to detect low altitude movements. Despite these limitations of the data, the resulting increased knowledge of regional and seasonal patterns in migratory movement offers guidance for future research and management as regulatory agencies and organizations implement bird conservation activities in the borderlands region.

Migrant ground speeds were higher in spring than fall, which is consistent with hypotheses concerning the selective pressures for Neotropical and Nearctic migrants to arrive early on breeding grounds in the spring. However, a number of factors may affect (reduce) migrant ground speeds in fall. (1) Greater variability in fall migrant directions of travel within a sweep results in lower measured ground speeds as a consequence of the way speed is measured using large Doppler radars. At their highest resolution, these radars quantify the Doppler velocity of all targets within relatively large volumes of airspace; for our sweeps these volumes were typically

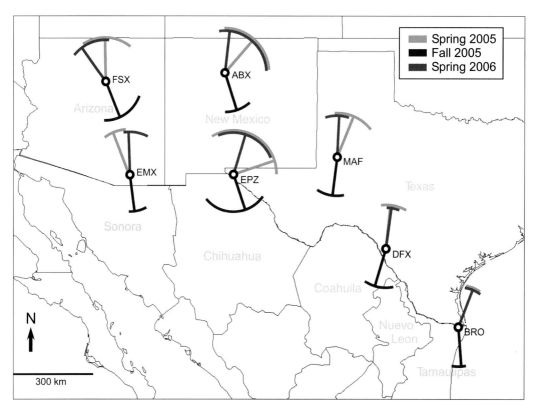

FIGURE 5. Directions of migration for spring and fall 2005 and spring 2006 at seven radar sites in the south-western US. Green, red, and blue flags indicate seasonal median migrant directions (with 25% and 75% quantile whiskers) traveling away from the radar site.

3.0×10^7 m^3 to 4.7×10^7 m^3 or more. When targets within those volumes travel in approximately the same direction, measured Doppler velocity is higher than when targets' directions vary, even if the actual speeds of individual targets within the volume were identical in both cases. (2) Birds experience less favorable winds in fall than in spring. (3) The proportion of naïve hatch-year birds that show more variable orientations (Ralph 1981, Woodrey 2000) is higher in fall. (4) Fall data retain a higher proportion of arthropods or non-migratory bats (Cleveland et al. 2006).

We attribute much of the seasonal variation in ground speed to differences at three sites, Midland, Del Rio, and Brownsville. These are the easternmost sites in the study area, making the greatest seasonal differences in ground speed somewhat concentrated geographically. This suggests that the causal factors are also geographically limited to the same area. Synoptic winds may be structured across the border-lands region such that birds migrating through Texas in fall encounter unfavorable winds. Alternatively, Del Rio's location in southcentral

Texas places it near a region of high insect and bat activity. Although insect migration through central Texas generally occurs below 1,000 m (Beerwinkle et al. 1994), foraging bats regularly reach altitudes characteristic of fall bird migration in this area. Despite efforts to retain data only from bird-dominated movements, this prospect of contamination by bats stresses the need for more sophisticated methods of target identification.

The direction of movement patterns we documented for spring and fall in 2005 and 2006 are consistent with a 5-day period in spring 2000 when data from the same radar locations showed the directions of travel of migrating birds in four overlapping altitude classes (Gauthreaux et al. 2003). They are also consistent with two major overland migratory systems suggested for North American wood warblers (Kelly and Hutto 2005), assuming that patterns in wood warbler migration are representative of more general passerine migration through the southwest captured by radar. Direction of movement patterns for our westernmost sites (Flagstaff and Tucson) in Arizona (Fig. 5) suggest dominance by species that migrate between the Sierra Madre Occidental or Baja California and the Pacific coast (Kelly and Hutto 2005; Cooke 1915). However, directions of travel in the central and eastern borderlands suggest that some component of these migrants may be from midwestern or eastern North America. High variation in directions of movement in the central sites in New Mexico (Albuquerque) and west Texas (El Paso and Midland) suggests that these areas may draw migrants from intermountain west and central-eastern North America in fall. This is consistent with Yong and Finch's (2002) findings that their sites on the Rio Grande in New Mexico (near Albuquerque) were used by both western and eastern breeding species. Paxton et al. (2007) found similar west-east patterns in the breeding destinations of migrating Wilson's Warblers (*Wilsonia pusilla*), although the easternmost borderlands site they studied was in southeastern Arizona. The directions of movement in the easternmost sites in Texas (Del Rio and Brownsville) to the NNE in spring and the SSW in fall are most consistent with species that migrate between various locations in Mexico (or further south) and central and eastern North America.

This paper focuses on migrant movement behavior (migrant altitude, speed, and direction) and not on the intensity of migration across the borderlands region. Our ongoing research addresses remaining questions concerning large-scale structure in migrant density, which may be particularly relevant if multiple migratory systems converge within the region.

ACKNOWLEDGMENTS

This research was funded jointly by the USGS Science Support Program, USDI Fish and Wildlife Service Region 2 Migratory Bird Office, the Sonoran Joint Venture, and the Lannan Foundation. The University of Wyoming provided sounding data. Barbara French at Bat Conservation International, Austin, Texas, provided data regarding bat colonies and the phenology of Mexican free-tailed bats in our study area. We also thank the USGS Fort Collins Science Center and University of Southern Mississippi Migratory Bird Group for general support in the conduct of this research. We thank J. J. Buler and J. F. Kelly for comments on earlier versions of this manuscript.

Studies in Avian Biology No. 37:138–144

APPLIED CONSERVATION PLANNING AND IMPLEMENTATION IN THE US-MEXICO BORDERLANDS

DAVID MEHLMAN

Abstract. The Nature Conservancy (TNC) and partners implement conservation strategies using an integrated framework with four components: setting goals and priorities, developing strategies, taking action, and measuring results. This framework, called Conservation by Design, is illustrated with specific examples that relate to US-Mexico borderland bird conservation, including the Chihuahuan Desert Ecoregional Plan, a conservation action planning process in this and surrounding regions, the acquisition of private lands, and the implementation of a comprehensive wintering grassland bird monitoring plan. For the specific purposes of long-term bird conservation, many of the elements of this process are captured by TNC's Prairie Wings project, an example of a large-scale conservation implementation plan.

Key Words: Conservation by Design, Chihuahuan Desert, The Nature Conservancy.

PLANEACIÓN PARA LA CONSERVACIÓN APLICADA Y SU IMPLEMENTACIÓN EN LA FRONTERA MÉXICO-EEUU

Resumen. The Nature Conservancy (TNC) y sus socios implementan estrategias de conservación usando un marco estratégico con cuatro elementos básicos: establecimiento de metas y prioridades, desarrollo de estrategias, toma de acciones, y medición de resultados. Este marco, se llama "Diseño para la Conservación", se ilustra con ejemplos que pertenecen a la conservación de las aves de la frontera México—EEUU. Los ejemplos incluyen el Plan Ecorregional del Desierto Chihuahuense, el proceso para Planeación para la Conservación de Areas como se ha sido implementado en esta ecorregión y sus alrededores, adquisición de tierras privadas, y el desarrollo de un plan de monitoreo para las aves de los pastizales del norte de México. Muchos de estos componentes de la conservación de aves para el largo plazo son parte del proyecto "Prairie Wings" de TNC, un ejemplo de un plan para la implementación de conservación de escala grande.

The long-term conservation of wide-ranging or migratory species requires coordination among conservation partners across numerous boundaries, both ecological and political. This need for coordination, coupled with widespread evidence of long-term declines in numerous taxa of migratory birds, has spawned efforts at conservation planning and, to some extent, implementation, across North America and at wider spatial scales (Brown et al. 2001, Kushlan et al. 2002, Rich et al. 2004, USDI Fish and Wildlife Service 2004). However, particularly when efforts must span complex ecological and political arenas, a strong need remains for a participatory and ecosystem-based regional conservation approach that can be facilitated by the non-governmental sector. This paper introduces the conservation approach applied by TNC to US-Mexico borderland birds as a means of addressing these needs.

TNC has used an integrated conservation framework called Conservation by Design since 1996 for all its activities (Baumgartner et al. 2006). This science-based conservation approach has four components: setting goals and priorities, developing strategies, taking action, and measuring results. Although TNC's broad conservation mission encompasses plants, animals, and ecological communities, specific bird conservation priorities have been incorporated throughout the Conservation by Design process. Given the current focus of modern conservation planning on ecosystem or ecoregional-based planning units, borderlands conservation projects provide a useful way of illustrating the application of these processes.

SETTING GOALS AND PRIORITIES

Goals and priorities are identified using a planning process applied at ecoregional scales and embedded within major habitat types. An example of this in the US-Mexico borderlands is the Chihuahuan Desert Ecoregional Plan (Cotera et al. 2004). This plan, a joint project of Pronatura Noreste, TNC, and World Wildlife Fund, identifies conservation priority sites with the aim of conserving biodiversity throughout the Chihuahuan Desert ecoregion (Fig. 1). This area encompasses a wide swath of the borderlands, including parts of the states of Texas and New Mexico in the US and Chihuahua, Coahuila, Durango, Zacatecas, San Luis Potosí, and Nuevo León in Mexico. The Chihuahuan Desert is known for its biological diversity,

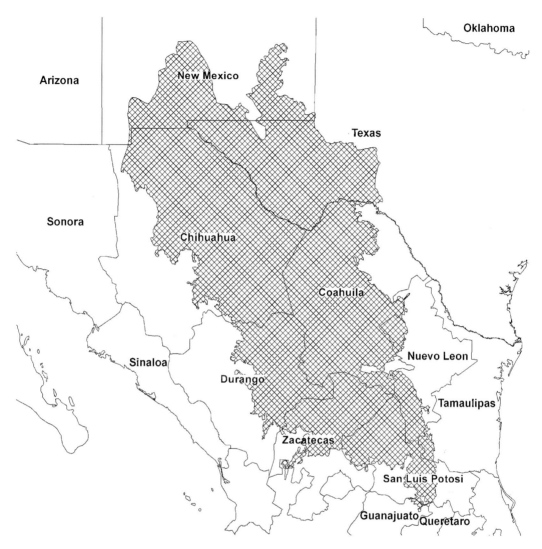

FIGURE 1. Map of the Chihuahuan Desert ecoregion, showing state boundaries in Mexico and the US (From Cotera et al. 2004).

particularly its endemic yuccas, cacti, and fish. In total, it supports more than 120 species of mammals, 300 species of birds, 110 species of fish, and more than 170 species of amphibians and reptiles (Cotera et al. 2004).

The goal of the ecoregional planning process is to generate a portfolio of areas that, if conserved, would protect the biodiversity of an ecoregion over the long-term. The process starts with identifying a broad suite of ecological targets of a variety of types (e.g., species or ecological systems) and a variety of geographic scales (Groves et al. 2000, Poiani et al. 2000). For the Chihuahuan Desert, initial lists of targets that met one or more of the following criteria were compiled:

1. Rare, having high global ranks (NatureServe 2007) or deemed rare by an expert.
2. Endemic to the Chihuahuan Desert.
3. Limited to two or three ecoregions including the Chihuahuan Desert.
4. Disjunct populations important for evolution.
5. Key indicators of quality habitat.
6. Keystone taxa, such as prairie dogs (*Cynomys* spp.)
7. Taxa for which the Chihuahuan Desert is key to the target's overall success, such as wintering migratory birds.
8. Taxa or plant communities for which there is evidence of serious immediate or impending decline.

9. Ecological systems that represent all naturally occurring plant communities in the ecoregion.

Initial lists of potential targets meeting these criteria were developed and reviewed by biologists and ecologists familiar with the Chihuahuan Desert and its flora and fauna. Of a grand total of 649 targets selected, 15 were birds (Table 1). Although birds appear at first glance to comprise only a small proportion of targets, a large number of additional bird taxa in the ecoregion were considered to be captured or subsumed by other targets at different scales, such as ecological systems. For example, the desert scrub ecological system was considered to include numerous shrubland birds, such as wintering Brewer's Sparrow (*Spizella breweri*), and the grassland ecological system to include Sprague's Pipit (*Anthus spragueii*).

To generate the actual portfolio of areas, known locations (occurrences) of all targets were plotted onto a planning grid of 2,000 ha hexagons across the entire ecoregion. Such locations were compiled from the literature, museum specimens, Natural Heritage Program databases, and scientists with knowledge of each taxon and the ecoregion. Goals were established for the number of occurrences of each target that needed to be captured in the final portfolio. Typically, the goal for any given target depended on its global rarity and the degree to which its distribution is confined to the ecoregion; rare species and those with restricted distributions had higher goals for the ecoregion than more common species with widespread distributions (Groves et al. 2000, Cotera et al. 2004). For many targets, goals were also specified for subregions or other strata within the ecoregion, to ensure appropriate spatial distribution of the target within the final portfolio (Groves 2003).

A map of the human impact on the Chihuahuan Desert ecoregion was developed, including relative area or density of urban areas, tilled agricultural lands, roads, railroads, powerlines, and protected areas. This map was used as a relative cost surface input to a software package (SITES; Davis et al. 2002) that helped design an efficient ecologically based portfolio of conservation areas that met the specified goals for each target while at the same time minimizing total area and cost from the human impact layer. The most efficient portfolio, as selected by the software package, was reviewed by biologists and staff from all institutions participating in the process to eliminate areas accidentally included, consolidate certain adjacent areas, and identify gaps in the resulting output. The final portfolio (Fig. 2) included 125 conservation areas which cover 24% of the entire ecoregion.

All of the 15 avian target taxa occurred within the final ecoregional portfolio (at least one site at which each taxon was known to occur was part of the portfolio). However, for only four of these taxa (27%) was the entire goal for that taxon completely captured within the portfolio. A primary cause for the failure to meet the entire goal for most taxa is the absence of accurate location data on the presence of viable occurrences. These data gaps are typical of planning for large ecoregions such as the Chihuahuan Desert and must be closed in future iterations of this planning process. The effort to make an efficient portfolio of the smallest total area probably also contributes to the failure to include more of the goal for each taxon, since single sites with one or a few total targets are unlikely to be included.

TABLE 1. AVIAN TAXA SELECTED AS CONSERVATION TARGETS IN CHIHUAHUAN DESERT ECOREGIONAL PLAN.

Species	Seasonal status	Reason for inclusion
Ferruginous Hawk (*Buteo regalis*)	wintering	Declining populations
Aplomado Falcon (*Falco femoralis*)	resident	Endemic subspecies
Snowy Plover (*Charadrius alexandrinus*)	breeding	High global rank, limited ecoregional distribution
Mountain Plover (*Charadrius montanus*)	breeding sites	High global rank, disjunct breeding population
Least Tern (*Sternula antillarum*)	breeding sites	Disjunct population
Burrowing Owl (*Athene cunicularia*)	resident	Declining populations
Spotted Owl (*Strix occidentalis*)	resident	High global rank
Willow Flycatcher (*Empidonax traillii*)	breeding	High global rank, US Endangered subspecies
Bell's Vireo (*Vireo bellii*)	breeding	Declining populations
Black-capped Vireo (*Vireo atricapilla*)	breeding	High global rank, limited ecoregional distribution; US Endangered
Gray Vireo (*Vireo vicinior*)	breeding	Disjunct population
Cave Swallow (*Petrochelidon fulva*)	breeding	Endemic subspecies
Colima Warbler (*Vermivora crissalis*)	breeding	Limited ecoregional distribution
Worthen's Sparrow (*Spizella wortheni*)	resident	Endemic
Baird's Sparrow (*Ammodramus bairdii*)	wintering	Limited ecoregional distribution

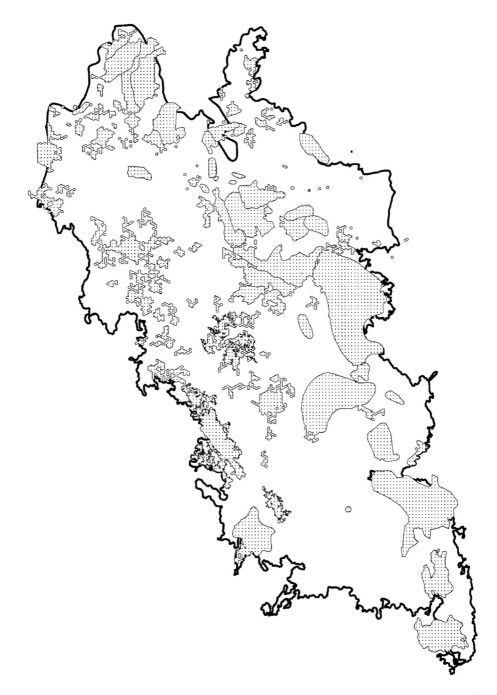

FIGURE 2. Chihuahuan Desert ecoregional portfolio of potential conservation areas (From Cotera et al. 2004). The heavy black line is the outline of the ecoregion, as in Fig. 1. The stippled areas are the portfolio sites, selected as described in the text.

DEVELOPING STRATEGIES

After conservation areas were identified through the ecoregional planning process, strategies and actions for the long-term conservation of biodiversity were developed. These strategies and actions were focused on abating the threats to one or more of the conservation targets at each area. In the borderlands region, this process was applied to a suite of conservation sites that shared common grassland bird species. Highly mobile conservation targets, such as birds, are often more easily dealt with in terms of suites of sites, because in addition to sharing targets, sites are likely to share threats and conservation strategies. A Conservation Action Planning process was carried out at five different conservation areas in the Chihuahuan Desert or adjacent ecoregions (The Nature Conservancy 2000). All were significantly important for shortgrass prairie and associated grassland birds and other taxa: Mescalero sandsheet, New Mexico; Marfa grasslands, Texas; San Pedro River, Sonora; Janos grasslands, Chihuahua; and Saltillo grasslands, Coahuila

and Nuevo León. For each site, teams of experts first identified a small subset of conservation targets that represented the biodiversity at the site, reflected conservation goals for the respective ecoregion, and faced some level of threat. Next, threats that were known or highly suspected to impact each target were tabulated. Each threat was also ranked on a four-level scale (very high, high, medium, low) by assessing the severity and scope of its effect. The results were then rolled up across all sites into a combined analysis (Table 2). Although a total of 28 threats were identified across the five sites, only two were common across all or nearly all sites: grazing practices and conversion to agriculture. The remaining threats, though potentially of high priority at individual sites, are more idiosyncratic in their nature and vary in rank across the larger grassland landscape.

The causes or sources of these threats were then identified and also ranked by their degree of contribution to each threat and the irreversibility of the threat. For highly ranked causes of threat, site teams then developed conservation strategies that were designed to address the

TABLE 2. SUMMARY OF COMBINED THREATS TO CONSERVATION TARGETS AT FIVE SITES IN THE CHIHUAHUAN DESERT OR ADJACENT ECOREGIONS, WITH THREAT RANK AT EACH SITE INDIVIDUALLY AND COMBINED ACROSS ALL SITES INDICATED. THREAT RANKS: VH = VERY HIGH; H = HIGH; M = MEDIUM; L = LOW.

Threat	San Pedro River	Mescalero sandsheet	Marfa grasslands	Janos grasslands	Saltillo grasslands	All Sites
Grazing practices	H	H	H	VH	VH	VH
Conversion to agriculture	L	H	M	H	VH	VH
Development of roads or utilities	L	-	-	M	H	H
Inappropriate herbicide use	-	H	-	-	-	H
Oil or gas development	-	H	-	-	-	H
Poisoning	-	-	-	H	-	H
Invasive species	H	-	L	-	M	H
Excessive extraction of subterranean water	M	-	-	-	M	M
Policies and programs for incompatible development	-	-	-	-	H	H
Agricultural practices	-	-	-	-	H	H
Subdivision and development	-	-	H	-	-	H
Watershed management	-	-	H	-	-	H
Dairies and associated development	-	M	-	-	-	M
Perception of competition between livestock and prairie dogs	-	-	-	M	-	M
Incompatible pasture and boundary fences	-	-	M	-	-	M
Construction of ditches, dikes, drainage or diversion systems	M	-	M	-	-	M
Irrigated agriculture	-	M	-	-	-	M
Parasites/pathogens	M	-	-	-	-	M
Altered fire regime	M	L	M	-	-	M
Commercial and industrial development	L	-	L	-	-	L
Recreational use	-	-	-	-	L	L
Water treatment	L	-	-	-	-	L
Off road vehicles	-	L	-	-	-	L
Erosion	-	-	-	-	L	L
Hunting practices	-	L	-	-	L	L
Wind energy	-	L	-	-	-	L

cause and mitigate the threat. Generally, such strategies include activities such as the protection of legal interests in land or water, implementation of adaptive management on public or private lands, implementation of policy measures, or the initiation of compatible development activities (The Nature Conservancy 2000). For the Mescalero sandsheet, New Mexico site, three initial conservation strategies of high priority and high potential to abate important threats were identified: protection of ranches at risk of conversion to agriculture, implementation of best management practices for oil and gas leases on federal lands, and creation of areas of restricted use on federal lands.

TAKING ACTION

Once strategies have been identified and prioritized, implementation of on-the-ground conservation begins. In this phase, private or public conservation partners, either based in Mexico or the US, initiate a wide variety of conservation actions. These actions use all methods in the conservation toolbox, from land protection by acquisition or easements, to invasive species control, to public policy implementation. Ideally, TNC seeks to use its limited resources for conservation as efficiently as possible while at the same time achieving as much leverage as possible.

An illustrative example of conservation action in the borderlands region is the ongoing conservation initiative for the grasslands in the Janos Valley of northern Chihuahua, Mexico. The Janos Valley has been identified by numerous priority setting exercises at a variety of spatial scales as being a top priority for biodiversity conservation. Some of these exercises and organizations include the Chihuahuan Desert ecoregional plan (Cotera et al. 2004), World Wildlife Fund (Dinerstein et al. 2000), Important bird areas program (Arizmendi and Márquez 2000), and the Commission for Environmental Cooperation (Karl and Hoth 2005). These planning efforts, as well as conservation area planning exercises conducted by TNC and partners, have identified and ranked numerous conservation strategies in the area, including the identification and acquisition of key tracts of land, establishment of a protected area over much of the intact grassland, community-based conservation education and landowner outreach, coalition building, partner capacity building, acquisition of grazing rights, and grass-banking.

A critically important step in beginning the implementation of conservation strategies was the acquisition in 2005 of the 18,545 ha Rancho El Uno near the town of Janos by TNC and Pronatura Noreste (PNE). This acquisition immediately halted two high-level threats to this property (overgrazing and unsustainable agriculture practices) and provides a solid platform from which to base more efficient and leveraged strategies such as implementation of sustainable grazing practices on private and communal lands in the area, habitat restoration, black-tailed prairie dog (*Cynomys ludovicianus*) recolonization, education, and community outreach. Bird species of conservation concern that occur regularly in the Janos Valley and that will benefit from the acquisition of Rancho El Uno and the implementation of other conservation strategies include Ferruginous Hawk (*Buteo regalis*), Mountain Plover (*Charadrius montanus*), Long-billed Curlew (*Numenius americanus*), Burrowing Owl (*Athene cunicularia*), Sprague's Pipit, Brewer's Sparrow, Baird's Sparrow (*Ammodramus bairdii*), Chestnut-collared Longspur (*Calcarius ornatus*), and at least 200 other avian species (Dieni et al. 2003, Manzano-Fischer et al. 2006).

This acquisition, coupled with the implementation of other strategies such as the declaration of a biosphere reserve and other protected areas at federal and state levels, use of conservation easements, and payments for environmental services, will be used to protect other key parts of the Chihuahuan Desert. These protection strategies, combined with environmentally compatible economic development alternatives and sustainable land management efforts that can be tested at Rancho El Uno, give hope for significantly increased quantity and quality of grassland and other habitats for birds in the US-Mexico borderlands over the decades to come.

MEASURING RESULTS

The final step in closing the loop of Conservation by Design is to measure the success of conservation strategies as they are applied, in order to continually refine the entire process in an adaptive manner. Measuring success is still in its infancy, as techniques that can provide the desired information and that are cost-effective and take reasonable time are still under vigorous discussion and development. A consensus is emerging among numerous conservation organizations that it is appropriate to measure conservation effectiveness by assessing the combination of biodiversity viability, threat status, and conservation management status (Higgins et al. 2007). It is when all three of these factors (fully viable biodiversity, lowered or eliminated threats, and effective land management) have been achieved that we can fully claim to have achieved conservation success. Such measures will have to be implemented at multiple spatial scales, such as the individual conservation site or project area, ecoregion, biome, or even the entire globe.

In many contexts, especially in the borderlands region, birds provide a valuable tool for monitoring conservation success, though undoubtedly many other techniques will have to be used. To test this hypothesis, TNC and Rocky Mountain Bird Observatory, in collaboration with numerous partners in Mexico, are implementing a large-scale initiative to monitor wintering grassland birds in northern Mexico (Panjabi 2007a). This project's immediate objectives are to gather better and more detailed data on the spatial, temporal, and habitat distribution of wintering grassland birds across the Chihuahuan Desert in Mexico. Efforts will be concentrated in several conservation areas identified through the above-mentioned planning processes and focused on avian priority conservation targets as selected by the ecoregional and conservation action planning processes. As this project continues over time, we expect to be able to measure the success of the variety of conservation strategies being implemented in this region, as well as to expand the project to cover a wider spatial scale.

Preliminary results from the first season of monitoring, in which a line-transect bird survey methodology was implemented at randomly points within randomly chosen 10 km × 10 km blocks overlapping previously identified conservation priority areas (Panjabi 2007b), reported a total of 131 species. Of this total, sample sizes sufficient for further analysis were obtained for 41 species (31%), of which nine are considered conservation priorities by one or more national initiatives. These species are Scaled Quail (*Callipepla squamata*), Northern Harrier (*Circus cyaneus*), Long-billed Curlew, Burrowing Owl, Loggerhead Shrike (*Lanius ludovicianus*), Sprague's Pipit, Brewer's Sparrow, Grasshopper Sparrow (*Ammodramus savannarum*), and Chestnut-collared Longspur. Several high priority birds, such as Mountain Plover, Cassin's Sparrow (*Aimophila cassinii*), and Baird's Sparrow were not found in numbers sufficient for analysis. These results suggest that implementation of broad scale surveys will yield useful data for conservation monitoring on many species of interest. However, a comprehensive survey effort will require additional, specialized surveys for certain species that are rare, difficult to find, or hard to identify.

CONCLUSION

The Conservation by Design framework is a useful process for achieving conservation success. Although implemented primarily by TNC, many of its components have been and can be used by other parties to achieve their particular conservation goals. Avian conservation has proved difficult to achieve for a variety of reasons, not the least of which are the broad spatial scale that many migratory birds traverse during their life cycles, the numerous threats they face, and the strategies that must be applied to address these threats. For these reasons, TNC and partners have developed large-scale conservation programs responsible for implementing the steps in the framework described in this paper. An example of these large-scale programs, applicable to many borderland bird species, is the Prairie Wings project (McCready et al. 2005). Such a fully integrated set of conservation planning tools and techniques, committed partners, and a framework to guide them are necessary to accomplish the long-term conservation of US-Mexico borderlands birds and other avian communities elsewhere.

LITERATURE CITED

Cactus Wren (*Campylorhynchus brunneicapillus*) © David J. Krueper

Studies in Avian Biology No. 37:146–165

LITERATURE CITED

ABARCA, F. J., M. F. INGRALDI, AND A. VARELA-ROMERO. 1993. Observaciones del perrito del desierto (*Cyprinodon macularius*), palmoteador de Yuma (*Rallus longirostris yumanensis*) y comunidades de aves playeras en la Ciénega de Santa Clara, Sonora México. Non-game and Endangered Wildlife Program Technical Report. Arizona Game and Fish Department, Phoenix, AZ.

ABLE, K. P. 1977. The flight behaviour of individual passerine nocturnal migrants: A tracking radar study. Animal Behaviour 25: 924–935.

ALBERS, M. T., AND F. R. GEHLBACH. 1990. Choices of feeding habitat by relict Montezuma Quail in central Texas. Wilson Bulletin 102: 300–308.

ALLRED, K. 1988. A field guide to the flora of the Jornada plain. New Mexico State University. Agricultural Experiment Station. Las Cruces, NM.

AMERICAN ORNITHOLOGISTS' UNION. 1998. Checklist of North American birds. Seventh Edition. American Ornithologists' Union. Washington, DC.

ANDERSEN, D. C. 1994. Demographics of small mammals using anthropogenic desert riparian habitat in Arizona. Journal of Wildlife Management 58:445–454.

ANDERSON, B. W., AND R. D. OHMART. 1977. Vegetation structure and bird use in the Lower Colorado River. Pp. 23–34 *in* R. R. Johnson, and D. A. Jones, Jr. (editors). Importance, preservation and management of riparian habitat: a symposium. USDA Forest Service General Technical Report RM-43. USDA Forest Service, Rocky Mountain Forest and Range Experiment Station, Fort Collins, CO.

ANDERSON, B. W., R. D. OHMART, AND J. RICE. 1983. Avian and vegetation community structure and their seasonal relationships in the Lower Colorado River Valley. Condor 85:392–405.

ANDERSON, B. W., P. E. RUSSELL, AND R. D. OHMART. 2004. Riparian revegetation: an account of two decades of experience in the arid Southwest. Avvar Books, Blythe, CA.

ANDERSON, D., J. KEITH, E. PALACIOS, E. VELARDE, F. GRESS, AND K. A. KING. 1999. El Niño 1997–98: Seabird responses from the southern California Current and Gulf of California. Pacific Seabirds 26:22.

ANDERSON, D. R., AND K. P. BURNHAM. 2002. Avoiding pitfalls when using information-theoretic methods. Journal of Wildlife Management 66:912–918.

ANDERSON, D. R., K. P. BURNHAM, AND G. C. WHITE. 1994. AIC model selection in over-dispersed capture-recapture data. Ecology 75:1780–1793.

ANDREWARTHA, H. G., AND L. C. BIRCH. 1954. The distribution and abundance of animals. University of Chicago Press, Chicago, IL.

ARIZMENDI, M. DEL C., AND L. MÁRQUEZ V. 2000. Areas de importancia para la conservación de las aves en México. CIPAMEX, Mexico City, Mexico.

AUTOMOBILE CLUB OF SOUTHERN CALIFORNIA. 1998. Baja California: U.S. border to Cabo San Lucas. Map 2401. Los Angeles, CA.

AVISE, J. C., AND D. WALKER. 1998. Pleistocene phylogeographic effects on avian populations and the speciation process. Proceedings of the Royal Society B: Biological Sciences 265:457–463.

BAHRE, C. J. 1991. A legacy of change: historic human impact on vegetation in the Arizona borderlands. University of Arizona Press, Tucson, AZ.

BAHRE, C. J. 1995. Human impacts on the grasslands of southeastern Arizona. Pp. 230–264 *in* M. P. McClaran, and T. R. Van Devender (editors). The desert grassland. University of Arizona Press, Tucson, AZ.

BAHRE, C. J., AND C. F. HUTCHINSON. 2001. Historic vegetation change in la Frontera west of the Rio Grande. Pp. 67–83 *in* G. L. Webster, and C. J. Bahre (editors). Changing plant life of la Frontera: observations on vegetation in the United States/Mexico borderlands. University of New Mexico Press, Albuquerque, NM.

BAHRE, C. J., AND R. A. MINNICH. 2001. Madrean oak woodlands along the Arizona/Sonora boundary. Desert Plants 17:3–14

BAHRE, C. J., AND M. L. SHELTON. 1993. Historic vegetation change, mesquite increases and climate in southeastern Arizona. Journal of Biogeography 20:489–504.

BAILEY, V. 1905. Biological survey of Texas. North. American Fauna No. 25. Washington, DC.

BAJA ALMANAC PUBLISHERS. 2003. Baja California almanac. Baja Almanac Publishers, Las Vegas, NV.

BALLING, R. C. JR. 1988. The climate impact of a Sonoran Desert vegetation discontinuity. Climate Change 13:99–109.

BALLING, R. C., AND G. B. GOODRICH. 2007. Analysis of drought determinants for the Colorado River Basin. Climatic Change 82: 179–184.

BANCROFT, G. 1927a. Breeding birds of Scammons Lagoon, Lower California. Condor 29: 29–57.

BANCROFT, G. 1927b. Notes on the breeding coastal and insular birds of central lower California. Condor 29:188–195.

BARNETT, T., R. MALONE, W. PENNELL, D. STAMMER, B. SEMTNER, AND W. WASHINGTON. 2004. The effects of climate change on water resources in the West: introduction and overview. Climatic Change 62:1–11.

BAUMGARTNER, J., T. COMENDANT, A. ERICKSON, J. HARDESTY, P. HARDY, M. HODGKINS, A. LEHNHOFF, M. LIPFORD, C. MACDONALD, AND B. NORTHRUP. 2006. Conservation by design: a strategic framework for mission success. The Nature Conservancy, Arlington, VA.

BEASON, R. C. 1995. Horned Lark (*Eremophila alpestris*). *In* A. Poole, and F. Gill (editors). The Birds of North America, No. 195. The Academy of Natural Sciences, Philadelphia, PA and The American Ornithologists' Union, Washington, DC.

BEERWINKLE, K. R., J. LOPEZ, J. D., J. A. WITZ, P. G. SCHLEIDER, R. S. EYSTER, AND P. D. LINGREN. 1994. Seasonal radar and meteorological observations associated with nocturnal insect flight at altitudes to 900 meters. Environmental Entomology 23:676–683.

BENDER, D. J., T. A. CONTRERAS, AND L. FAHRIG. 1998. Habitat loss and population decline: a meta-analysis of the patch size effect. Ecology 79:517–533.

BENKMAN, C. W., AND H. R. PULLIAM. 1988. The comparative feeding rates of North American sparrows and finches. Ecology 69: 1195–1199.

BENSON, K. L. P., AND K. A. ARNOLD. 2001. The Texas breeding bird atlas. Texas A&M University System, College Station and Corpus Christi, TX. <http://txtbba.tamu.edu> (22 March 2008).

BIBBY, C. J., N. D. BURGESS, D. A. HILL, AND S. MUSTOE. 2000. Bird census techniques. Second Edition. Academic Press, London, UK.

BLENDINGER, P. G., AND R. A. OJEDA. 2001. Seed supply as a limiting factor for granivorous bird assemblages in the Monte Desert, Argentina. Austral Ecology 26:413–422.

BOAL, C. W., T. S. ESTABROOK, AND A. E. DUERR. 2003. Productivity and breeding habitat of Loggerhead Shrikes in a southwestern urban environment. Southwestern Naturalist 48:557–562.

BOCK, C. E., AND J. H. BOCK. 1988. Grassland birds in southeastern Arizona: impacts of fire, grazing, and alien vegetation. Pp. 43–58 *in* P. D. Goriup (editor). Ecology and conservation of grassland birds. International Council for Bird Preservation, Technical Publication No. 7, Cambridge, UK.

BOCK, C. E., AND J. H. BOCK. 1999. Response of winter birds to drought and short-duration grazing in southeastern Arizona. Conservation Biology 13:1117–1123.

BOCK, C. E., AND Z. F. JONES. 2004. Avian habitat evaluation: should counting birds count? Frontiers in Ecology and the Environment 2:403–410.

BOCK, C. E., AND B. WEBB. 1984. Birds as grazing indicator species in southeastern Arizona. Journal of Wildlife Management 48:1045–1049.

BOCK, C. E., Z. F. JONES, AND J. H. BOCK. 2008. The oasis effect: response of birds to exurban development in a southwestern savanna. Ecological Applications 18:1093–1106.

BOCK, C. E., J. H. BOCK, W. R. KENNEY, AND V. M. HAWTHORNE. 1984. Responses of birds, rodents, and vegetation to livestock exclosure in a semidesert grassland site. Journal of Range Management 37:239–242.

BOJÓRQUEZ-TAPIA, L. A., R. AGUIRRE, AND A. ORTEGA. 1985. Rio Yaqui watershed, northwestern Mexico: use and management. Pp. 475–478 *in* R. R. Johnson, C. D. Ziebell, P. F. Patton, P. F. Ffolliott, and R. E. Hamre (editors). Riparian ecosystems and their management: reconciling conflicting issues. USDA Forest Service General Technical Report RM-12., USDA Forest Service, Rocky Mountain Forest and Range Experiment Station, Fort Collins, CO.

BOWERS, R. K., AND J. B. DUNNING. 1997. Buff-collared Nightjar (*Caprimulgus ridgwayi*). *In* A. Poole, P. Stettenheim, and F. Gill (editors). The Birds of North America, No. 267. The Academy of Natural Sciences, Philadelphia, PA and The American Ornithologists' Union, Washington, DC.

BRANDT, H. W. 1940. Texas bird adventures. The Bird Research Foundation, Cleveland, OH.

BRANDT, H. 1951. Arizona and its bird life. The Bird Research Foundation, Cleveland, OH.

BRODRICK, H. 1960. Check-list of the birds of Big Bend National Park. Big Bend Natural History Association, Big Bend National Park, TX.

BRODRICK, H., C. P. ALLEN, AND A. LESASSIER. 1966. Check-list of Birds of Big Bend National Park. Big Bend Natural History Association, Big Bend National Park, TX.

BROWN, D. 1982. Biotic communities of the America southwest United States and Mexico. Desert Plants 4:123–179.

BROWN, D. E. (EDITOR). 1994. Biotic communities: southwestern United States and northwestern Mexico. University of Utah Press, Salt Lake City, UT.

BROWN, D. E., P. J. UMACK, AND T. C. BRENNAN. 2007. Digitized map of biotic communities for plotting and comparing distributions of North American animals. Southwestern Naturalist 52:610–616.

BROWN, H. 1900. The conditions governing bird life in Arizona. Auk 17:31–34.

BROWN, H. 1904. Masked Bob-white (*Colinus ridgwayi*). Auk 21:209–213.

BROWN, J. H. 1995. Macroecology. University of Chicago Press, Chicago, IL.

BROWN, J. H., O. J. REICHMAN, AND D. W. DAVIDSON. 1979. Granivory in desert ecosystems. Annual Review of Ecology and Systematics 10:201–227.

BROWN, S., C. HICKEY, B. HARRINGTON, AND R. GILL (EDITORS). 2001. The U.S. shorebird conservation plan, 2nd edition. Manomet Center for Conservation Sciences, Manomet, MA.

BROWNING, K. A., AND R. WEXLER. 1968. The determination of kinematic properties of a wind field using Doppler radar. Journal of Applied Meteorology 7:105–113.

BRUDERER, B. 1997. The study of bird migration by radar, Part 2: Major achievements. Naturwissenschaften 84:45–54.

BRUSH, T. 2000. Nesting of Rose-throated Becard *Pachyramphus aglaiae* (Passeriformes: *Incertae sedis*) and Clay-colored Robin *Turdus grayi* (Passeriformes: Turdidae) in Hidalgo County, Texas. Texas Journal of Science 52:165–168.

BRUSH, T. 2005. Nesting birds of a tropical frontier, the Lower Rio Grande Valley of Texas. Texas A&M University Press, College Station, TX.

BRUSH, T., AND A. CANTU. 1998. Changes in the breeding bird community of subtropical evergreen forest in the Lower Rio Grande Valley of Texas, 1970s–1990s. Texas Journal of Science 50:123–132.

BRUSH, T. In press. Range expansions and new breeding records of birds in Tamaulipas, Mexico. Southwestern Naturalist 53.

BRYAN, K. B., AND J. KARGES. 2001. Recent changes to the Davis Mountains avifauna. Texas Birds 3:41–53.

BRYCE, S. A., R. M. HUGHES, AND P. R. KAUFMANN. 2002. Development of a bird integrity index: using bird assemblages as indicators of riparian condition. Environmental Management 30:294–310.

BUCKLEY, F. G., AND P. A. BUCKLEY. 1972. The breeding ecology of Royal Terns *Sterna* (*Thalasseus*) *maxima maxima*. Ibis 114: 344–359.

BUCKLEY, F. G., AND P. A. BUCKLEY. 1974. Comparative feeding ecology of wintering adult and juvenile Royal Terns (Aves: Laridae: Sterninae). Ecology 55:1053–1063.

BUCKLEY, P. A., AND F. G. BUCKLEY. 1977. Hexagonal packing of Royal Tern nests. Auk 94:36–43.

BUCKLEY, P. A., AND F. G. BUCKLEY. 2002. Royal Tern (*Sterna maxima*). *In* A. Poole, and F. Gill (editors). The Birds of North America, No. 700. The Academy of Natural Sciences, Philadelphia, PA and The American Ornithologists' Union, Washington, DC.

BUFFINGTON, L. C., AND C. H. HERBEL. 1965. Vegetational changes on a semidesert grassland range from 1858 to 1963. Ecological Monographs 35:139–164.

BURNHAM, K. P., AND D. R. ANDERSON. 1998. Model selection and inference: a practical information-theoretic approach. Springer-Verlag, New York, NY.

BURNHAM, K. P., AND W. S. OVERTON. 1979. Robust estimation of population size when capture probabilities vary among animals. Ecology 60:927–936.

BÚRQUEZ, A. A., AND A. MARTÍNEZ-YRÍZAR. 2007. Conservation and landscape transformations in northwestern Mexico. Pp. 537–547 *in* R. S. Felger, and B. Broyles (editors). Dry borders: great nature reserves of the Sonoran Desert. University of Utah Press, Salt Lake City. UT.

CADE, T. J., AND C. P. WOODS. 1997. Changes in distribution and abundance of the Loggerhead Shrike. Conservation Biology 11:21–31.

CANTERBURY, G. E., T. E. MARTIN, D. R. PETIT, L. J. PETIT, AND D. F. BRADFORD. 2000. Bird communities and habitat as ecological indicators of forest condition in regional monitoring. Conservation Biology 14:544–558.

CARLISLE, J. D., S. L. STOCK, G. S. KALTENECKER, AND D. L. SWANSON. 2004. Habitat associations, relative abundance and species richness of autumn land-bird migrants in southwestern Idaho. Condor 106:549–566.

CARTRON, J.-L. E., G. CEBALLOS, AND R. S. FELGER (EDITORS). 2005. Biodiversity, ecosystems, and conservation in northern Mexico. Oxford University Press, New York, NY.

CASTELLANOS, A., F. SALINAS, AND A. ORTEGA-RUBIO. 2001. Inventory and conservation of breeding waterbirds at Ojo de Liebre and Guerrero Negro Lagoons, Baja California Sur, Mexico. Ciencias Marinas 27:351–373.

CHRISTENSEN, N. S., A. W. WOOD, N. VOISIN, D. P. LETTENMAIER, AND R. N. PALMER. 2004. The effect of climate change on the hydrology and water resources of the Colorado Basin. Climatic Change 62:337–363.

CLEVELAND, C. J., M. BETKE, P. FEDERICO, J. D. FRANK, T. G. HALLAM, J. HORN, J. LÓPEZ, J. D., G. F. MCCRACKEN, R. A. MEDELLÍN, A. MORENO-VALDEZ, C. G. SANSONE, J. K. WESTBROOK, AND T. H. KUNZ. 2006. Economic value of the pest control service provided by Brazilian free-tailed bats in south-central Texas. Frontiers in Ecology and the Environment 4:238–243.

COGSWELL, H. L. 1977. Waterbirds of California. University of California Press, Los Angeles, CA.

COHN, J. P. 2007. The environmental impacts of a border fence. BioScience 57:96.

COLEMAN, B. D., M. A. MARES, M. R. WILLIG, AND Y. HSIEH. 1982. Randomness, area and species richness. Ecology 63:1121–1133.

COLLINS, C. T. 2006. Banding studies of Elegant Terns in southern California. North American Bird Bander 31:17–22.

COLLINS, C. T., AND P. F. DOHERTY, JR. 2006. Survival estimates for Royal Terns in southern California. Journal of Field Ornithology 77:310–314.

COLLINS, C. T., W. A. SCHEW, AND E. BURKETT. 1991. Elegant Terns breeding in Orange County, California. American Birds 45:393–395.

CONANP. 2007. Plan de Conservación y Manejo de la Reserva de la Biosfera Alto Golfo de California y delta del Río Colorado. Comisión Nacional de Áreas Naturales Protegidas, México, D.F.

CONLEY, W., AND M. R. CONLEY. 1984. New Mexico State University College Ranch and Jornada Experimental Range: a summary of research 1900–1983. Special report. New Mexico State Agricultural Experimental Station. Las Cruces, NM.

CONWAY, C. 2002. Standardized protocols for monitoring marshbirds in North America. Arizona Cooperative Fish and Wildlife Research Unit, USGS and School of Renewable Natural Resources, University of Arizona, Tucson, AZ.

CONWAY, C. J., AND J. P. GIBBS. 2005. Effectiveness of call-broadcast surveys for monitoring marshbirds. Auk 122:26–35.

CONWAY, C. J., AND C. P. NADEAU. 2005. Effects of fire on Yuma Clapper Rails and California Black Rails, 2004 Annual Report. Wildlife Research Report Number 2005-01. Arizona Cooperative Fish and Wildlife Research Unit, Tucson, AZ.

COOKE, W. W. 1915. Bird migration. USDA Bulletin 185:1–47.

COOPER, B. A., A. A. STICKNEY, AND T. J. MABEE. 2004. A radar study of nocturnal bird migration at the proposed Chautauqua Wind Energy Facility, New York, Fall 2003: Final Report for Chautauqua Windpower LLC. ABR Inc. Environmental Research and Services, Forest Grove, OR.

COPPEDGE, B. R., D. M. ENGLE, R. E. MASTERS, AND M. S. GREGORY. 2001. Avian response to landscape change in fragmented southern Great Plains grasslands. Ecological Applications 11:47–59.

CORMAN, T. E., AND G. MONSON. 1995. First United States nesting records of the Streak-backed Oriole. Western Birds 26:49-53.

CORMAN, T. E., AND C. WISE-GERVAIS (EDITORS). 2005. Arizona breeding bird atlas. University of New Mexico Press, Albuquerque, NM.

COTERA, M., E. GUADARRAMA, J. BRENNER, A. M. ARANGO, M. E. GARCIA GARZA, G. P. BELL, S. YANOFF, T. SULLIVAN, S. NAJERA, P. GRONEMEYER, J. WEIGEL, J. KARGES, B. MCCREADY, D. MEHLMAN, J. BERGAN, J. KING, M. GALLYOUN, D. L. CERTAIN, R. POTTS, J. WRINKLE, J. BEZAURY, H. M. ARIAS, J. ATCHLEY MONTOYA, I. E. PARRA, E. MULDAVIN, T. NEVILLE, AND G. KITTEL. 2004. Ecoregional conservation assessment of the Chihuahuan Desert, 2nd edition. Pronatura Noreste, Monterrey, N.L., Mexico.

CRUM, T. D., R. L. ALBERTY, AND D. W. BURGESS. 1993. Recording, archiving, and using WSR-88D data. Bulletin of the American Meteorological Society 74:645–653.

CRUMPTON, L. S. 1991. Baja explorer topographic atlas directory. ALTI Publishing. La Jolla, CA.

CRUMPTON, L. S. 1997. Baja California Sur almanac: topographic maps. Baja Almanac Publishers, Las Vegas, NV.

CUETO, V. R., L. MARONE, AND J. LOPEZ DE CASENAVE. 2006. Seed preferences in sparrow species of the Monte Desert, Argentina: implications for seed-granivore interactions. Auk 123:358–367.

DANEMANN, G. D., AND R. CARMONA. 2000. Breeding birds of the Guerrero Negro saltworks, Baja California Sur, Mexico. Western Birds 31:195–199.

DANEMANN, G. D., AND J. R. GUZMAN. 1992. Notes on the birds of San Ignacio Lagoon, Baja California Sur, Mexico. Western Birds 23:11–19.

DAUBENMIRE, R. F. 1959. Canopy coverage method of vegetation analysis. Northwest Scientist 33:43–64.

DAVIS, F., S. ANDELMAN, AND D. STOMS. 2002. SITES: an analytical toolbox for ecoregional planning. <Internet site:<http://www.biogeog.ucsb.edu/projects/tnc/toolbox.html> (9 April 2008).

DAVIS, L. I. 1945. Yellow-green Vireo nesting in Cameron County, Texas. Auk 62:146.

DAVIS, L. I. 1966. Birds of the Rio Grande delta, an annotated checklist. Published by the author, Austin, TX.

Davis, L. I. 1974. Birds of the Rio Grande delta, an annotated checklist. Published by the author, Austin, TX.

Davis, S. K. 2004. Area sensitivity in grassland passerines: effects of patch size, patch shape, and vegetation structure on bird abundance and occurrence in southern Saskatchewan. Auk 121:1130–1145.

DeBano, L. F. (editor). 1995. Biodiversity and management of the Madrean Archipelago: the sky islands of southwestern United States and northwestern Mexico. USDA Forest Service General Technical Report RM-GTR-264. USDA Forest Service, Rocky Mountain Forest and Range Experiment Station, Fort Collins, CO.

DeSante, D. F., and T. L. George. 1994. Population trends in the landbirds of western North America. Studies in Avian Biology 15:173–190.

Desmond, M. J. 2004. Effects of grazing practices and fossorial rodents on a winter avian community in Chihuahua, Mexico. Biological Conservation 116:235–242.

Desmond, M. J., K. Young, B. Thompson, R. Valdez, and A. Lafón Terrazas. 2005. Habitat associations and conservation of grassland birds in the Chihuahuan Desert region: two case studies in Chihuahua Mexico. Pp. 439–451 in J. L. E. Carton, G. Ceballos, and R. S. Felger (editors). Biodiversity, ecosystems and conservation in northern Mexico. Oxford University Press, New York, NY.

Diario Oficial de la Federación. 2002. Norma Oficial Mexicana NOM-059-ECOL-2001, Protección ambiental—especies nativas de México de flora y fauna silvestres—categorías de riesgo y especificaciones para su inclusión, exclusión o cambio-lista de especies en riesgo. Secretaría de Medio Ambiente y Recursos Naturales. México, D.F.

Diaz, M. 1990. Interspecific patterns of seed selection among granivorous passerines: effects of seed size, seed nutritive value and bird morphology. Ibis 132:467–476.

Dick-Peddie, W. A. 1993. New Mexico vegetation: past, present, and future. University of New Mexico Press, Albuquerque, NM.

Dick-Peddie, W. A., W. H. Moir, and R. Spellenberg. 1993. New Mexico vegetation: past, present, and future. University of New Mexico Press, Albuquerque , NM.

Diehl, R. H., and R. P. Larkin. 2005. Introduction to the WSR-88D (NEXRAD) for ornithological research. Pp. 876–888 in C. J. Ralph, and T. D. Rich (editors). Bird conservation implementation and integration in the Americas: Proceedings of the Third International Partners in Flight Conference 2002. USDA Forest Service General Technical Report PSW-GTR-191. USDA Forest Service, Pacific Southwest Research Station, Albany, CA. <http://www.fs.fed.us/psw/ publications/documents/psw_gtr191/ Asilomar/pdfs/876-888.pdf> (10 April 2008).

Dieni, J. S., W. H. Howe, S. L. Jones, P. Manzano-Fischer, and C. P. Melcher. 2003. New information on wintering birds of northwestern Chihuahua. American Birds 103:26–31.

Dinerstein, E., D. Olson, J. Atchley, C. Loucks, S. Contreras-Balderas, R. Abell, E. Iñigo, E. Enkerlin, C. Williams, and G. Castilleja. 2000. Ecoregion-based conservation in the Chihuahuan Desert: a biological assessment. World Wildlife Fund, Washington, DC.

Dinsmore, J. J., and S. J. Dinsmore. 1993. Range expansion of Great-tailed Grackles in the 1900s. Journal of the Iowa Academy of Science 100:54–59.

Dooley, J. L., and M. A. Bowers. 1998. Demographic responses to habitat fragmentation: experimental tests at the landscape and patch scale. Ecology 79:969–980.

Dunning, J. B., and J. H. Brown. 1982. Summer rainfall and winter sparrow densities: a test of the food limitation hypothesis. Auk 99: 123–129.

Ecton, K. 2003. Spatial and temporal migration patterns of Wilson's Warblers revealed by stable hydrogen isotopes. M.S. thesis, Northern Arizona University, Flagstaff, AZ.

Eddleman, W. R. 1989. Biology of the Yuma Clapper Rail in the southwestern U.S. and northwestern México. Final Report. Intra-Agency of Agreement No. 4-AA-30-02060. U.S. Bureau of Reclamation, Yuma Projects Office, Yuma, AZ.

Eddleman, W. R., and C. J. Conway. 1998. Clapper Rail (Rallus longirostris). In A. Poole, and F. Gill (editors). The Birds of North America, No. 340. The Academy of Natural Sciences, Philadelphia, PA and The American Ornithologists' Union, Washington, DC.

Eitniear, J. C. 1997. White-collared Seedeater (Sporophila torqueola). In A. Poole, and F. Gill (editors). The Birds of North America, No. 278. The Academy of Natural Sciences, Philadelphia, PA and The American Ornithologists' Union, Washington, DC.

Eitniear, J. C. 2004. Diet of the white-collared seedeater Sporophila torqueola (Passeriformes: Emberizidae) in Texas. Texas Journal of Science 56:77–80.

Ellison, K., and S. G. Sealy. 2007. Small hosts infrequently disrupt laying by Brown-headed

Cowbirds and Bronzed Cowbirds. Journal of Field Ornithology 78:379–389.

ENVIRONMENTAL SYSTEMS RESEARCH INSTITUTE. 1990. PC ARC/INFO Version 3.2. Environmental Systems Research Insitute, Redlands, CA.

ERWIN, R. M. 1977. Foraging and breeding adaptations to different food regimes in three seabirds: Common Tern, *Sterna hirundo*, Royal Tern, *S. maxima*, and Black Skimmer, *Rynchops niger*. Ecology 58:389–397.

ERWIN, R. M. 1979. Species interactions in a mixed colony of Common Terns, *Sterna hirundo*, and Black Skimmers, *Rynchops niger*. Animal Behaviour 27:1054–1062.

ESCALANTE, T., G. RODRÍGUEZ, AND J. J. MORRONE. 2004. The diversification of Nearctic mammals in the Mexican transition zone. Biological Journal of the Linnean Society 83: 327–339.

EVERETT, W. T., AND D. W. ANDERSON. 1991. Status and conservation of the breeding seabirds of offshore Pacific Islands of Baja California and the Gulf of California. Pp. 115–139 *in* J. P. Croxall (editor), Seabird status and conservation: a supplement. ICBP Technical Publication 11. International Council for Bird Preservation, Cambridge, UK.

FARLEY, G. H., L. M. ELLIS, J. N. STUART, AND N. J. SCOTT. 1994a. Avian species richness in different-aged stands of riparian forest along the middle Rio Grande, New Mexico. Conservation Biology 8:1098–1108.

FARLEY, G. H., L. M. ELLIS, J. N. STUART, AND N. J. SCOTT. 1994b. Birds of restored and mature riparian woodlands in the middle Rio Grande Valley. New Mexico Ornithological Society Bulletin 22:25–33.

FELGER R. S., B. BROYLES, M. F. WILSON, G. P. NABHAN, AND D. S. TURNER. 2007. Six grand reserves, one grand desert. Pp. 3–26 *in* R. S. Felger, and B. Broyles (editors). Dry borders: great nature reserves of the Sonoran Desert. University of Utah Press, Salt Lake City. UT

FINCH, D. M. (EDITOR). 2004. Assessment of grassland ecosystem conditions in the southwestern United States, Volumes 1 and 2. USDA Forest Service General Technical Report RMRS-GTR-135. USDA Forest Service, Rocky Mountain Research Station, Fort Collins, CO.

FINCH, D. M., AND W. YONG. 2000. Landbird migration in riparian habitats of the Middle Rio Grande: a case study. Studies in Avian Biology 20:88–98.

FLEISHMAN, E., G. T. AUSTIN, P. F. BRUSSARD, AND D. D. MURPHY. 1999. A comparison of butterfly communities in native and agricultural riparian habitats in the Great Basin, USA. Biological Conservation 89:209–218.

FLEISHMAN, E., N. McDONAL, R. MacNALLY, D. D. MURPHY, J. WALTERS, AND T. FLOYD. 2003. Effects of floristics, physiognomy, and non-native vegetation on riparian bird communities in a Mojave Desert watershed. Journal of Animal Ecology 72:484–490.

FLESCH, A. D. 1997. Distribution and abundance of breeding grassland birds on the Buenos Aires National Wildlife Refuge: a monitoring program. Report prepared for USDI Fish and Wildlife Service, Sasabe, AZ.

FLESCH, A. D. 2003. Distribution, abundance, and habitat of Cactus Ferruginous Pygmy-Owls in Sonora Mexico. M.S. thesis, University of Arizona, Tucson, AZ.

FLESCH, A. D. 2008. Status and population size of breeding grassland birds on Rancho Los Fresnos, northern Sonora, Mexico. Report. School of Natural Resources, University of Arizona, Tucson, AZ.

FLESCH, A. D., AND L. A. HAHN. 2005. Distribution of birds and plants at the western and southern edges of the Madrean Sky Islands in Sonora, Mexico. Pp. 80–87 *in* G. J. Gottfried, B. Gebow, L. G. Eskew, and E. Carleton (editors). Connecting mountain islands and desert seas: biodiversity and management of the Madrean Archipelago II. USDA Forest Service General Technical Report RMRS-P-36. USDA Forest Service, Rocky Mountain Research Station, Ft. Collins, CO.

FLESCH, A. D., AND R. J. STEIDL. 2006. Population trends and implications for monitoring Cactus Ferruginous Pygmy-Owls in northern Mexico. Journal of Wildlife Management 70:867–871.

FLESCH, A. D., AND R. J. STEIDL. 2007. Detectability and response rates of Ferruginous Pygmy-Owls. Journal of Wildlife Management 71: 981–990

FORD, H. A., N. FORDE, AND S. HARRINGTON. 1982. Non-destructive methods to determine the diets of birds. Corella 6:6–10.

FREDRICKSON, E., K. M. HAVSTAD, R. ESTELL, AND P. HYDER. 1998. Perspectives on desertification: southwestern United States. Journal of Arid Environments 39:191–207.

FRETWELL S. D. 1972. Populations in a seasonal environment. Princeton University Press, Princeton, NJ.

FUERTES, L. A. 1903. With the Mearn's Quail in southwestern Texas. Condor 5:113–116.

GALLOP, F. N., AND B. H. BAILEY. 1960. Elegant and Royal Terns nesting in California. Condor 62:65–66.

GARCÍA-HERNÁNDEZ, J., O. HINOJOSA-HUERTA, E. GLENN, D. BAUMGARTNER, S. DeSTEFANO, AND W. SHAW. 1999. Impacts of salinity increase in the bypass drain (MODE) on the ecology of the Cienega de Santa Clara wetland. Report to USDI, Bureau of Reclamation, Yuma Office. Yuma. AZ.

GARRETT, K., AND J. DUNN. 1981. The Birds of southern California. Los Angeles Audubon Society, Los Angeles, CA.

GARZA-TORRES, H. A., J. R. HERRERA-HERRERA, G. ESCALONA-SEGURE, J. A. VARGAS-CONTRERAS, AND A. G. NAVARRO-S. 2003. New bird records from Tamaulipas, Mexico. Southwestern Naturalist 48:707–710.

GATZ, T. A., M. D. JAKLE, R. L. GLINSKI, AND G. MONSON. 1985. First nesting record and current status of the Black-shouldered Kite in Arizona. Western Birds 16:57–61.

GAUTHREAUX, S. A., AND C. G. BELSER. 1998. Displays of bird movements on the WSR-88D: patterns and quantification. Weather and Forecasting 13:453–464.

GAUTHREAUX, S. A., C. G. BELSER, AND D. VAN BLARICOM. 2003. Using a network of WSR-88D weather surveillance radars to define patterns of bird migration at large spatial scales. Pp. 335–346 in P. Berthold, E. Gwinner, and E. Sonnenschein (editors). Avian migration. Springer-Verlag. Berlin, Germany.

GIBBENS, R. P., AND R. F. BECK. 1988. Changes in grass basal area and forb densities over a 64–year period on grassland types of the Jornada Experimental Range. Journal of Range Management 41:186–192.

GIBBENS, R. P., J. M. TROMBLE, J. T. HENNESY, AND M. CARDENAS. 1983. Soil movement in mesquite dune lands and former grass grasslands of southern New Mexico from 1933 to 1980. Journal of Range Management 36: 145–148.

GIBBENS, R. P., R. P. MCNEELY, K. M. HAVSTAD, R. F. BECK, AND B. NOLEN. 2005. Vegetation changes in the Jornada Basin from 1858 to 1998. Journal of Arid Environments 61: 651–668.

GIBBS, J. P. 1995. Users manual for MONITOR 6.2. Yale University, New Haven, CT.

GINTER, D. L., AND M. J. DESMOND. 2005. Influence of foraging and roosting behavior on home-range size and movement patterns of Savannah Sparrows wintering in south Texas. Wilson Bulletin 117:63–71.

GLENN, E. P., AND P. L. NAGLER. 2005. Comparative ecophysiology of Tamarix ramosissima and native trees in western U.S. riparian zones. Journal of Arid Environments 61:419–446.

GLENN, E. P., C. LEE, R. FELGER, AND S. ZENGEL. 1996. Effects of water management on the wetlands of the Colorado River delta, Mexico. Conservation Biology 10:1175–1186.

GLENN, E. P., F. ZAMORA-ARROYO, P. L. NAGLER, M. BRIGGS, W. SHAW, AND K. FLESSA. 2001. Ecology and conservation biology of the Colorado River delta, Mexico. Journal of Arid Environments 49:5–15.

GLÜCK, E. E. 1985. Seed preference and energy intake of Goldfinches Carduelis carduelis in the breeding season. Ibis 127:421–429.

GÓMEZ DE SILVA, H. 2004. Mexico. North American Birds 58:607–610

GÓMEZ DE SILVA, H. 2007. The nesting season; Mexico. North American Birds 60:584–587.

GOODWIN, S. L. 2000. Conservation connections in a fragmented desert environment: the U.S.-Mexico border. Natural Resource Journal 40:898–1016.

GORDON, C. E. 2000. Movement patterns of wintering grassland sparrows in Arizona. Auk 117:748–759.

GRAHAM, C. H., AND J. G. BLAKE. 2001. Influence of patch- and landscape-level on bird assemblages in a fragmented tropical landscape. Ecological Applications 11:1709–1721.

GRANT, P. R. 1966. Preliminary experiments on the foraging of closely related species of birds. Ecology 47:148–151.

GREENBERG, R. 1995. Insectivorous migratory birds in tropical ecosystems: the breeding currency hypothesis. Journal of Avian Biology 26:260–264.

GREENBERG, R., P. BICHIER, AND J. STERLING. 1997. Acacia, cattle and migratory birds in southeastern Mexico. Biological Conservation 80: 235–247.

GREGORY, S. V., F. J. SWANSON, W. A. MCKEE, AND K. W. CUMMINS. 1991. An ecosystem perspective of riparian zones. BioScience 41:540–551.

GREIG-SMITH, P. W., AND D. R. CROCKER. 1986. Mechanisms of food size selection by bullfinches (Pyrrula-pyrrula L) feeding on sunflower seeds. Animal Behaviour 34:843–859.

GREIG-SMITH, P. W., and M. F. WILSON. 1985. Influence of seed size, nutrient composition and phenolic content on the preference of bullfinches feeding in ash trees. Oikos 44: 47–54.

GRINNELL, J. 1928. A distributional summation of the ornithology of Lower California. University of California Publications in Zoology 32:1–300.

GRINNELL, J., AND A. H. MILLER. 1944. The distribution of the birds of California. Pacific Coast Avifauna 27:1–608.

GRISCOM, L., AND M. S. CROSBY. 1926. Birds of the Brownsville region, southern Texas. Auk 43: 18–36.

GROSCHUPF, K. 1994. Current status of Five-striped Sparrow in Arizona. Western Birds 25:192–197.

GROSS, K. L., AND K. A. RENNER. 1989. A new method for estimating seed numbers in the soil. Weed Science 37:836–839.

GROVES, C. 2003. Drafting a conservation blueprint: A practitioner's guide to planning for biodiversity. Island Press, Washington, DC.

GROVES, C., L. VALUTIS, D. VOSICK, B. NEELY, K. WHEATON, J. TOUVAL, AND B. RUNNELS. 2000. Designing a geography of hope: a practitioner's handbook to ecoregional conservation planning, second edition. The Nature Conservancy, Arlington, VA.

GRZYBOWSKI, J. A. 1982. Population structure in grassland bird communities during winter. Condor 84:137–152.

GRZYBOWSKI, J. A. 1983. Sociality of grassland birds during winter. Behavioral Biology and Sociobiology 13:211–219.

GUTIÉRREZ-LACAYO, M., AND O. HINOJOSA-HUERTA. 2007. Manual de Adquisición de Derechos de Agua en el delta del Río Colorado. Technical Publication of Pronatura Noroeste. San Luis Río Colorado, Sonora, México.

GUTZWILLER, K. J., AND W. C. BARROW. 2002. Does bird community structure vary with landscape patchiness? A Chihuahuan Desert perspective. Oikos 98:284–298.

HALFFTER, G. 1987. Biogeography of the montane entomofauna of Mexico and Central America. Annual Review in Entomology 32:95–114.

HARPER, J. L., P. H. LOVELL, AND K. G. MOORE. 1970. The shapes and sizes of seeds. Annual Review of Ecology and Systematics 1: 327–356.

HAVSTAD, K. M., J. E. HERRICK, AND W. H. SCHLESINGER. 2000. Desert rangelands, degradation and nutrients. Pp. 77–87 in O. Arnalds, and S. Archer (editors). Rangeland desertification. Kluwer Academic Publishers, Dordrecht, The Netherlands.

HEALD, W. F. 1993. The Chiricahuas sky island. Bantlin Publishers, Tucson, AZ.

HEGLUND, P. J., AND S. K. SKAGEN. 2005. Ecology and physiology of en route Nearctic-Neotropical migratory birds: a call for collaboration. Condor 107:193–196.

HELZER, C. J., AND D. E. JELINSKI. 1999. The relative importance of patch area and perimeter-area ratio to grassland breeding birds. Ecological Applications 9:1448–1458.

HENDERSON, C. B. 1990. The influence of seed apparency, nutrient content and chemical defenses on dietary preference in *Dipodomys ordii*. Oecologia 82:333–341.

HERKERT, J. R. 1994. The effects of habitat fragmentation on midwestern grassland bird communities. Ecological Applications 4: 461–471.

HERKERT, J. R., AND F. L. KNOPF. 1998. Research needs for grassland bird conservation. Pp. 273–282 in J. M. Marzluff, and R. Sallabanks (editors) Avian conservation: research and management. Island Press, Washington, DC.

HERRICK, J. E., K. M. HAVSTAD, AND D. P. COFFIN. 1997. Rethinking remediation technologies for desertified landscapes. Journal of Soil and Water Conservation 52:220–225.

HIGGINS, J., R. UNNASCH, AND C. SUPPLES. 2007. Ecoregional status measures version 1.0: framework and technical guidance to estimate effective conservation. The Nature Conservancy, Arlington, VA.

HINES, J. E. 1996. SPECRICH software to compute species abundance from empirical species abundance distribution data. USGS Patuxent Wildlife Research Center, Patuxent, MD. <http://www.mbr-pwrc.usgs.gov/software/specrich.html> (5 April 2008).

HINOJOSA-HUERTA, O. 2000. Abundance, distribution, and habitat use of the Yuma Clapper Rail (*Rallus longirostris yumanensis*) in the Colorado River delta, Mexico. M.S. thesis, University of Arizona, Tucson, AZ.

HINOJOSA-HUERTA, O., S. DESTEFANO, AND W. SHAW. 2001. Abundance and distribution of the Yuma Clapper Rail (*Rallus longirostris yumanensis*) in the Colorado River delta, Mexico. Journal of Arid Environments 49: 171–182.

HINOJOSA-HUERTA, O., J. GARCÍA-HERNÁNDEZ, Y. CARRILLO-GUERRERO, AND E. ZAMORA-HERNÁNDEZ. 2007. Hovering over the Alto Golfo: status and conservation of birds from the Rio Colorado to the Gran Desierto. Pp. 383–407 in R. S. Felger, and B. Broyles (editors). Dry borders: great natural areas of the Sonoran Desert. University of Utah Press, Salt Lake City, UT.

HINOJOSA-HUERTA, O., M. GUTIÉRREZ-LACAYO, Y. CARRILLO-GUERRERO, AND F. ZAMORA-ARROYO. 2007. Water acquisition for wetland restoration in the Colorado River delta. Final Report from Pronatura Noroeste presented to the USDI Fish and Wildlife Service, Grant MX-N391. San Luis Río Colorado, Sonora, México.

HINOJOSA-HUERTA, O., Y. CARRILLO-GUERRERO, S. DESTEFANO, W. SHAW, AND C. VALDÉS-CASILLAS. 2004. Waterbird communities and associated wetlands of the Colorado River delta, Mexico. Studies in Avian Biology 27: 52–60.

HINOJOSA-HUERTA, O., H. ITURRIBARRÍA-ROJAS, Y. CARRILLO-GUERRERO, M. DE LA GARZA-TREVIÑO, AND E. ZAMORA-HERNÁNDEZ. 2004.

Bird conservation plan for the Colorado River delta. Pronatura Noroeste, Dirección de Conservación Sonora. San Luis Río Colorado, Sonora, México.

HOLDERMANN, D. A., S. SOROLA, JR., AND R. SKILES. 2007. Recent photo and audio-documentation of Montezuma Quail from the Chisos Mountains, Big Bend National Park (BBNP), Texas. Bulletin of the Texas Ornithological Society 40:62–67.

HOLMES, R. T., AND T. W. SHERRY. 2001. Thirty-year bird population trends in an unfragmented temperate deciduous forest: importance of habitat change. Auk 118:589–609.

HORN, M. H., P. A. COLE, AND W. E. LOEFFLER. 1996. Prey resource base of the tern and skimmer colonies at the Bolsa Chica Ecological Reserve, Orange, County, and the Western Saltworks, south San Diego Bay. Final Report to USDI Fish and Wildlife Service, Carlsbad, CA.

HORN, M. H., W. E. LOEFFLER, J. F. WILSON, AND P. A. COLE. 1994. Monitoring of foraging patterns of terns and skimmers at the Bolsa Chica Ecological Reserve in 1994. Final Report to USDI Fish and Wildlife Service, Carlsbad, CA.

HOWELL, A. B. 1917. Birds of the islands off the coast of southern California. Pacific Coast Avifauna 12:1–127.

HOWELL S. N. G., AND S. WEBB. 1995. A guide to the birds of Mexico and northern Central America. Oxford University Press, New York, NY.

HUBBARD, J. P. 1971. The summer birds of the Gila Valley, New Mexico. Neumoria Occasional Papers of the Delaware Museum of Natural History 2:1–35.

HUNT, C. 1985. The need for riparian habitat protection. National Wetlands Newsletter 7:5–8.

HUTTO, R. L. 1980. Winter habitat distribution of migratory land birds in western Mexico, with special reference to small foliage-gleaning insectivores. Pp. 181–203 in A. E. Keast, and E. S. Morton (editors). Migrant birds in the Neotropics. Smithsonian Institution Press, Washington, DC.

HUTTO, R. L. 1985. Habitat selection by non-breeding, migratory land birds. Pp. 455–476 in M. L. Cody (editor). Habitat selection in birds. Academic Press, Inc., Orlando, FL.

HUTTO, R. L. 1995. Can patterns of vegetation change in western Mexico explain population trends in western neotropical migrants? Pp. 48–58 in M. H. Wilson, and S. A. Sader (editors). Conservation of neotropical migratory birds in Mexico. Maine Agricultural and Forest Experiment Station, Misc. Publ. 727. Orono, ME.

HUTTO, R. L. 1998. On the importance of stopover sites to migrating birds. Auk 115:823–825.

HUTTO, R. L. 2000. On the importance of en-route periods to the conservation of migratory landbirds. Studies in Avian Biology 20: 109–114.

HUTTO, R. L., S. M. PLETSCHET, AND P. HENDRICKS. 1986. A fixed-radius point count method for nonbreeding and breeding season use. Auk 103:593–602.

HYLANDER, K. 2006. Riparian zones increase regional species richness by harboring different, not more, species: comment. Ecology 87:2126–2128.

HYRENBACH, K. D., AND R. R. VEIT. 2003. Ocean warming and seabird communities of the southern California Current System (1987–98): response at multiple temporal scales. Deep-Sea Research II 50:2537–2565.

IGL, L. D., AND B. M. BALLARD. 1999. Habitat associations of migrating and over wintering grassland birds in southern Texas. Condor 101:771–782.

INEGI. 2000. Síntesis de Información Geográfica del Estado de Sonora., Second edition. Instituto Nacional de Estadística, Geografía e Informática INEGI, Aguascalientes, Ags. México.

INTERNATIONAL BOUNDARY AND WATER COMMISSION. 2007. Colorado River at southerly international boundary. <http://www.ibwc.state.gov/wad/ddqsibco.htm> (14 April, 2008).

JOHNSON, D. H. 1980. The comparison of usage and availability measurements for evaluating resource preference. Ecology 61:65–71.

JOHNSON, M. D., A. M. STRONG, AND T. W. SHERRY. 2006. Migrants in tropical bird communities: the balanced breeding limitation hypothesis. Journal of Avian Biology 37:229–237.

JOHNSON, M. D., T. W. SHERRY, A. M. STRONG, AND A. MEDORI. 2005. Migrants in Neotropical bird communities: an assessment of the breeding currency hypothesis. Journal of Animal Ecology 74:333–341.

JOHNSON, N. K. 1994. Pioneering and natural expansion of breeding distributions in western North American birds. Studies in Avian Biology 15:27–44.

JONES, Z. F., AND C. E. BOCK. 2002. Conservation of grassland birds in an urbanizing landscape: a historical perspective. Condor 104: 643–651.

JORNADA BASIN LONG TERM ECOLOGICAL RESEARCH NETWORK. 2006. Jornada Basin long term ecological research. <http://jornada-www.nmsu.edu/> (5 April 2008).

KARL, J. W., AND J. HOTH. 2005. North American grassland priority conservation areas:

technical report and documentation. Commission for Environmental Cooperation, Montreal, Quebec, Canada and The Nature Conservancy, Arlington, VA.

KELLY, J. F., AND R. L. HUTTO. 2005. An east-west comparison of migration in North American wood warblers. Condor 107:197–211.

KELLY, J., D. L. HAWKSWORTH, AND R. A. MEYER. 2006. Abundance of non-breeding Horned Larks and Chestnut-collared Longspurs on grazed and rested semiarid grassland. Southwestern Naturalist 51:172–180.

KELLY, J., R. SMITH, D. D. FINCH, F. MOORE, AND W. YONG. 1999. Influence of summer biogeography on Wood Warbler stopover abundance. Condor 101:76–85.

KENYON, K. W. 1947. Notes on the occurrence of birds in Lower California. Condor 49: 210–211.

KERLEY, G. I., AND W. G. WHITFORD. 2000. Impact of grazing and desertification in the Chihuahuan Desert: plant communities, granivores and granivory. American Midland Naturalist 144:78–91.

KIRKPATRICK, C., S. DeSTEPHANO, R. W. MANNAN, AND J. LLOYD. 2002. Trends in abundance of grassland birds following a spring prescribed burn in southern Arizona. Southwestern Naturalist 47:282–292.

KNOPF, F. L. 1985. Significance of riparian vegetation to breeding birds across an altitudinal cline. Pp.105–111 in R. R. Johnson, C. D. Ziebell, D. R. Patton, P. F. Ffolliott, and R. E. Hamre (editors). Riparian ecosystems and their management: reconciling conflicting issues. First North American Riparian Conference. USDA Forest Service General Technical Report RM-120. USDA Forest Service, Rocky Mountain Forest and Range Experiment Station, Fort Collins, CO.

KNOPF, F. L. 1994. Avian assemblages on altered grasslands. Studies in Avian Biology 15: 247–257.

KNOPF, F. L. 1996. Prairie legacies—birds. Pp. 135–148 in F. B. Samson, and F. L. Knopf (editors). Prairie conservation: preserving North America's most endangered ecosystem. Island Press, Washington, DC.

KNOPF, F. L., AND F. B. SAMSON. 1994. Scale perspectives on avian diversity in western riparian ecosystems. Conservation Biology 8:669–676.

KNOPF, F. L., R. R. JOHNSON, T. RICH, F. B. SAMSON, AND R .C. SZARO. 1988. Conservation of riparian ecosystems in the United States. Wilson Bulletin 100:272–284.

KOSTECKE, R. M., K. ELLISON, AND S. G. SUMMERS. 2004. Continued range expansion by Bronzed Cowbird in the southwestern United States. Southwestern Naturalist 49: 487–492.

KRICHER, J. C., AND W. E. DAVIS. 1992. Patterns of avian species richness in disturbed and undisturbed habitats in Belize. Pp. 240–246 in J. M. Hagan, and D. W. Johnston (editors). Ecology and Conservation of Neotropical Migrant Landbirds. Smithsonian Institution Press, Washington, DC.

KRUEPER, D., J. BART, AND T. RICH. 2003. Response of vegetation and breeding birds to the removal of cattle on the San Pedro River, Arizona (U.S.A.). Conservation Biology 17: 607–615.

KUSHLAN, J. A., M. J. STEINKAMP, K. C. PARSONS, J. CAPP, M. ACOSTA CRUZ, M COULTER, I. DAVIDSON, L. DICKSON, N. EDELSON, R. ELLIOT, R. M. IRWIN, S. HATCH, S. KRESS, R. MILKO, S. MILLER, K. MILLS, R. PAUL, R. PHILLIPS, J. E. SALIVA, B. SYDEMAN, J. TRAPP, J. WHEELER, AND K. WOHL. 2002. Waterbird conservation for the Americas. The North American Conservation Plan. Version 1. Waterbird Conservation for the Americas, Washington, DC.

LAND, H. C. 1970. Birds of Guatemala. Livingston Publishing Company, Wynnewood, PA.

LARISON, B., S. A. LAYMON, P. L. WILLIAMS, AND T. B. SMITH. 2001. Avian responses to restoration: nest-site selection and reproductive success in Song Sparrows. Auk 118: 432–442.

LARKIN, R. P. 1991. Flight speeds observed with radar, a correction: slow "birds" are insects. Behavioral Ecology and Sociobiology 29: 221–224.

LARKIN, R. P. 2005. Radar techniques for wildlife biology. Pp. 448–464 in C. E. Braun (editor). Techniques for wildlife investigations and management. The Wildlife Society, Bethesda, MD.

LATTA, M. J., C. J. BEARDMORE, AND T. E. CORMAN. 1999. Arizona Partners in Flight Bird Conservation Plan. Version 1.0. AGFD Nongame and Endangered Wildlife Program Technical Report 142. Arizona Game and Fish Department, Phoenix, AZ.

LITTELL, R. C., W. W. STROUP, AND R. J. FREUND. 2002. SAS for linear models. Fourth Edition. SAS Institute, Inc., Cary, NC.

LIVERMAN, D. M., R. G. VARADY, O. CHÁVEZ, AND R. SÁNCHEZ. 1999. Environmental issues along the United States-Mexico border: drivers of change and responses of citizens and institutions. Annual Review of Energy and the Environment 24:60–643.

LOCKWOOD, M. W. 2002. Texas Bird Records Committee report for 2001. Bulletin of the Texas Ornithological Society 35:1–10.

LOCKWOOD, M. W. 2004. Texas Bird Records Committee report for 2003. Bulletin of the Texas Ornithological Society 37:17–24.

LOCKWOOD, M. W. 2005. Texas Bird Records Committee report for 2004. Bulletin of the Texas Ornithological Society 38:21–28

LOCKWOOD, M. W. 2006. Texas Bird Records Committee report for 2005. Bulletin of the Texas Ornithological Society 39:33–42.

LOCKWOOD, M. W. 2007. Texas Bird Records Committee report for 2006. Bulletin of the Texas Ornithological Society 40:41–49

LOCKWOOD, M. W., AND B. FREEMAN. 2004. The Texas Ornithological Society handbook of Texas birds. Texas A&M University Press, College Station, TX.

LOCKWOOD, M. W., R. PINKSTON, AND R. WEEKS. 2006. Texas. North American Birds 59:620–624.

LONARD, R. I., AND F. W. JUDD. 1991. Comparison of the effects of the severe freezes of 1983 and 1989 on native woody plants of the Lower Rio Grande Valley, Texas. Southwestern Naturalist 36:213–217.

LORENZ, S., C. BUTLER, AND J. PAZ. 2006. First nesting record of the Gray-crowned Yellowthroat (Geothlypis poliocephala) in the United States since 1894. Wilson Journal of Ornithology 118:574–576.

LOWTHER, P. E., C. CELADA, N. K. KLEIN, C. C. RIMMER, AND D. A. SPECTOR. 1999. Yellow Warbler (Dendroica petechia). In A. Poole, and F. Gill (editors). The Birds of North America, No. 454. The Academy of Natural Sciences, Philadelphia, PA and The American Ornithologists' Union, Washington, DC.

MACARTHUR, R. H. 1964. Environmental factors affecting bird species diversity. American Naturalist 68:387–397.

MACARTHUR, R. H. 1972. Geographical ecology: patterns in the distribution of species. Harper and Row, New York, NY.

MACCALL, A. D. 1979. Population estimates for the waning years of the Pacific sardine fishery. California Cooperative Fisheries Investigations Report 20:72–82.

MACMYNOWSKI, D. P., T. L. ROOT, G. BALLARD, AND G. R. GEUPEL. 2007. Changes in spring arrival of Nearctic-Neotropical migrants attributed to multiscalar climate. Global Change Biology 13:1–13.

MANLY, B. F. J. 2004. Multivariate statistical methods: a primer. Third Edition, Chapman and Hall/CRC. Boca Raton, FL.

MANNAN, R. W., M. L. MORRISON, AND E. C. MESLOW. 1984. Comment: the use of guilds in forest bird management. Wildlife Society Bulletin 12:426–430.

MANVILLE, A. M. II. 2001. The ABCs of avoiding bird collisions at communication towers: next steps. Pp. 85–103 in R. L. Carlton (editor). Avian interactions with utility and communication structures. EPRI Technical Report. Concord, CA.

MANZANO-FISCHER, P., R. LIST, G. CEBALLOS, AND J.-L. E. CARTRON. 2006. Avian diversity in a priority area for conservation in North America: The Janos-Casas Grandes prairie dog complex and adjacent habitats in northwestern Mexico. Biodiversity and Conservation 15:3801–3825.

MARESH, J. 2004. Survey of Black-capped Vireo, Big Bend National Park, Brewster County, Texas, Spring 2004. Report to Big Bend National Park, TX.

MARONE, L., B. E. ROSSI, AND J. LOPEZ. 1998. Granivore impact on soil-seed reserves in the central Monte Desert Argentina. Functional Ecology 12:640–645.

MARSHALL, J. T. JR. 1957. Birds of pine-oak woodland in southern Arizona and adjacent Mexico. Pacific Coast Avifauna 32:1–125.

MARTIN, T. G., S. MCINTYRE, C. P. CATTERALL, AND H. P. POSSINGHAM. 2006. Is landscape context important for riparian conservation? Birds in grassy woodland. Biological Conservation 127:201–214.

MASON, L., M. J. DESMOND, AND M. S. AGUDELO. 2005. Influence of grassland type, nest type and shrub encroachment on predation of artificial nests in Chihuahuan Desert grasslands. Western North American Naturalist 65:196–201.

MASSEY, B. W., AND E. PALACIOS. 1994. Avifauna of the wetlands of Baja California, Mexico: current status. Studies in Avian Biology 15: 45–57.

MASSEY, B. W., D. W. BRADLEY AND J. L. ATWOOD. 1992. Demography of a California Least Tern colony including effects of the 1982–1983 El Niño. Condor 94:976–983.

MAURER, B. A. 1985. Avian community dynamics in desert grasslands: observational scale and hierarchical structure. Ecological Monographs 55:295–312.

MCCLARAN, M. P., AND T. R. VAN DEVENDER (EDITORS). 1995. The desert grassland. University of Arizona Press, Tucson, AZ.

MCCOMB, B. C., D. BILSLAND, AND J. J. STEINER. 2005. Associations of winter birds with riparian condition in the lower Calapooia watershed, Oregon. Northwest Science 72: 164–171.

MCCREADY, B., D. MEHLMAN, D. KWAN, AND B. ABEL. 2005. The Nature Conservancy's Prairie Wings project: a conservation strategy for the grassland birds of the western Great Plains. Pp. 1158–1161 in C. J. Ralph and T. D. Rich (editors). Bird conservation implementation and integration in the Americas: Proceedings of the third international partners in flight conference. USDA Forest Service General Technical Report PSW-GTR-191. USDA Forest Service, Pacific Southwest Research Station, Albany, CA.

McCune, B., and M. J. Mefford. 1997. Multivariate analysis of ecological data. PC-ORD. Version 3.17. MjM Software, Gleneden Beach, OR.

Mearns, E. A. 1907. Mammals of the Mexican boundary of the United States. Bulletin of the United States National Museum, 56:1–530.

Meents, J. K. 1979. Avian community structure in Chihuahuan Desert grasslands. Ph.D. dissertation, New Mexico State University, Las Cruces, NM.

Mellink, E., E. Palacios, and E. Amador. 2007. Colonies of four species of terns and the Black Skimmer in western Mexico. Waterbirds 30:358–366.

Merola-Zwartjes, M. 2004. Biodiversity, functional processes, and the ecological consequences of fragmentation in southwestern grasslands. Pp. 49–85 in D. M. Finch (editor). Assessment of grassland ecosystem conditions in the southwestern United States Volume 1. USDA Forest Service General Technical Report RMRS-GTR-135. USDA Forest Service, Rocky Mountain Research Station, Fort Collins, CO.

Mills, G. S. 1982. Status report: *Ammodramus savannarum ammolegus* (H. C. Oberholser). Arizona Natural Heritage Program, Tucson, Report to Office of Endangered Species, USDI Fish and Wildlife Service, Albuquerque, NM.

Misenhelter, M. D., and R. T. Rotenberry. 2000. Choices and consequences of habitat occupancy and nest site selection in Sage Sparrows. Ecology 81:2892–2901.

Mittermeier, R. A., C. F. Kormos, C. G. Mittermeier, P. R. Gil, T. Sandwith, and C. Besançon. 2005. Transboundary conservation: a new vision for protected areas. University of Chicago Press, Chicago IL.

Monson, G., and A. R Phillips. 1981. An annotated checklist of the birds of Arizona. University of Arizona Press, Tucson, AZ.

Moorcroft, D., M. J. Whittingham, R. B. Bradbury, and J. D. Wilson. 2002. The selection of stubble fields by wintering granivorous birds reflects vegetation cover and food abundance. Journal of Applied Ecology 39: 535-547.

Moore, F. R. (editor). 2001. Stopover ecology of Nearctic-Neotropical landbird migrants: habitat relations and conservation implications. Studies in Avian Biology 20.

Moore, F. R., and T. R. Simons. 1992. Habitat suitability and stopover ecology of Neotropical landbird migrants. Pp. 345–355 in J. M. Hagan, and D. H. Johnson (editors). Ecology and conservation of Neotropical migrant landbirds. Smithsonian Institution Press, Washington, DC.

Moore, F. R., P. Kerlinger, and T. R. Simmons. 1990. Stopover on a gulf coast barrier island by spring trans-gulf migrants. Wilson Bulletin 102:487–500.

Moore, F. R., S. A. Gauthreaux, Jr., P. Kerlinger, and T. R. Simons. 1995. Habitat requirements during migration: important link in conservation. Pp. 121–144 in T. E. Martin, and D. M. Finch (editors). Ecology and management of Neotropical migratory birds, a synthesis and review of critical issues. Oxford University Press, New York, NY.

Moore, R. T. 1938. Unusual birds and extensions of ranges in Sonora, Sinaloa, and Chihuahua. Condor 40:23–28.

Mosconi, S. L., and R. L. Hutto. 1982. The effect of grazing on the land birds of a western Montana riparian habitat. Pp. 221–233 in L. Nelson, and J. M. Peek (editors). Proceedings of the wildlife-livestock relationships symposium. Forest, Wildlife and Range Experiment Station, University of Idaho, Moscow, ID.

Nabhan, G. P., and A. R. Holdsworth. 1999. State of the desert biome: uniqueness, biodiversity, threats and the adequacy of protection in the Sonoran bioregion. Arizona-Sonora Desert Museum, Tucson, AZ.

Nagler, P. L., O. Hinojosa-Huerta, E. P. Glenn, J. García-Hernández, R. Romo, C. Curtis, A. R. Huete, and S. G. Nelson. 2005. Regeneration of native tress in the presence of invasive saltcedar in the Colorado River delta, Mexico. Conservation Biology 19:1842–1852.

Naiman, R. J., H. Décamps, and M. E. McClain. 2005. Riparia: ecology, conservation, and management of streamside communities. Elsevier Academic Press, Burlington, MA.

NatureServe. 2007. NatureServe conservation status. <http://www.natureserve.org/explorer/ranking.htm> (9 April 2008).

Neff, J. A. 1947. Notes on some birds of Sonora, Mexico. Condor 49:32–34.

Nelson, S. M., and B. W. Anderson. 1999. Butterfly (Papilionoidea and Hesperoidea) assemblages associated with natural, exotic, and restored riparian habitats along the Lower Colorado River, USA. Regulated Rivers: Research and Management 15: 485–504.

Nentvig, J., A. F. Pradeau, and R. R. Rasmussen. 1980. Rudo Ensayo: a description of Sonora and Arizona in 1764. University of Arizona Press, Tucson AZ.

NEW MEXICO PARTNERS IN FLIGHT. 2007. New Mexico bird conservation plan. Version 2.1. C. Rustay, and S. Norris (compilers). New Mexico Partners in Flight, Albuquerque, NM.

NIELSON, R. P. 1986. High resolution climatic analysis and southwest biography. Science 232:27–33.

NIEMELA, S. A. 2002. The influence of habitat heterogeneity and seed distribution on a Chihuahuan Desert avifauna. M.S. thesis, New Mexico State University, Las Cruces, NM.

NOAA. 2002. NOAA Satellite and Information Service and the National Climatic Data Center. <http://www.ncdc.noaa.gov/oa/climate/stationlocator.html> (18 April 2008).

NOAA. 2003. NOAA Satellite and Information Service and the National Climatic Data Center. <http://www.ncdc.noaa.gov/oa/climate/stationlocator.html> (18 April 2008).

NORRIS, D. R., P. P. MARRA, T. K. KYSER, T. W. SHERRY, AND L. M. RATCLIFFE. 2004. Tropical winter habitat limits reproductive success on the temperate breeding grounds in a migratory bird. Proceedings of the Royal Society of London 271:59–64.

NORTH AMERICAN ORNITHOLOGICAL ATLAS COMMITTEE. 1990. Handbook for atlasing North American breeding birds. <http://www.bsc-eoc.org/norac/atlascont.htm> (4 April 2008).

NORWINE, J., AND K. JOHN (EDITORS). 2007. The changing climate of south Texas, 1900–2100: problems and prospects, impacts and implications. Texas A & M University-Kingsville, Kingsville,TX.

OBERHOLSER, H. C. 1902. Some notes from western Texas. Auk 19:300–301.

OBERHOLSER, H. C. 1942. Description of a new race of the Grasshopper Sparrow. Proceedings of Biological Society, Washington 55:15–16.

OBERHOLSER, H. C. 1974. The bird life of Texas. University of Texas Press, Austin, TX.

OFFICE OF THE FEDERAL COORDINATOR FOR METEOROLOGY. 1997. Federal meteorological handbook No. 3, Rawinsonde and Pibal Observations. FCM-H3-1997. <http://www.ofcm.gov/fmh3/text/default.htm> (10 April 2008).

OHMART, R. D. 1994. The effects of human-induced changes on the avifauna of western riparian habitats. Studies in Avian Biology 15:273–285.

PALACIOS, E., AND E. MELLINK. 1993. Additional records of breeding birds from Montague Island, northern Gulf of California. Western Birds 24:259–262.

PANJABI, A. 2007a. RMBO launches initiative to monitor wintering grassland birds in Mexico. The Primary Source 24:1, 3

PANJABI, A. 2007b. Wintering grassland bird inventory and monitoring in northern Mexico: an interim narrative report. Rocky Mountain Bird Observatory, Brighton, CO.

PANKRATZ, C. 1994. PREFER—Preference assessment program. v5.1. Northern Prairie Science Center. Jamestown, ND.

PARKES, K. C., AND R. W. DICKERMAN, 1967. A new subspecies of Mangrove Warbler (*Dendroica petechia*) from Mexico. Annals of Carnegie Museum 39:85–89.

PARMESAN, C. 2006. Ecological and evolutionary responses to recent climate change. Annual Review of Ecology, Evolution, and Systematics 37:637–669.

PARMESAN, C., AND G. YOHE. 2003. A globally coherent fingerprint of climate change impacts across natural systems. Nature 421:37–42.

PATTEN, M. A., E. MELLINK, H. GÓMEZ DE SILVA, AND T. E. WURSTER. 2001. Status and taxonomy of the Colorado desert avifauna of Baja California. Monographs in Field Ornithology 3:29–63.

PAXTON, K. L., C. VAN RIPER III, T. C. THEIMER, AND E. H. PAXTON. 2007. Spatial and temporal patterns of Wilson's Warbler (*Wilsonia pusilla*) in the Southwest as revealed by stable isotopes. Auk 124:162–175.

PEARSON, S. M., AND T. R. SIMONS. 2002. Spatial analysis of stopover habitats of Neotropical migrant birds. Pp. 581–593 *in* J. M. Scott, P. Heglund, and M. Morrison (editors). Predicting species occurrences: issues of scale and accuracy. Island Press, Washington, DC.

PETERJOHN, B. G., AND J. R. SAUER. 1999. Population status of North American grassland birds from the North American breeding bird survey, 1966–1996. Studies in Avian Biology 19:27–44.

PETERSON, J. J., G. W. LASLEY, K. B. BRYAN, AND M. LOCKWOOD. 1991. Additions to the breeding avifauna of the Davis Mountains. Bulletin of the Texas Ornithological Society 24:39–48.

PHILLIPS, A. R. 1968. The instability of the distribution of land birds in the Southwest. Pp. 129–162 *in* A. H. Schroeder (editor). Collected papers in honor of Lyndon Lane Hargrave, Papers of the Archaeological Society of New Mexico: 1.

PHILLIPS, A. R. 1986. The known birds of North and Middle America. Part I. Published by the author, Denver, CO.

PHILLIPS, A. R. 1991. The known birds of North and Middle America. Part II. Published by the author, Denver, CO.

PHILLIPS, A. R., AND D. AMADON. 1952. Some birds of northwestern Sonora, Mexico. Condor 54: 163–168.

PHILLIPS, A. R., J. T. MARSHALL, JR., AND G. MONSON. 1964. The birds of Arizona. University of Arizona Press, Tucson, AZ.

PIDGEON, A. M., N. E. MATHEWS, R. BENOIT, AND E. NORDHEIM. 2001. Response of avian communities to historic habitat change in northern Chihuahuan Desert. Conservation Biology 15:1772–1788.

PIDGEON, A. M., V. C. RADELOFF, AND N. E. MATHEWS. 2006. Contrasting measures of fitness to classify habitat quality for the Black-throated Sparrow (Amphispiza bilineata). Biological Conservation 132:199–210.

PLUMPTRE, A. J., D. KUJIRAKWINJA, A. TREVES, I. OWIUNJI, AND H. RAINER. 2007. Transboundary conservation in the greater Virunga landscape: its importance for landscape species. Biological Conservation 134:279–287.

POIANI, K. A., B. D. RICHTER, M. G. ANDERSON, AND H. E. RICHTER. 2000. Biodiversity conservation at multiple scales: functional sites, landscapes, and networks. BioScience 50: 133–146.

POOLE, A. (EDITOR). 2005. The Birds of North American. Cornell Laboratory of Ornithology, Ithaca, NY. <http://bna.birds.cornell.edu/BNA/> (4 April 2008).

POWELL, B. F., AND R. J. STEIDL. 2000. Nesting habitat and reproductive success of southwestern riparian birds. Condor 102:823-831.

PROUDFOOT, G. A., AND R. R. JOHNSON. 2000. Ferruginous Pygmy-Owl (Glaucidium brasilianum). In A. Poole, and F. Gill (editors). The Birds of North America, No. 498. The Academy of Natural Sciences, Philadelphia, PA and The American Ornithologists' Union, Washington, DC.

PULICH, W. M., SR., AND W. M. PULICH, JR. 1963. The nesting of the Lucifer Hummingbird in the United States. Auk 80:370–371.

PULLIAM, H. R. 1975. Coexistence of sparrows: a test of community theory. Science 189: 474–476.

PULLIAM, H. R. 1980. Do Chipping Sparrows forage optimally? Ardea 68:75–82.

PULLIAM, H. R. 1985. Foraging efficiency, resource and partitioning, and the coexistence of sparrow species. Ecology 66:1829–1836.

PULLIAM, H. R. 1986. Niche expansion and contraction in a variable environment. American Zoologist 26:71–79.

PULLIAM, H. R., AND G. S. MILLS. 1977. The use of space by wintering sparrows. Ecology 58: 1393–1399.

PULLIAM, H. R., AND J. B. DUNNING. 1987. The influence of food supply on local density and diversity of sparrows. Ecology 68: 1009–1014.

PULLIAM, H. R., AND M. R. BRAND. 1975. The production and utilization of seeds in plains grassland of southeastern Arizona. Ecology 56:1158–1166.

PULLIAM, H. R., AND T. A. PARKER III. 1979. Population regulation of sparrows. Fortschritte der Zoologie 25:137–147.

RAITT, R. J., AND S. L. PIMM. 1976. Dynamics of bird communities in the Chihuahuan Desert, New Mexico. Condor 78:427–442.

RALPH, C. J. 1981. Age ratios and their possible use in determining autumn routes of passerine migrants. Wilson Bulletin 93:164–188.

RALPH, C. J., AND J. M. SCOTT (EDITORS). 1981. Estimating numbers of terrestrial birds. Studies in Avian Biology 6.

RALPH, C. J., G. R. GEUPEL, P. PYLE, T. E. MARTIN, AND D. F. DESANTE. 1993. Handbook of field methods for monitoring landbirds. USDA Forest Service General Technical Report PSW-GTR-144. USDA Forest Service, Pacific Southwest Research Station, Albany, CA.

RALPH, C. J., G. R. GEUPEL, P. PYLE, T. E. MARTIN, D. F. DESANTE, AND B. MILA. 1996. Manual de métodos de campo para el monitoreo de aves terrestres. USDA Forest Service General Technical Report PSW-GTR-159. USDA Forest Service, Pacific Southwest Research Station, Albany, CA.

RAMÍREZ-ALBORES, J. E., F. MARTÍNEZ V., AND J. CLEMENTE VÁSQUEZ S. 2007. Listado avifaunístico de un matorral tamaulipeco del noreste de México. Huitzil 8:1–10.

RANGO, A., L. HUENNEKE, M. BUONOPANE, J. HERRICK, AND K. M. HAVSTAD. 2005. Using historic data to assess effectiveness of shrub removal in southern New Mexico. Journal of Arid Environments 62:75–91.

RENFREW, R. B., AND C. A. RIBIC. 2002. Influence of topography on density of grassland passerines in pastures. American Midland Naturalist 147:315–325.

REYNOLDS, J. F., R. A. VIRGINIA, P. R. KEMP, A. G. DESOYZA, AND D. C. TREMMEL. 1999. Impact of drought on desert shrubs: effects of seasonality and degree of resource island development. Ecological Monographs 69: 69–106.

RICH, T. D., C. J. BEARDMORE, H. BERLANGA, P. J. BLANCHER, M. S. W. BRADSTREET, G. S. BUTCHER, D. W. DEMAREST, E. H. DUNN, W. C. HUNTER, E. E. IÑIGO-ELIAS, J. A. KENNEDY, A. M. MARTELL, A. O. PANJABI, D. N. PASHLEY, K. V. ROSENBERG, C. M. RUSTAY, J. S. WENDT, AND T. C. WILL. 2004. Partners in Flight North American landbird conservation plan. Cornell Lab of Ornithology, Ithaca, NY.

RICHARDSON, J. W. 1978. Timing and amount of bird migration in relation to weather: A review. Oikos 30:224–272.

RICHTER, B. D., AND H. E. RICHTER. 2000. Prescribing flood regimes to sustain riparian ecosystems along meandering rivers. Conservation Biology 14:1467–1478.

RISING, J. D. 2005. A guide to the identification and natural history of the sparrows of the United States and Canada. Academic Press, Inc., San Diego, CA.

ROBBINS, M. B., AND D. A. EASTERLA. 1981. Range expansion of the Bronzed Cowbird with the first Missouri record. Condor 83:270–272.

ROBERSON, D. 2002. Monterey Birds. 2nd Edition, Monterey Peninsula Audubon Society, Carmel, CA.

ROJAS-SOTO, O., F. PUEBLA-OLIVARES, E. M. FIGUEROA-ESQUIVEL, L. A. SÁNCHEZ-GONZÁLEZ, Y. J. NAKAZAWA-UEJI, C. A. RÍOS-MUÑÓZ, AND A. G. NAVARRO S. 2002. Avifauna de Isla Tiburón, Sonora, México. Anales del Instituto de Biología. Serie Zoología 73: 73–89.

ROMAGOSA, C. M. 2002. Eurasian Collared-Dove (*Streptopelia decaocto*). *In* A. Poole, and F. Gill (editors). The Birds of North America, No. 630. The Academy of Natural Sciences, Philadelphia, PA and The American Ornithologists' Union, Washington, DC.

ROMAGOSA, C. M., AND T. MCENEANEY. 1999. Eurasian Collared-Dove in North America and the Caribbean. North American Birds 53:348–353.

ROOT, T. L., J. T. PRICE, K. R. HALL, S. H. SCHNEIDER, C. ROSENZWEIG, AND J. A. POUNDS. 2003. Fingerprints of global warming on wild animals and plants. Nature 421:57–60.

ROSENBERG, G. H. 2001. Arizona Bird Committee report: 1996–1999 records. Western Birds 32: 50–70.

ROSENBERG, G. H., AND J. L. WITZEMAN. 1998. Arizona Bird Committee report, 1974–1996: part 1 (nonpasserines). Western Birds 29: 199–224.

ROSENBERG, G. H., AND J. L. WITZEMAN. 1999. Arizona Bird Committee report, 1974–1996: part 2 (passerines). Western Birds 30: 94–120.

ROSENBERG, K. V., AND R. J. COOPER. 1988. Approaches to avian diet analysis. Studies in Avian Biology 13:80–90.

ROSENBERG, K. V., R. D. OHMART, W. C. HUNTER, AND B. W. ANDERSON. 1991. Birds of the lower Colorado River valley. University of Arizona Press, Tucson, AZ.

RUIZ-CAMPOS, G., AND M. RODRÍGUEZ-MERAZ. 1997. Composición taxonómica y ecológica de la avifauna de los ríos El Mayor y Hardy, y áreas adyacentes, en el Valle de Mexicali, Baja California, México. Anales del Instituto de Biología, Universidad Nacional Autónoma de México, Serie Zoología 68:291–315.

RUSSELL, K. R., AND S. A. GAUTHREAUX. 1998. Use of weather radar to characterize movements of roosting Purple Martins. Wildlife Society Bulletin 26:5–16.

RUSSELL, S. M., AND D. W. LAMM. 1978. Notes on the distribution of birds in Sonora, Mexico. Wilson Bulletin 90:123–131.

RUSSELL, S. M., AND G. MONSON. 1998. The birds of Sonora. University of Arizona Press, Tucson, AZ.

RUTH, J. M. (EDITOR). 2007. Applying radar technology to migratory bird conservation and management: strengthening and expanding a collaborative. U.S. Geological Survey, Biological Resources Discipline, Open-File Report 2007-1361. Fort Collins, CO.

RUTH, J. M., W. C. BARROW, R. S. SODJA, D. K. DAWSON, R. H. DIEHL, A. MANVILLE, M. T. GREEN, D. J. KRUEPER, AND S. JOHNSTON. 2005. Advancing migratory bird conservation and management by using radar: an interagency collaboration. USGS Biological Resources Discipline, Open-File Report 2005-1173. USGS Fort Collins Science Center. <http://www.fort.usgs.gov/Products/Publications/pub_abstract.asp?PubID=21469> (10 April 2008).

SAAB, V. 1999. Importance of spatial scale to habitat use by breeding birds in riparian forests: a hierarchical analysis. Ecological Applications 9:135–151.

SAAB, V. A., C. E. BOCK, T. D. RICH, AND D. S. DOBKIN. 1995. Livestock grazing effects in western North America. Pp. 311–353 *in* T. E. Martin, and D. M. Finch (editors). Ecology and management of Neotropical migratory birds: a synthesis and review of critical issues. Oxford University Press, New York, NY.

SABO, J. L., AND C. SOYKAN. 2006. Riparian zones increase regional richness by supporting different, not more, species: reply. Ecology 87:2128–2131.

SALL, J., AND A. LEHMAN. 1996. JMP start statistics. Duxbury Press, Belmont, CA.

SANDERS, T. A., AND W. D. EDGE. 1998. Breeding bird community composition in relation to riparian vegetation structure in the western United States. Journal of Wildlife Management 62:461–473.

SAS INSTITUTE. 1990. SAS/STAT user's guide, version 6, fourth edition. SAS Institute Inc., Cary, NC.

SAS INSTITUTE. 1999. SAS/STAT user's guide. Version 8. SAS Institute Inc., Cary, NC.

SAS Institute. 2003. SAS/STAT user's guide. Version 9.1 SAS Institute Inc., Cary, NC.

Sauer, J. R., J. E. Hines, and J. Fallon. 2006. The North American breeding bird survey, results and analysis 1966–2006. Version 6.2.2006. USGS Patuxent Wildlife Research Center, Laurel, MD.

Schaefer, G. W. 1976. Radar observations of insect flight. Pp. 157–197 in R. C. Rainey (editor). Insect flight. Blackwell Scientific Publications, London, UK.

Schaffner, F. C. 1985. Royal Tern nesting attempts in California: isolated or significant incidences? Western Birds 16:71–80.

Schlesinger, W. H. 1994. Long term ecological studies in the Chihuahuan Desert. The Jornada LTER - III Consortium, Duke University, Durham, NC.

Schlesinger, W. H. 2002. Desertification. Pp. 253–256 in A. S. Goudie, and D. J. Cuff (editors). Encyclopedia of global change. Oxford University Press, New York, NY.

Schlesinger, W. H., J. F. Reynolds, G. L. Cunningham, L. F. Huenneke, W. M. Jarrell, R. A. Virginia, and W. G. Whitford. 1990. Biological feedbacks in global desertification. Science 247:1043–1048.

Schluter, D., and R. R. Repasky. 1991. Worldwide limitation of finch densities by food and other factors. Ecology 72: 1763–1774.

Schmitt, C. G. 1976. Summer birds of the San Juan Valley, New Mexico. New Mexico Ornithological Society Bulletin 4.

Scott, M. L., S. K. Skagen, and M. F. Merigliano. 2003. Relating geomorphic change and grazing to avian communities in riparian forests. Conservation Biology 17:284–296.

Seidel, D. J., Q. Fu, W. J. Randel, and T. J. Reichler. 2008. Widening of the tropical belt in a changing climate. Nature Geoscience 1: 21–24.

SEMARNAT. 2002. Norma Oficial Mexicana NOM-059-SEMARNAT-2001, Protección ambiental—especies nativas de México de flora y fauna silvestres—categorías de riesgo y especificaciones para su inclusión, exclusión o cambio—lista de especies en riesgo. Diario Oficial de la Federación 582(4) wa. Sección:1–80.

Sennett, G. B. 1878. Notes on the ornithology of the lower Rio Grande of Texas, from observations made during the season of 1877. Bulletin of the U.S. Geological and Geographical Survey of the Territories 4:1–66.

Sexton, C. S. 2001. Texas. North American Birds 55:321–325.

Shackelford, C. E., and M. W. Lockwood. 2000. Rare and declining birds of Texas: conservation needed. Texas Parks and Wildlife Department, Austin, TX.

Sher, A. A., D. L. Marshall, and S. A. Gilbert. 2000. Competition between native Populus deltoides and invasive Tamarix ramosissima and the implications for reestablishing flooding disturbance. Conservation Biology 14:1744–1754.

Sherbrooke, W. C. 1974. Differential acceptance of toxic jojoba seed (Simmondsia chilensis) by four Sonoran Desert heteromyid rodents. Ecology 57:596–602.

Sherry, T. W., and R. T. Holmes. 1995. Summer versus winter limitation of populations: what are the issues and what is the evidence? Pp. 85–120 in T. E. Martin, and D. M. Finch (editors). Ecology and management of Neotropical migratory birds: a synthesis and review of critical issues. Oxford University Press, New York, NY.

Short, L. L. 1974. Nesting of southern Sonora birds during the summer rainy season. Condor 76:21–32.

Shreve, F. 1951. Vegetation of the Sonoran Desert. Carnegie Institute of Washington, Publication Number 591. Washington DC.

Sillett, T. S., and R. T. Holmes. 2002. Variation in survivorship of a migratory songbird throughout its annual cycle. Journal of Animal Ecology 71:296–308.

Sims, P., J. S. Singh, and W. K. Lauenroth. 1978. The structure and function of ten western North American grasslands. Journal of Ecology 66:251–285.

Sisk, T. D., A. E. Castellanos V, and G. W. Koch. 2007. Ecological impacts of wildlife conservation units policy in Mexico. Frontiers in Ecology and the Environment 5:209–212.

Skagen, S. K., C. P. Melcher, W. H. Howe, and F. L. Knopf. 1998. Comparative use of riparian corridors and oases by migrating birds in southeast Arizona. Conservation Biology 12:896–909.

Skagen, S. K., J. F. Kelly, C. van Riper III, R. L. Hutto, D. M. Finch, D. J. Krueper, and C. P. Melcher. 2005. Geography of spring landbird migration through riparian habitats in southwestern North America. Condor 107: 212–227.

Small, A. 1994. California birds: their status and distribution. Ibis Publishing Co., Vista, CA.

Snell-Rood, E. C., and D. A. Cristol. 2003. Avian communities of created and natural wetlands: bottomland forests in Virginia. Condor 105:303–315.

Sogge, M. K., R. M. Marshall, S. J. Sferra, and T. J. Tibbitts. 1997. A southwestern Willow Flycatcher natural history summary and survey protocol. USGS Colorado Plateau Research Station, Northern Arizona University, Flagstaff, AZ.

SPSS. 2002. Data analysis software. SPSS, Inc., Chicago, IL.

STALLCUP, R. 1990. Ocean birds of the nearshore Pacific. Point Reyes Bird Observatory, Stinson Beach, CA.

STAMP, N. E. 1978. Breeding birds of riparian woodland in south-central Arizona. Condor 80:64–71.

STEPHENS, F. 1885. Notes of an ornithological trip in Arizona and Sonora. Auk 2:225–231.

STOLESON, S. H., R. S. FELGER, G. CEBALLOS, C. RAISH, M. F. WILSON, AND A. BÚRQUEZ. 2005. Recent history of natural resource use and population growth in northern Mexico. Pp. 52–86 in J.-L. E. Cartron, G. Ceballos, and R. S. Felger (editors). Biodiversity, ecosystems, and conservation in northern Mexico. Oxford University Press, NY.

STROMBERG, J. C., AND M. K. CHEW. 2002. Flood pulses and restoration of riparian vegetation in the American Southwest. Pp. 11–50 in B. A. Middleton (editor). Flood pulsing in wetlands: restoring the natural hydrological balance. John Wiley and Sons, New York, NY.

STRONG, T. R. 1988. Status of the Arizona Grasshopper Sparrow (Ammodramus savannarum ammolegus Oberholser). Arizona Game and Fish Department, report to Office of Endangered Species, USDI Fish and Wildlife Service, Albuquerque, NM.

STRONG, T. R., AND C. E. BOCK. 1990. Bird species distribution patterns in riparian habitats in southeastern Arizona. Condor 92:866-885.

SWARTH, H. S. 1914. A distributional list of the birds of Arizona. Pacific Coast Avifauna 10: 1–133.

SWETNAM, T. W., AND J. L. BETANCOURT. 1998. Mesoscale disturbance and ecological response to decadal climatic variability in the American Southwest. Journal of Climate 11: 3128–3147.

SYKES, G. 1937. The Colorado delta. American Geographical Society Special Publication 19.

TEJAS, A., R. SERVÍN, AND S. GALLINA. 1991. Delimitación, zonificación y tenencia de la tierra. Pp. 53–68 in A. Ortega, and L. Arriaga (editors), La reserva de la biósfera El Vizcaino en la península de Baja California. Centro de Investigaciones Biológicas de Baja California Sur, A.C. No. 4. La Paz, B.C.S., México.

TERRILL, S. B. 1981. Notes on the winter avifauna of two riparian sites in northern Sonora, Mexico. Continental Birdlife 2:11–18.

THAYER, J. E., AND O. BANGS. 1906. Breeding birds of the Sierra de Antonez, north central Sonora. Proceedings of the Biological Society of Washington 19:17–22.

THE NATURE CONSERVANCY. 2000. The five-S framework for site conservation: a practitioner's handbook for site conservation planning and measuring conservation success. The Nature Conservancy, Arlington, VA.

THOMAS, L., J. L. LAAKE, S. STRINDBERG, F. F. C. MARQUES, S. T. BUCKLAND, D. L. BORCHERS, D. R. ANDERSON, K. P. BURNHAM, S. L. HEDLEY, AND J. H. POLLARD. 2002. Distance 5.0. Research Unit for Wildlife Population Assessment, University of St. Andrews, UK. <http://www.ruwpa.st-and.ac.uk/distance/> (4 April 2008).

TROY, J. R. 2006. Survey of Black-capped Vireo, Big Bend National Park, Brewster County, Texas, Spring 2006. Report to Big Bend National Park, TX.

TUNNELL, J. W., JR., AND F. W. JUDD (EDITORS). 2002. The Laguna Madre of Texas and Tamaulipas. Texas A&M University Press, College Station, TX.

TURNER, R. M., J. E. BOWERS, AND T. L. BURGESS. 1995. Sonoran Desert plants: an ecological atlas. University of Arizona Press, Tucson, AZ.

TURNER, R. M., R. H. WEBB, J. E. BOWERS, AND J. R. HASTINGS. 2003. The changing mile revisited. University of Arizona Press, Tucson, AZ.

U.S. BUREAU OF RECLAMATION. 2005. Report to the Congress: the Yuma Desalting Plant and other actions to address alternatives. Colorado River Basin Salinity Control Act, Title I, August 2005. U.S. Bureau of Reclamation, Washington, DC.

UNITED NATIONS. 1992. Managing fragile ecosystems: combating desertification and drought, chapter 12 of Agenda 21. United Nations. New York, NY.

UNITT, P. 1984. The birds of San Diego County. San Diego Society of Natural History, Memoir 13:1–276.

UNITT, P. 2004. San Diego County bird atlas. Proceedings of the San Diego Society of Natural History 39:1–645.

USDI BUREAU OF LAND MANAGEMENT. 1996. Birds of the San Pedro Riparian National Conservation Area and upper San Pedro River Valley. BLM/AZ/GI-96/006. San Pedro National Conservation Area, Bureau of Land Management, Safford, AZ.

USDI BUREAU OF LAND MANAGEMENT. 1998. Birds as indicators of riparian vegetation condition in the western U.S. BLM/ID/PT-98/004+6635. Bureau of Land Management, Partners in Flight, Boise, ID.

USDI Bureau of Reclamation. 2007. Colorado River interim guidelines for lower basin shortages and coordinated operations for Lake Powell and Lake Mead final environmental impact statement. USDI Bureau of Reclamation, Upper and Lower Colorado Regions, Boulder City, NV.

USDI Fish and Wildlife Service. 2000. Yuma Clapper Rail revised survey protocol. memorandum to Yuma Clapper Rail interested parties. USDI Fish and Wildlife Service, Arizona Ecological Services Field Office, Phoenix, AZ.

USDI Fish and Wildlife Service. 2002. Birds of conservation concern 2002. USDI Fish and Wildlife Service, Division of Migratory Bird Management, Arlington, VA. <http://www.fws.gov/migratorybirds/reports/BCC2002.pdf> (26 March 2008).

USDI Fish and Wildlife Service. 2004. North American waterfowl management plan: Strengthening the biological foundation, 2004 strategic guidance. North American Waterfowl Management Plan, USDI Fish and Wildlife Service, Arlington, VA.

USGS National Gap Analysis Program. 2004. Provisional digital land cover map for the southwestern United States. Version 1.0. RS/GIS Laboratory. College of Natural Resources, Utah State University, Logan, UT.

Valdez, R., J. C. Guzman-Aranda, F. J. Abarca, L. A. Tarango-Arambula, and F. Clemente-Sanchez. 2006. Wildlife conservation and management in Mexico. Wildlife Society Bulletin 34:270–282.

van der Meij, M. A. A., and R. G. Bout. 2000. Seed selection in the Java Sparrow (*Padda oryzivora*): preference and mechanical constraint. Canadian Journal of Zoology 78:1668–1673.

Van Horne, B. 1983. Density as a misleading indicator of habitat quality. Journal of Wildlife Management 47:893–901.

van Rossem, A. J. 1931. Report on a collection of land birds from Sonora, Mexico. Transactions of the San Diego Society of Natural History 6:237–304.

van Rossem, A. J. 1945. A distributional survey of the birds of Sonora, Mexico. Occasional Papers Museum of Zoology, Louisiana State University 21:1–379.

Van Tyne, J. 1936. The discovery of the nest of the Colima Warbler (*Vermivora crissalis*). Miscellaneous Publications of the University of Michigan 33, Flint, MI.

Van Tyne, J., and G. M. Sutton. 1937. The birds of Brewster County, Texas. Miscellanous Publications of the University of Michigan 37, Flint, MI.

Velarde, E., J.-L. E. Cartron, H. Drummond, D. W. Anderson, F. R. Garrardo, E. Palacios and C. Rodriquez. 2005. Nesting seabirds of the Gulf of California's offshore islands: diversity, ecology, and conservation. Pp. 452–470 *in* J.-L. Catron, G. Ceballos, and R. S. Felger (editors). Biodiversity, ecosystems and conservation in northern Mexico. Oxford Univ. Press, New York, NY.

Vickery, P. D. 1996. Grasshopper Sparrow (*Ammodramus savannarum*). *In* A. Poole, and F. Gill (editors). The Birds of North America, No. 239. The Academy of Natural Sciences, Philadelphia, PA and the American Ornithologists' Union, Washington, DC.

Vickery, P. D., M. L. Hunter, Jr., and J. V. Wells. 1992. Is density an indicator of breeding success? Auk 109:706–710.

Vickery, P. D., P. L. Tubarro, J. M. Cardoso da Silva, B. G. Peterjohn, J. R. Herkert, and R. B. Cavalcanti. 1999. Conservation of grassland birds in the western hemisphere. Studies in Avian Biology 19:2–26.

Villaseñor, J. F. 2006. Habitat use and the effects of disturbance on wintering birds using riparian habitats in Sonora, Mexico. Ph.D. dissertation, University of Montana, Missoula MT.

Villaseñor-Gómez, J. F., and R. L. Hutto. 1995. The importance of agricultural areas for the conservation of neotropical migratory landbirds in western Mexico. Pp. 59–80 *in* M. H. Wilson, and S. A. Sader (editors). Conservation of Neotropical migratory birds in Mexico. Maine Agricultural and Forest Experiment Station, Misc. Publ. 727.

Warkentin, I. G., R. Greenberg, and J. S. Ortiz. 1995. Songbird use of gallery woodlands in recently cleared and older settled landscapes of the Selva Lacandona, Chiapas, Mexico. Conservation Biology 9:1095–1106.

Warshall, P. 1995. The Madrean Sky Island Archipelago: a planetary overview. Pp. 7–18 *in* L. F. DeBano, P. F. Ffolliott, A. Ortega-Rubio, G. J. Gottfried, R. H. Hamre, and C. B. Edminster (editors). Biodiversity and management of the Madrean Archipelago: the Sky Islands of southwestern United States and northwestern Mexico. USDA Forest Service General Technical Report RM-GTR 264. USDA Forest Service, Rocky Mountain Research Station, Ft. Collins, CO.

Wauer, R. H. 1973. Birds of Big Bend National Park and vicinity. University of Texas Press, Austin, TX.

Wauer, R. H. 1996. A field guide to birds of the Big Bend. Gulf Publishing, Houston, TX.

WAUER, R. H. 1998. Avian population survey of a Tamaulipan scrub habitat, Tamaulipas, Mexico. Cotinga 10:13–19.

WAUER, R. H., AND DAVIS, D. G. 1972. Cave Swallows in Big Bend National Park, Texas. Condor 74:482.

WAUER, R. H., AND D. J. LIGON. 1977. Distributional relations of breeding avifauna of four southwestern mountain ranges. Pp. 567–578 *in* R. H. Wauer, and D. H. Riskind (editors). Transactions of the symposium on the biological resources of the Chihuahuan Desert region, U.S. and Mexico. USDI National Park Service, Transactions and Proceedings Series, No. 3. Washington, DC.

WEBB, R. H., S. A. LEAKE, AND R. M. TURNER. 2007. The ribbon of green: change in riparian vegetation in the southwestern United States. University of Arizona Press, Tucson, AZ.

WEBER, M., G. GARCÍA-MARMOLEJO, AND R. REYNA-HURTADO. 2006. The tragedy of the commons: wildlife management units in southeastern Mexico. Wildlife Society Bulletin 34: 1480–1488.

WEBSTER, G. L., AND C. J. BAHRE (EDITORS). 2001. Changing plant life of La Frontera: observations on vegetation in the United States/Mexico borderlands. University of New Mexico Press, Albuquerque, NM.

WELLS, D., B. W. ANDERSON, AND R. D. OHMART. 1979. Comparative avian use of southwestern citrus orchards and riparian communities. Journal of the Arizona-Nevada Academy of Science 14:58.

WHITFORD, W. G. 1997. Desertification and animal biodiversity in the desert grasslands of North America. Journal of Arid Environments 37:709–720.

WHITFORD, W. G. 2002. Ecology of desert systems. Elsevier Science Ltd., London, UK.

WHITMORE, R. C. 1979. Temporal variation in the selected habitats of a guild of grassland sparrows. Wilson Bulletin 91:592–598.

WHITMORE, R. C. 1981. Structural characteristics of Grasshopper Sparrow habitat. Journal of Wildlife Management 45:811–814

WILBUR, S. A. 1987. Birds of Baja California. University of California Press, Los Angeles, CA.

WILLIAMS, S. O. III. 1991. Discovery and status of the Arizona Grasshopper Sparrow in New Mexico. New Mexico Ornithological Society Bulletin 19:32–33.

WILLIAMS, S. O. III. 1997. Trends in Arizona Grasshopper Sparrow breeding populations in New Mexico: value of long-term studies. New Mexico Ornithological Society Bulletin 25:35.

WILLIAMS, S. O. III. 2007. Status of the Arizona Grasshopper Sparrow on the Diamond A (Gray) Ranch, Hidalgo County, New Mexico. New Mexico Department of Game and Fish, Santa Fe, NM.

WILLIAMS, S. O. III, J. P. DELONG, AND W. H. HOWE. 2007. Northward range expansion by the Short-tailed Hawk, with first nesting records for New Mexico and Chihuahua. Western Birds 38:2–10.

WINTER, M., D. JOHNSON, AND J. FAABORG. 2000. Evidence for edge effects on multiple levels in tallgrass prairie. Condor 102:256-266.

WITH, K. A., AND T. CRIST. 1995. Critical thresholds in species responses to landscapes structures. Ecology 76:2446–2459.

WOLF, S. B. 2002. The relative status and conservation of island breeding seabirds in California and northwest Mexico. M.S. thesis, University of California, Santa Cruz, CA.

WOLF, S. B., B. KEITT, A. AGUIRRE-MUNOZ, B. TERSHY, E. PALACIOS, AND D. CROLL. 2006. Transboundary seabird conservation in an important North American marine ecoregion. Environmental Conservation 33:294–305.

WOODIN, M. C., M. K. SKORUPPA, AND G. C. HICKMAN. 1998. Breeding bird surveys at the Galvan Ranch, Webb County, Texas. Final report, prepared for the Ed Rachal Foundation, Corpus Christi, TX.

WOODIN, M. C., M. K. SKORUPPA, G. W. BLACKLOCK, AND G. C. HICKMAN. 1999. Discovery of a second population of White-collared Seedeaters (Passeriformes: Emberizidae) along the Rio Grande in Texas. Southwestern Naturalist 44:535–537.

WOODREY, M. 2000. Age-dependent aspects of stopover biology of passerine migrants. Studies in Avian Biology 20:43–52.

YAHNER, R. H. 1993. Effects of long term forest clear cutting on wintering and breeding birds. Wilson Bulletin 105:239–255.

YONG, W., AND D. M. FINCH. 2002. Stopover ecology of landbirds migrating along the Middle Rio Grande in spring and fall. USDA Forest Service General Technical Reporty RMRS-GTR-99. USDA Forest Service, Rocky Mountain Research Station, Ogden, UT.

YUMA DESALTING PLANT/CIENEGA DE SANTA CLARA WORKGROUP. 2005. Balancing water needs in the Lower Colorado Basin: recommendations of the Yuma Desalting Plant/Cienega de Santa Clara Workgroup. White Paper of the Yuma Desalting Plant/Cienega de Santa Clara Workgroup, Yuma, AZ.

ZAMORA-ARROYO, F., P. CULP, AND O. HINOJOSA-HUERTA. 2006. Looking beyond the border: environmental consequences of the All-American Canal project in Mexico and potential binational solutions. Pp. 21–57 *in* V. Sánchez-Mungía (editor). Lining the

All-American Canal: competition or cooperation for the water in the U.S.-Mexican Border? San Diego State University Press, San Diego, CA.

ZAMORA-ARROYO, F., P. L. NAGLER, M. BRIGGS, D. RADTKE, H. RODRÍGUEZ, J. GARCÍA, C. VALDÉS, A. HUETE, AND E. P. GLENN. 2001. Regeneration of native trees in response to flood releases from the United States into the delta of the Colorado River, Mexico. Journal of Arid Environments 49:49–64.

ZAMORA-ARROYO, F., J. PITT, S. CORNELIUS, E. GLENN, O. HINOJOSA-HUERTA, M. MORENO, J. GARCÍA, P. NAGLER, M. DE LA GARZA, AND I. PARRA. 2005. Conservation priorities in the Colorado River delta, Mexico and the United States. Prepared by the Sonoran Institute, Environmental Defense, University of Arizona, Pronatura Noroeste Dirección de Conservación Sonora, Centro de Investigación en Alimentación y Desarrollo (CIAD) and World Wildlife Fund-Gulf of California Program, Tucson, AZ.

ZAR, J. H. 1999. Biostatistical analysis, 4th ed. Prentice Hall, Upper Saddle River, NJ.

ZENGEL, S., V. MERTETSKY, E. GLENN, R. FELGER, AND D. ORTIZ. 1995. Cienega de Santa Clara, a remnant wetland in the Rio Colorado delta (Mexico): vegetation distribution and the effects of water flow reduction. Ecological Engineering 4:19–36.